Living Earth

Ari Trausti Guðmundsson

Living Earth
Outline of the Geology of Iceland

with contribution by Halldór Kjartansson
Translated by George Douglas

Mál og menning

Living earth – Outline of the Geology of Iceland

© Ari Trausti Guðmundsson 2007
© English translation: George Douglas

Mál og menning
Reykjavík 2013

Cover design: Alexandra Buhl/Forlagið
Pages: Næst
Maps and diagrams: Næst
Printed by Almarose, Slovenia

1st edition 2007
Reprinted 2010, 2013

Photography:
ATG   Ari Trausti Guðmundsson
GH   Guðmundur Hannesson
HB   Hjálmar Bárðarson
HK   Halldór Kjartansson
JJ   Jón Jóhannsson
OS   Oddur Sigurðsson
ÓR   Ómar Þ. Ragnarsson
PI   Páll Imsland
RTH   Ragnar Th. Sigurðsson
SÞ   Sigurður Þórarinsson
ÆJ   Ævar Jóhannsson

ISBN 978-9979-3-3360-9

Mál og menning is an imprint of ❦ Forlagið ehf.
www.forlagid.is

Contents

Introduction

There is great interest in Iceland's geology for obvious reasons. The country is young and active, lies on top of a mantle plume and astride a divergent plate margin, has extensive glaciers and, in addition, most geological processes there are rapid and dynamic. Research into Icelandic geology by Icelandic and foreign scientists features prominently at conferences and in respected books and journals. By far the majority of published works are in English. Two earth-science journals are published in Iceland: Jökull, which is in English, and *Náttúrufræðingurinn*, which contains articles in Icelandic with English summaries.

Literally hundreds of articles or book chapters on Iceland's geology appear every four to five years. As a result there has always been a need for a readily accessible summary of their findings for foreign readers. These may include university students at various stages of study, university professionals in geology-related subjects, earth scientists who require a general knowledge of Iceland's geology, and laymen who have a particular interest in the subject.

Only a few Icelandic books have addressed this need. The present authors published *A Guide to the Geology of Iceland (Wegweiser durch die Geologie Islands)* in 1984, *Earth in Action (Land im Werden)* and *Volcanoes in Iceland* in 1996. English and German translations of Þorleifur Einarsson's book on the geology of Iceland have been published since 1991 *(The Geology of Iceland)*. Foreign authors, in particular from Germany, have also written general books of this kind, and in 2002 a travel guide to the geology of Iceland was compiled by Þorvaldur Þórðarson (pen name Thor Thordarson) and Ármann Höskuldsson (*Iceland* in the European series *Classic Geology*, publ. Terra). The latest additions are *100 Geosites in South Iceland*, of Swedish origin, and *Iceland Geodynamics – Crustal deformation and divergent plate tectonics* by Freysteinn Sigmundsson.

Living earth is a fresh overview of all the main features of Iceland's geology, based on a detailed review of the literature as well as the authors' long experience of teaching geology and promoting it through the media of radio, television and books. Relevant references (chiefly in English) are given at the end of each chapter but are not cited in the text, in keeping with popular-science-book style. Explanatory diagrams have been redrawn and simplified, and their source acknowledged in the text where applicable. Illustrations have been selected for relevance to the subject matter rather than pictorial value. References to useful study sites are also provided.

My valued colleague and co-author for many years, the geologist Halldór Kjartansson, wrote chapter two, for which I am most grateful. His intention of writing half the book was cut short by his sad death in late 2005. This publication is dedicated to his memory.

I would also like to thank the staff at Edda for their cooperation, and Dr. Olgeir Sigmarsson and Dr. Ágúst Guðmundsson for reading part of the text and for their constructive criticism. Finally I would like to thank George Douglas and Victoria Cribb for their work on the English translation.

Ari Trausti Guðmundsson

1 Iceland: a geological laboratory and showcase

Iceland's main geological features are prominent and popular objects of study among both geologists and laymen. The island is a land-born or supramarine section of the divergent plate margins, otherwise only evident as the submarine North-Atlantic Ridge. It boasts spreading ridge segments, intraplate lateral eruptive zones, transverse fracture zones and a hot spot. The lively tectonic and volcanic activity, as well as the geothermal activity, stem from the Iceland hot spot, the plate separation, the upwelling of ductile rocks from below and the associated production of magma. Iceland's arctic elements include ice caps, active glaciers, permafrost regions and other interesting periglacial phenomena. These are easily accessible for study, as are many other geomorphological features. All in all, Iceland provides a highly recommended and interesting single region for studying many geological processes or phenomena, which would otherwise involve travelling to far-flung corners of the world. The central highlands of Iceland have even stood in for lunar and Martian landscapes in simulations and learning centers.

Key words

Plate tectonics • plate spreading • rift zone • rifting • fracture zone • hot spot • mantle plume • crust aggregation • oceanic volcanism • MORB (basalts) • evolved basalts • acid eruptive rock • continental volcanism • volcanic system • central volcano • volcanic centre • submarine volcanic activity • subglacial eruption • glacier burst • fissure • fissure swarm • graben • fault • rift • geothermal activity • ice cap (temperate) • surging glacier • glacial erosion • periglacial phenomena • permafrost features • desertification • mechanical erosion • chemical and mechanical weathering

1. On top of a spreading ridge and a hot spot

Iceland is not very large on an international scale: its area is 103,000 km². It rises to 1,500–2,000 m above sea level. Its location close to the Arctic Circle and on the North-Atlantic plate margins make Iceland extremely important to those interested in the natural sciences such as geology and geophysics and their many branches. These include volcanology, petrology, the chemistry of weathering, geothermal science, the physics of the crust and mantle, tectonics and seismology, glaciology, periglacial studies, palaeoclimatology, sedimentology, palaeontology and finally geomorphology.

Iceland is often referred to as a supramarine section of the Mid-Atlantic Ridge and the only part which is large and accessible. Nowhere else is it as easy to examine an ocean ridge on dry land. The Mid-Atlantic Ridge measures 14,000–15,000 km in length and forms a broad threshold which runs the length of the sea floor from the Arctic Ocean southwards past Africa. The ridge is formed by the accumulation of eruptive material and the drifting of the plates which float on top of a plastic (mobile) layer in the earth's mantle. They support continents in the east (Europe, Asia and Africa) and the west (South and North America). The drift or rifting rate is approximately 2 cm per year on average, but in reality the spreading is localised and a long time usually elapses between periods of drifting in a particular area. The stress increases within the crustal layers of a particular part of the plate margin until they fail. In each rifting episode the plates move apart with associated earthquakes and fracture formation, or movement on existing faults.

During rifting, magma normally rises to shallow depths within the crust to form intrusions, or less frequently reaches the surface in a single eruption or several eruptions during the rifting episode. Most of this activity occurs on the sea floor in rifting zones which have a northerly orientation, but the zones are also displaced along transform fracture zones (tending stepwise east-west) where earthquakes are frequent, some very severe, but there is considerably less volcanic activity.

Where plates collide, one will sink into the earth's mantle. Plate margins of this type are the site of earthquakes and volcanic eruptions, and deep ocean trenches and fold mountains often form there.

Askja 1961 (SÞ)

The Mid-Atlantic Ridge rises gradually from a depth of 2,000–3,000 m. Along the crest where it is delimited by rifting zones, the ridge is characterised by rift valleys, which run more or less parallel to the crest, often in an offset manner, and many elongate eruptive piles. Isolated volcanoes and geothermal areas also occur. Here the earth's crust is formed in volcanic eruptions and by intrusions. In the North Atlantic, the ridge southwest of Iceland is known as the Reykjanes Ridge, while north of the country the Kolbeinsey Ridge extends towards the Arctic Ocean. On dry land the plate margin runs northeast, thus making it possible to witness and study geological activity that would generally occur unseen on the sea-floor ridge. Inland, interaction during glacial periods between the ice cover and volcanism has produced mountains formed of hyaloclastites (i.e. cemented tuff) that are called *móberg* in Icelandic. The other main component of such mountains is pillow lava which is common on the sea floor. The so-called *Móberg* formation in Iceland is therefore a good example of some of the eruptive formations found on active ocean ridges around the world.

Just to the east of the axial rift lies the centre of the Iceland hot spot, which has long been active in the North Atlantic. It is actually the top of a mantle plume of upwelling ductile rock which is somewhat hotter than the mantle rock found within the mobile and relatively light mass that rises along the entire length of the ridge rifting zones, including Iceland. Where the hot spot and plate margin coincide, the production of magma and resultant crustal aggregation is so great that eruptive rock has created a large island: a kind of thickening of the crust. Iceland and its surrounding shelf form a 200,000 km^2 platform on the Mid-Atlantic Ridge, which reaches at least 3,000–4,000 m above the distant sea floor. It is sometimes said that the country floats on a relatively lighter "cushion" of hot mantle material. The formation of the country and the surrounding shelf area has been governed by the joint action of plate movement and the position of the hot spot over the past 20–24 million years.

Some hypotheses explain volcanism without resorting to the idea of a deep-rooted mantle plume, while others take account of the relatively shallower cycle within the mantle as an explanation for volcanism

A fissure eruption, Krafla, November 1981. (RTH)

and plate movement, or refer to yet other mechanisms and explanations.

Dynamic crustal formation and destruction

In Iceland, volcanic eruptions occur on average every four to five years (based on the past thousand years). Hundreds of fractures and dozens of central volcanoes are organised in around 30 well-delineated volcanic systems on dry land, while others are found in tectonically active areas on the sea floor. On land most of the volcanic systems are arranged obliquely (en echelon) in the volcanic zones which account for more than 25% of the land area. Volcanism is varied for a number of reasons: the crust is relatively thick and part of it is remelted, and intraplate lateral volcanic zones or belts occur outside the rifting zones. The volcanic products are also varied. Within the rifting zones basaltic fracture eruptions typical of sea-floor volcanism are common and central volcanoes also occur. In the lateral volcanic zones or belts, however, eruptions tend to be more explosive in nature, where evolved basalts or intermediate and acid magma are extruded through towering volcanoes and fractures. In these cases the volcanism is reminiscent of continental central volcanoes. Almost all the different types of volcanic structures can be found: crater rows with spatter cones, scoria and pumice craters cut up into offset sections, rows of explosion craters, lava shields reminiscent of the volcanoes of Hawaii, large mountain ranges with calderas, stratovolcanoes, volcanic domes and circular ash craters resembling those of the Moon. Submarine eruptions are common, and huge ice caps cover parts of some volcanic systems with the result that subglacial eruptions often occur with associated *jökulhlaups*. The latter are catastrophic floods that transport enormous amounts of material to the sea, including chemical substances which are variously beneficial or detrimental to marine life. Peculiarly shaped *móberg* mountains are left behind following eruptions under glaciers or the sea, in particular hyaloclastic *móberg* cones (made of tuff and breccias), table mountains (Icel. *stapi*) and serrated ridges composed of pillow lavas and hyaloclastites (*móberg*).

The plate margins, i.e. a continuous system of rift zones and transform faults or fracture zones, are the playground of giant forces. Numerous earthquakes of Ms = 5–7+ on the Richter scale occur in these regions as a result of plate movement. In addition the earthquakes are accompanied by volcanic eruptions. Thus thousands of measurable earthquakes can be expected in Iceland every year, while earthquakes in the range Ms = 6–7+ occur several times every century. Consequently it is easy to examine open fractures and faults of various types. These visual manifestations of plate movement can be found in the volcanic systemes and transform fracture zones and also in the oldest part of the country's bedrock. The latter is a fairly complex formation of 3.2–17 million years old. The bulk of it comprises severely eroded lava piles which overlap. They contain intrusions, including dykes and sills, and a considerable number of laccoliths composed of plutonic rocks. These are the remains of volcanoes or magma chambers and inactive volcanic systems. Tectonic features can also be found. These formations form the western and eastern parts of the country.

Subglacial volcanic eruption, Grímsvötn caldera
1998. (RTH)

From geysers to ice caps

The shallow depth to the magma or unusually hot crustal rocks, in addition to their high permeability and the presence of plentiful groundwater, means that geothermal activity is a striking feature in Iceland. The active volcanic zones contain many powerful and extremely hot geothermal areas with mud and steam springs (solfataras and fumaroles). In the older parts of the crust (east and west) there are still more geothermal areas, but with lower energy output and typified by boiling or lukewarm water springs. Iceland stands at the forefront of countries

15

Strokkur in action, Geysir geothermal field. (RTH)

that exploit geothermal energy, using it for domestic heating and electricity production, although most of the country's electricity is still
produced by hydroelectric power plants.

The recent snowline in Iceland has ranged between 600 and 1,700
metres above sea level, depending on the location in the country and
fluctuations in the climate over the past four to six decades. Around
50% of the country lies above 400 m and many individual mountains
or upland areas are capped by small or large glaciers: the largest are
termed ice caps. Five of these measure 200–8,000 km^2 in area and classify as temperate glaciers (ice temperature at freezing point). Ice thickness measurements yield up to 900 m. Numerous outlet glaciers of
varying thickness extend from these ice caps, including many surging
glaciers. There are volcanoes situated underneath four large ice caps,

The large ice cap Langjökull and a smaller one,
Hrútfell, in the central highlands. (RTH)

while a few other large or free-standing volcanoes are topped by glaciers. Iceland was for the most part covered by glacial ice during the
repeated glacial periods of the Ice Age and this has eroded and sculpted
large areas of the present-day landscape, particularly in the older western, northern and eastern parts of the country. The active valley glaciers
of today display all the features associated with glacier movement,
retreating glaciers and their sedimentation. All the larger rivers of the
country have their source in glaciers which cover a total of about 11.3%
of the land area. In addition, there are spring-fed rivers, direct run-off
rivers and mixtures of all three types. Lakes are numerous, though not
large, and owe their origin to glacial erosion, accumulation of marine
sediments, volcanism, debris flow and other processes. Fluvial erosion
and coastal marine erosion are rapid and their effects obvious, while
inland, wind erosion and frost weathering are dominant and have a
major impact on the landscape.

The climate of Iceland is relatively mild, generally windy and wet,
and characterised by frequent frost and thaw cycles. Chemical weather-

A surging glacier, western Langjökull ice cap
1999 (Hagafellsjökull eystri). (RTH)

ing is rapid in the basaltic crustal rocks and there are large amounts of
volcanic glass in the soils, classified as andosol, while the clay content
results in itbeing rather loosely bound. It is fertile but easily eroded,
which led to desertification in earlier centuries, a situation which has
been considerably retarded in recent times by the planting or fertilizing
and protecting of large land areas. Many different frost formations can
easily be seen in the soil, from stone polygons to vegetated hummocks
(Icel. þúfur) and large earth mounds in restricted permafrost areas
(tundras), as well as most of the erosion features associated with cold
climate soil around the world.

A geological "hot spot"

Iceland has played a key role in research into topics such as hot spots,
plate movement, volcanism, glaciology, Quarternary stratigraphy and
palaeoclimate, to name but a few. With the emergence of the space age

The cliffs of Dyrhólaey and a flat, sandy beach in southern Iceland. (RTH)

the country proved to be a suitable location for preparatory research on the Moon and for understanding processes there. More recently, experts on Martian geology have examined Iceland closely, for example in connection with research on glacial floods *(jökulhlaups)*, submarine geothermal springs, basaltic volcanism on dry land and subglacial eruptions. The country can therefore be regarded as a "hot spot" in more than one sense.

The first Icelandic geologists and geographers emerged between 1890 and 1930. They usually worked on special projects for the Danish or Icelandic authorities or taught in academic institutions in Iceland. The first geological map of the entire country was compiled by Þorvaldur Thoroddsen and published in 1912. Between 1930 and 1960 the number of geologists increased to around 10 or 15 specialists, and the first natural history institutions outside the University of Iceland appeared, including The Natural History Museum of Iceland (*Náttúrugripasafnið/ Náttúrufræðistofnun Íslands*). Its work included the compilation of a new geological map and the initiation of volcanological research. The teaching of geology as a specialist subject at the university did not start until around 1970, although some geology was taught as part of the engineering and geography courses from the mid 20th century onwards. Since the very beginning, in around 1930, the Meteorological Office has carried out seismological measurements and conducted geophysical research, while increased geothermal and hydroenergy production led to the setting up of the National Energy Authority around 1960, with associated research departments. In the period between 1938 and 1960 only one volcanic eruption occurred in Iceland (the Hekla eruption of 1947–48) and as a result volcanological research in this period tended to concentrate on the history and basic nature of volcanism in the country, including tephrochronology. Its main proponent, Dr. Sigurður Þórarinsson, was one of the country's most internationally recognised earth scientists between 1950 and 1970. For some time geology was a compulsory subject at high-school level (two terms), which is unusual in comparison to other countries. As the number of students increased, geology became a university subject, energy exploitation boomed, volcanological research thrived and an ever-increasing number of people sought a geological education and associated work within Iceland. Registered members of the Geoscience Society of Iceland now number almost 400 (2005). Some specialists are from abroad, and a considerable number of Icelandic earth scientists are employed in other countries.

Several of the country's specialists are well known for their work internationally. As the subject evolved, so did specialisation and the variety of the research. During this period the geophysics branch of the Meteorological Office was strengthened, the Nordic Volcanological Institute was founded, its work including further education, and the Science Institute at the University of Iceland attracted many specialists in the field of earth science to its staff. The United Nations Geothermal Training Program also began its work in Reykjavík, providing up to 20–30 foreign specialists with training each year. A large number of conferences, workshops and courses in specialist branches of earth science are held annually and hundreds or even thousands of researchers specialising in the geology of Iceland visit the country every year. In

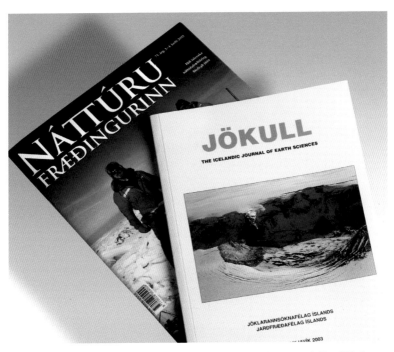

The two Icelandic journals publishing papers and articles on the geosciences in English or with an English abstract: *Jökull and Náttúru-fræðingurinn.* (RTH)

the autumn of 2003 the impressive new Askja natural science building was opened at the University of Iceland. As well as the geology department, many specialists in the field of geoscience moved to this building and various research institutes underwent considerable reorganisation. A few small private companies are also involved in geological research.

Note: In January 2007, Journal of Geoclynamics publisted a special issue (1) on Iceland with many interesting papers (vol. 43).

RESEARCH INSTITUTES AND THEIR WEBSITES

As of 2005 the following key institutions carry out geological research and other research projects within the field of earth sciences in Iceland. For addresses and contact information, please check the websites:

Department of Geology and Geography at the University of Iceland (Jarð- og landfræðiskor Háskóla Íslands)

Lectures and studies in geology and geography, research into Quaternary geology, volcanology, mineralogy, petrology, chemical geology, palaeontology, etc. Geophysics is studied within the Physics Dept. and both departments belong to the Faculty of Science. www.hi.is

Institute of Earth Sciences at the University of Iceland (Jarðvísindastofnun Háskóla Íslands)

Most branches of geology, theoretical and applied glaciology, volcanology, volcanic hazards, seismic research, tectonics, geophysical surveys and modelling, participation in the overall network of earthquake, tectonic movement and volcano monitoring (incl. the SIL-network), etc. www.jardvis.hi.is

Iceland GeoSurvey (Íslenskar orkurannsóknir)

Formerly, research in the fields of geothermal resources, hydropower, hydrology, etc. was conducted within the National Energy Authority (*Orkustofnun,* www.os.is) but it is now carried out by an independent entity. Activities include geological mapping, hydrology, glaciology, geothermal research and technology, geochemical research and environmental issues. An extensive stock of research reports and geological maps is available. www.isor.is

Icelandic Institute of Natural History (Náttúrufræðistofnun Íslands)

Geological mapping, museum and curatorial activities, mineralogy and petrology, work on volcanic hazards, etc. The institute operates a small museum of natural history with a geological section. www.ni.is

The Geophysical Department of the Icelandic Meteorological Office (Jarðeðlisfræðisvið Veðurstofu Íslands)
Geophysical monitoring, seismic monitoring and research. Operation of the SIL-system for monitoring tectonic activity, earthquakes and volcanoes, etc. Avalanche and landslide hazards. **www.vedur.is**

The Nordic Volcanological Institute (Norræna eldfjallasetrið)
Geophysical and geological research into volcanic activity, isostatic movements and tectonics. Mineralogy, trace element mass spectrometer analysis, geophysical modelling and participation in the overall network of monitoring tectonic activities, earthquakes and volcanoes (incl. the SIL-network). **www.norvol.hi.is**

Soil research is carried out by the Hvanneyri Agricultural University (**www. lbhi.is**) and the Soil Conservation Agency (**www.land.is**). An overview can be found at **www.rala.is/kvasir**

EXHIBITIONS
Mineral, rock and geology exhibitions
Several exhibitions of Icelandic rocks and minerals can be found in towns outside Reykjavík (see **www.ni.is**), including Akranes, Akureyri, Húsavík, Neskaupstaður, Stöðvarfjörður, Vestmannaeyjar and Kópavogur (ask for information locally or at tourist information offices).

Exhibitions with information on general or regional geology are found, for example, at the Svartsengi Geothermal Power Plant close to the Blue Lagoon (Eldborg), at Geysir, Höfn/Hornafjörður (on glaciers and ice caps), Lake Mývatn (in summer) and at the visitor centres of the national parks.

Further projects are currently (2007) in preparation.

The Institute of Earth Sciences of the University
of Iceland is housed in *Askja* close to the Nordic
House in the centre of Reykjavík. (RTH)

SOCIETIES, PUBLICATIONS AND THEIR WEBSITES

The Geoscience Society of Iceland (Jarðfræðafélag Íslands)

Issues the annual geoscientific magazine *Jökull* (Glacier) along with the
Iceland Glaciological Society (see IGS), in addition to other activities.
Most articles are in English. **www.jfi.is**

Hið íslenska náttúrufræðifélag (The Society for Natural Sciences)

Issues the magazine *Náttúrufræðingurinn* (The Naturalist; 2–4 times
p.a., housed at the Icelandic Institute of Natural History) in Icelandic
with English abstracts of the main articles which commonly cover geological issues. Contact: through **www.ni.is**

The Iceland Glaciological Society
(IGS, Jöklarannsóknafélag Íslands)

Participates in glaciological research and issues the annual scientific magazine *Jökull* (Glacier) in cooperation with the Geoscience Society of Iceland. The magazine carries articles/scientific papers in English on glaciology and various aspects of geology and geophysics. **www.jorfi.is**

A useful website is maintained by the lecturer and geologist George Douglas at the Hamrahlíð High School and contains many links: **www. ismennt.is/vefir/earth**

GEOLOGICAL MAPS AND WEBSITES

The National Energy Authority has issued different types of geological maps of regions with relevance to hydropower and geothermal power projects (**www.os.is**). So have Sudurnes Regional Heating (Hitaveita Suðurnesja, **www. hs.is**) and Reykjavík Energy (Orkuveita Reykjavíkur, **www.or.is**). The Icelandic Institute of Natural History, in cooperation with the National Land Survey of Iceland (or Geodetic Survey, **www. li.is**), recently issued six geological maps covering the whole of Iceland (1:250,000). The publishing house Edda (formerly Mál og menning, **www.edda.is**) has also published three maps, illustrating the bedrock of Iceland, the tectonics and the vegetation cover (1:500,000), in cooperation with the Icelandic Institute of Natural History.

Basalt columns, Reynisfjall, South Iceland.
(RTH)

2 The foundation
by Halldór Kjartansson

Rocks and minerals

Iceland is a large isolated basaltic mass in the middle of the North Atlantic. The island is in most respects understandably different from the bedrock of the continents, since its origin is quite different. Iceland was formed when the Mid-Atlantic Ridge became positioned over one of the most powerful mantle plumes in the world. Production from the plume and rising material beneath the ridge are sufficient to form an approximately 40 km thick crustal expanse of basalt which has such a low density that it sits above sea level. This basalt platform is well over 200,000 km^2 in total area. About 103,000 km^2 of this rise above sea level as the island of Iceland. Iceland is therefore a very young country compared to the continental landmasses. The oldest dated rocks above sea level are about 16 million years old. This means furthermore that Iceland is petrologically very homogenous. About 90% of the bedrock is igneous, of which about 80% is basalt and only about 10% sedimentary. The remaining 10% are acid (SiO$_2$-rich) rocks and intermediate eruptives. Metamorphic rocks hardly exist.

The most famous minerals in Iceland are secondary pore and crack infills or amygdales. These include, on the one hand, a variety of calcite known as Iceland spar and, on the other, zeolites which are common and well known. Eighteen types of the latter have been found in Iceland, including the largest and most beautiful zeolite crystals in the world.

> ### Key words
>
> Magmatic rocks • basalt • basic rocks • intermediate rocks • acid rocks • Tertiary formation • Quaternary formation • primary minerals • secondary minerals • tholeiitic series • transitional series • alkali series • evolution of magma • plutonic/intrusive rocks • classification of eruptives • palagonite

Mostly basalt

Basalt is the most widely distributed rock in the world. The entire sea floor, over 50% of the Earth's surface, is composed of basalt, and basalt is continually solidifying in the wake of eruptions on the sea floor or as intrusions in the crust somewhere at the ocean ridges of the world. There, a submarine eruption generally occurs at great depth (>1,000 m) so that the pressure of the sea contains the eruption. Only in certain locations are there hot spots underneath the oceans where magma production is sufficient to allow islands to form, among the most significant being Iceland, the Galapagos islands and the Hawaiian islands. On the continental landmasses, on the other hand, basalt is relatively rare, although there are quite large expanses of basalt such as the Deccan basalt plateau in India, the Colorado basalt plateau in the USA and others. These are also attributed to hot spots.

Iceland consists, therefore, from a geological viewpoint, of elevated sea floor and, moreover, the largest area of sea floor above sea level. Here (as in Hawaii) it is possible to closely monitor basalt eruptions and investigate different types of basalt. And there is yet another unique aspect to Iceland. The Mid-Atlantic Ridge runs right through the country and coincides with the mantle plume which forms one of the more active hot spots in the world. Drifting of plates in opposite directions at the central part of the ridge is slow (rifting amounts to about 2 cm per year on average) and the Icelandic crust is thick (up to 40 km). Basalt has evolved in central volcanoes or changed composition in other ways to partly form intermediate and acid igneous rocks. Plate drifting, the formation of the country's bedrock, the origin and evolution of basalt, volcanism and geothermal heat, and the geological history of Iceland will be covered in the following chapters. This chapter deals with the appearance of various igneous rocks and the way in which the crust is composed of them. Minerals, especially primary minerals and amygdales, will also be examined.

Although almost all the bedrock of Iceland is composed of basalt, its appearance varies greatly depending on the conditions of its formation and age. If eruption occurs on dry land the basalt magma flows as lava and forms layers measuring from a few metres to tens of metres thick.

A flank cross-section of a lava shield on the Reykjanesskagi peninsula. The thin, belted basalt layers (picrite) formed during one prolonged eruption. (RTH)

If, on the other hand, eruption takes place under glaciers or the sea, water quenches the magma and causes flash boiling, commmonly with tephra production (loose eruptives) as a result. Under thick glaciers (hundreds of metres), or at great depth in the sea, the eruption is contained by water and ice pressure, leading to the formation of pillow lava. When the pillow lava has formed a thick mound, causing water depth to decrease, the eruption becomes explosive (Surtseyan). The magma becomes fragmented and forms tephra, mainly as ash, which builds up and later hardens into *móberg* (palagonite tuff, also termed hyaloclastite). When the glacier ice disappears, it leaves behind *móberg* mountains, commonly rising up to several hundred metres above their surroundings. The above-mentioned conditions occurred in Iceland during the glacial periods of the Pleistocene and in fact still persist, for example beneath the western Vatnajökull, Mýrdalsjökull and Eyjafjallajökull ice caps (dormant but active volcanoes).

Classification of the Icelandic bedrock
- Tertiary bedrock (*Blágrýtismyndunin*): Ca. 16–3 million years ago.
- The Older Pleistocene formation (*Eldri ísaldarmyndunin*): 3–0.78 million years ago.
- The Younger Pleistocene formation (*Yngri ísaldarmyndunin*): 780,000–10,000 years ago.
- The Holocene formation: last 10,000 years.

Tertiary formation (ca. 16 million–3 million years ago)

This is the oldest part of the bedrock. The oldest rock occurs furthest east and west, and the youngest towards the central axis of the country, all of which can be explained by plate drifting (spreading plate movements). There is therefore no longer any volcanism within the Tertiary formation and only trace evidence of previous plate drifting and volcanic activity is found there. The Icelandic term *Blágrýtismyndun* refers to the dark basalt rock. This formation accumulated during the latter part of the Tertiary, that is before the Pleistocene, and all indications point to a climate much warmer than in Quaternary times. There is almost no evidence of glaciation in the Tertiary lava piles. On the other hand, Pleistocene glaciers have eroded the upper parts of the lava piles in many areas and cut deep valleys and fjords into them. Good sections in the bedrock can be studied on mountainsides in western, northwestern and eastern parts of Iceland. These generally consist of a pile of trap basalt strata, with thin interbasaltic layers, dipping 5–15° towards the nearest inland volcanic belt. A number of vertical dykes cut the lava pile. Eroded ancient central volcanoes are widespread and testify to great activity and high temperatures. In these areas the lava pile is disturbed, the dip becomes irregular and the rocks are commonly green coloured due to alteration. Dykes are numerous and form dense swarms. Some dykes dip, indicating intrusive activity close to a magma

Basalt veins in an eruptive complex. While dykes are emplaced in straight fissures, veins are generally thinner, bent or crooked. (RTH)

Characteristics of the Tertiary formation are as follows:
- Piles of dark-coloured, altered lavas with amygdales.
- Red interbasaltic layers.
- Lignite coal (Icel. *surtarbrandur*)

chamber or caldera formation. Small intrusive bodies (laccoliths) composed of gabbro and granophyre also occur.

The lava layers are usually altered by geothermal heat and are therefore dark brown or almost black in colour (thus the Icel. term "dark" or "blue rock" or *blágrýti*). They are also more or less amygdaloidal. The Tertiary landscape appears to have consisted of lava plains (the lavas are practically flat) and little else apart from shallow valleys, isolated volcanoes and crater rows.

Sediments occur between most lavas. Most common are the red interbasaltic sediments. These are red-coloured sands and clays, probably lateritic soils formed by chemical weathering in a fairly hot and humid climate, much warmer than our present one. The sediments are coloured red right through and most of them are thin (<1 m), which suggests frequent eruptions, but in some localities they are up to 15 m thick, which suggests a longer period of volcanic quiescence.

Fluvial sediment is also widespread. It consists of brown sandstones and clays which generally form fairly thick layers. In places these layers contain up to 1 m thick seams of lignite coal (Icel. *surtarbrandur*).

Tephra layers can also be found in the lava pile, particularly close to central volcanoes. Strata which cannot be found in the Tertiary formation are mainly:
- Unaltered grey lavas without amygdales.
- *Móberg* (palagonite tuff), although certain sediments may resemble *móberg*.
- Glacial tillites (with a few exceptions).
- Marine sediments (the oldest marine sediments are in the Tjörnes strata from the Tertiary-Quaternary boundary).

Fluvial sediments are common in Iceland,
especially in the Quaternary regions. (RTH)

The boundary between the Tertiary and Quaternary formations is by no means clear. Towards the end of the Tertiary the temperature gradually decreased but there was no sudden onset of the Ice Age. The boundary is most obvious in Iceland in the sedimentary succession at Tjörnes. According to this, the Pleistocene in Iceland began with a long glacial period a little over 3 million years ago.

Characteristics of the Pleistocene formations:
- Little-altered or unaltered lavas which are lighter in colour (greyer) than the older rocks.
- *Móberg* (palagonite tuff), forming mountains or thick tuff layers.
- Glacial tillites and glaciofluvial sediments (often varve clays).
- Marine sediments (often with the appearance of varves), sometimes containing shells.

Pleistocene formations (ca. 3 million–10,000 years ago)

The difference between the rocks from the Tertiary and the Pleistocene lies in the much colder climate that characterised the onset of the latter and in widespread glaciation. Glaciers covered almost the entire country for most of the period. The rocks are also younger and therefore less eroded than the older "*Blágrýti* formation". Few deep valleys or fjords cut the succession. Sections are therefore less common, although they can be found in mountainsides and river valleys lining the present volcanic zone.

Visible lavas are little or unaltered and not amygdaloidal. For this reason they are generally greyish and thus lighter in colour than Tertiary lava. The Icelandic term *grágrýti* ("grey rock") applies to the main types of lava.

As explained before, *móberg* forms in volcanic eruptions under glaciers and the resulting mountains often tend to be of low profile. Glaciers easily erode the soft *móberg*. In the older parts of the Pleistocene formations the móberg is not very conspicuous, occurring mainly as thick layers and in the bedrock. However, in the younger parts of the Pleistocene formation the móberg in a number of cases tends to be more obvious and the *móberg* mountains form impressive features in the active volcanic belt, such as table mountains (Icel. *stapi*) and multi-summit ridges.

Tillite is common over a wide area as interbasaltic material. The most common lacustrian sediment is that from the bottom of proglacial lakes, often with varve clays at the base and overlain by sandy sediments.

Marine sediments are found in several places, usually as a succession from the deltas of past glacial rivers.

Soil layers are brown in colour, resembling those of today.

As already indicated, the Pleistocene formation is divided in two, according to age. The older formation is known in Icelandic as the "Grágrýti formation" or the "Older grágrýti and móberg formation" while the younger has been termed the "Móberg formation" or the "Younger grágrýti and móberg formation". Lavas are more common in the older part of the formation and móberg in the younger part. There has been some confusion over the term grágrýti which has been used for the grey olivine-tholeiite shield-volcano lava and has been translated as dolerite in non-Icelandic literature. However, the term dolerite is now used purely to denote fine-grained gabbro which is an intrusive rock and not lava, so that the grágrýti formation cannot be referred to as a dolerite formation. On the other hand, it is acceptable to translate móberg formation as palagonite formation. It is therefore simplest to use the terms Older and Younger Pleistocene or Ice Age formations. But there are other considerations. The Ice Age had already begun in Iceland in the Pliocene about 3 million years ago, or about 1.5 million years earlier than in the northern hemisphere in general. The accepted boundary between Pliocene and Pleistocene is set at 1.6 million years ago. It is therefore hardly appropriate to call the Ice Age in Iceland the Pleistocene without elaboration. And it can be confusing to use the term Plio-Pleistocene formation for the Older Ice-Age formation which can be up to 3 million years old, although this is often done.

There is no clear stratigraphic division between the Older and Younger Ice Age or Pleistocene formations. For this reason the boundary is set in conjunction with the last geomagnetic reversal which was 780,000 years ago. Thus the Younger Ice Age formation spans the normally magnetised Bruhnes period up until the Holocene which began 10,000 years ago, and the Older Ice Age formation spans the Matuyama (reverse) and Gauss (normal) geomagnetic periods.

The Older Ice Age Formation (ca. 3–0.8 million years ago)
This formation forms broad stripes running along the active volcanic belt and extends over central southern Iceland. Here volcanic activity is

The Eystrahorn mountain massif is defined as an intrusive body of magma or a former magma chamber. It contains both acid and basic rocks from a series of successive magma injections, in a net-veined complex. (RTH)

no longer evident but some of the most active seismic zones belong to this formation. A good example of a section from the Older Ice Age formation is the glacially eroded mountain of Esja which is easily visible from Reykjavík. At the base of the mountain are ancient (about 2–3 million years old) central volcanoes and altered rocks (light grey), as well as intrusive rocks (dolerite, dark). On top of this is the rock succession, mainly composed of lavas with thick *móberg* layers (light brown) between the lavas.

The Younger Ice Age formation (780,000–10,000 years ago)

This formation lies in the active volcanic belt and as a result features much volcanism and tectonic activity. The lavas of this formation are glacially eroded, as is observed in the bedrock of Reykjavík, and relate generally as an olivine-tholeiite lava pile to one or more late, interglacial periods of the Ice Age. Móberg mountains are common and much more conspicuous than the flat lavas, in particular the stately móberg ridges and table mountains. Examples of such mountains lie to the east and southeast of Reykjavík: Hengill (a central volcano), Langahlíð, Bláfjöll, Sveifluháls and Keilir.

Phenocrysts are common in Icelandic basalt. The clear or white crystals are feldspars, green specks are olivine, and brownish or black dots are pyroxene. (RTH)

Recent postglacial lavas

When the glaciers of the last glacial period (Weichselian) disappeared about 10,000 years ago, volcanism continued to build up a new rock foundation. Presently, Holocene lavas cover about 10,000 km^2 (10% of the country). These lavas are easily recognised as they have not been eroded by glaciers and are rough and often difficult to traverse. The road between Reykjavík and Keflavík lies to a great extent through this type of lava.

The hard rocks

As has already been mentioned, the igneous rocks of Iceland are more varied than those found on the sea floor, the crust is thicker and volcanism more complex. The thickness of the crust means, for example, that underneath the active volcanic belts partially and completely melted rock occurs at relatively shallow depths. The magma can accumulate in reservoirs beneath the surface, i.e. large masses at great depth that have been called magma reservoirs, and also in smaller volumes nearer the surface, termed magma chambers. Central volcanoes gradually

37

The chief primary minerals

- The Feldspar group is divided into two serial end members:
- Plagioclase as Ca-Al silicate in primitive igneous rocks and Na-Al silicate in acid igneous rocks. Intermediate rocks contain Ca-Na mixed phases.
- Potassium feldspar: K-Al silicate in acid (and intermediate) igneous rocks.
- Quartz (SiO_2) in acid igneous rocks.
- Olivine (Mg-Fe silicate) in basic igneous rocks.
- Pyroxene (Ca-Mg-Fe-Al silicate; mainly augite) in all (Icelandic) igneous rocks.
- Hornblende is rare and biotite is hardly found in Icelandic igneous rocks although these primary minerals are common in acid and intermediate igneous rocks on the continents.
- Magnetite (mixed Fe-oxide) occurs mainly in basic igneous rocks.

form on the surface above such magma bodies. The volcanoes erupt frequently and in most cases obtain their magma from these sources. In fact, a key characteristic of central volcanoes is that they erupt magma of varied composition, covering a range from basic (52% SiO_2) through intermediate (52–65% SiO_2) to acid magma (65% SiO_2).

Solidification of magma involves crystallisation of different primary minerals, of which there are a relatively small number of main types.

Phenocrysts are crystals of the primary minerals, one type or more, distributed through the rock and much bigger than the groundmass, often of fingernail size.

Grain size of igneous rocks

- Glassy: structureless, no crystals. Lustre. Very rapid cooling.
- Microcrystalline: crystals microscopic. Matt. Rapid cooling.
- Finely crystalline: crystals 0.5–2 mm. Quite rapid cooling.
- Coarsely crystalline: crystals 2 mm (up to several centimetres). Slow cooling.

In addition to the primary minerals various others are found in small quantities.

Characteristics of the main primary minerals (seen with the naked eye)
- Plagioclase: white or almost clear.
- Potassium feldspar: fine grained (sanidine), white or clear (commonest in Icelandic rocks) or coarse grained (orthoclase), reddish colour (found in Iceland).
- Quartz: clear or milky, appears to be grey in rocks.
- Olivine: olive green (characteristic and easily recognisable).
- Pyroxene: Dark green to black, with small streaks.

The commonest Icelandic igneous rocks are often displayed in table form and these types can as a rule be easily identified in a hand specimen. It can be somewhat difficult to distinguish between intermediate and basic rocks (see later).

Confusion over terminology is common, particularly in Icelandic publications.

Basalt is often divided into *blágrýti* and *grágrýti* according to appearance and this is a well-established division, although it is based on nothing more than the fact that finely crystalline basalt is grey in colour (*grágrýti*=grey stone), while finely crystalline and microcrystalline basalt is dark in colour (*blágrýti*=blue stone, dark stone). It is inadvisable to translate *grágrýti* as dolerite or diabase.

Icelandic petrologists increasingly distinguish intermediate eruptive rocks in Iceland from continental andesite and call them Icelandite. The dark mineral in Icelandite is pyroxene and not the hornblende of continental andesite, while in addition Icelandite is richer in iron and poorer in aluminium.

The term liparite is still commonly used in Icelandic for the light-coloured acid eruptive rock instead of the more correct term rhyolite, and its use may prove difficult to eradicate. Rhyolite is, however, used in all scientific journals.

Icelandic igneous rocks (Tholeiitic series)

	Primary minerals	Eruptive rock	Intrusive rock
Basic rock 52% SiO_2	Ca-plagioclase, pyroxene, +/- olivine, magnetite	Basalt	Coarse grained: gabbro Fine grained: dolerite
Intermediate rock 52–65% SiO_2	Intermediate-plagioclase, pyroxene	Icelandite (andesite)	Diorite
Acid rock 65% SiO_2	Na-plagioclase, potassium feldspar, quarz, pyroxene	Rhyolite (liparite)	Coarse grained: granite Fine grained: granophyre

The term granophyre is used for the light-coloured fine-coloured acid intrusive rock which is widespread in Iceland, but is not necessarily based on analysis of its texture or structure.

The English geologist G.P.L. Walker pioneered stratigraphical studies of the Tertiary basalt formation (1959–62). He divided the basalts into three archetypes according to their appearance in hand specimens (grain size, colour and flow-banding), but used terms from petrology, which are unfortunate and have caused confusion. He uses the terms porphyritic basalt, olivine basalt and tholeiite basalt in spite of the fact that the Tertiary basalts all belong to the tholeiitic rock series.

Magma evolution

There are two main types of volcanism in Iceland. On the one hand there are shield volcanoes with eruptions of the Hawaiian effusive type. These have mainly erupted during and immediately after the close of glacial periods and are associated with large vertical isostatic movement related to the formation and disappearance of ice caps. This in turn causes pressure changes in the crust. On the other hand there are the elongated, en-echelon-spaced volcanic systems of the volcanic zones. The volcanic systems comprise mainly crater rows which form

Rapid cooling of magma in the open air or in contact with water may turn the eruptive rocks into amorphous, glassy material: volcanic glass. Obsidian (right) is a well-known variety, composed of acid rocks (e.g. rhyolite, left). (RTH)

in eruptions of Hawaiian to Strombolian type. Near the centre of the volcanic systems central volcanoes usually evolve and erupt frequently with variable eruption type from Strombolian to Plinian. The rocks also vary from basalt to rhyolite. It is likely that magma reservoirs of different sizes exist beneath the volcanic systems, while under each central volcano there is a smaller magma chamber where magma can evolve from the original basalt to rhyolite. This evolution can result from fractional crystallisation in the magma chamber, partial melting of the host rock or mixing of magmas of different acidity.

Regionally, the postglacial igneous rocks are divided into three evolutionary series, each with a compositional SiO_2-range from basic to acid:

a) The tholeiite series occurs in the active rifting zones of the ocean-ridge system. The rocks have a low alkaline content, a high proportion of Fe and Ti and are low in Al and Ca.

b) The alkali series occurs on volcanic islands outside the spreading ridge system. In Iceland it is found in the lateral volcanic belts where there is no rifting. This is the case in the Westman Islands and in the Holocene volcanism of the Snæfellsnes peninsula. The rocks have a high alkaline content with a relatively high proportion of Al.

c) The transitional basalt series is found as a continuation of the active northeastern volcanic rift zone, i.e. in an area including the Torfajökull volcanic system and extending to Eyjafjallajökull (the Westman Islands come next to the south). Rocks of the transitional series have a relatively high proportion of Fe and Ti but are low in Al.

The top photo shows micro-crystalline acid eruptive rocks (rhyolite) but the pink variety is an igneous, intrusive, coarser-grained counterpart (granophyre). The lower photo displays two varieties of gabbro and behind them is common tholeiitic basalt. (RTH)

Each of the series has an independent origin. They develop separately and evolve side by side, divided by the so-called Hawaiian line, as can be seen in the alkali/SiO_2 diagram.

Eruptive rock types of the Holocene

The tholeiite series comprises: picrite, olivine tholeiite, tholeiite (all basic rock types); basaltic Icelandite, Icelandite (two intermediate rock types); dacite, rhyolite (the acid rock types).

Picrite

The rock is grey, fine grained and finely vesicular. The groundmass resembles that of olivine tholeiite. The main characteristic of picrite is a high content of olivine phenocrysts, often around 20%, and black chromite phenocrysts (small); plagioclase and pyroxene phenocrysts can also often be seen. A peculiarity is that the olivine phenocrysts sink rapidly in the hot magma (1,300°C) and as a result they occur at the bottom of the lava rather than at the top, so that there is a risk of confusing them with olivine tholeiite. However, the chromite phenocrysts help in identification since they occur only in picrite. This phenomenon is very clearly illustrated in pillow lavas at Stapafell on the Reykjanes peninsula. Picrite is a very primitive basalt with a very high proportion of MgO and Cr_2O_3. The magma has a very low viscosity and forms mainly small flat shield volcanoes. It is a rare rock type, found mainly on the Reykjanes peninsula.

Olivine tholeiite

The rock is grey (*"grágrýti"*), fine grained and finely vesicular. There are no large phenocrysts. The rock often displays individual mineral grains (0.3–1 mm) in the groundmass visible to the naked eye (white plagioclase, yellow olivine, black pyroxene, magnetite). Olivine tholeiite is a primitive basalt, the proportion of MgO>8%. It probably erupts directly from the mantle, since the magma is hot and very liquid and usually solidifies as pahoehoe or plate lava. The volcanic centres are chiefly large lava shields or móberg table mountains (stapis) but volcanic slag craters may sometimes consist of this rock type. It is one of the commonest rocks in the country after tholeiite.

Tholeiite

The rock varies from almost black (microcrystalline, aphanitic) to dark grey (fine grained). It is so fine grained that groundmass crystals can generally not be discerned. It is often vesicular, with large (often 2–8 mm) irregular vesicles. Phenocrysts are common, often white plagioclase, less commonly pyroxene (augite) or olivine, with more than one phenocryst in the same lava. The proportion of plagioclase phenocrysts is sometimes high, 10% or more. Tholeiite is usually associated

A xenolite embedded in a lava bomb. The xenolite is an "alien" rock that rising magma has broken from the host rock. (RTH)

with volcanic systems, probably originates from magma reservoirs or magma chambers and is therefore somewhat evolved with the proportion of MgO<5–8%. The eruption is usually on fissures, often very long ones, and the volcanic edifices are scoria and volcanic-slag crater rows. The magma is more viscous and usually solidifies as aa or scoria lava. Tholeiite is the commonest rock in Iceland.

Basaltic Icelandite and Icelandite (andesite)

These are both intermediate rocks and are so alike that it can be difficult to distinguish between them. Both are invariably microcrystalline and almost without phenocrysts, flow-banded and tend to break down into plates. Basaltic Icelandite is dark grey and often slightly brownish in colour. Icelandite is also dark grey, often with purple streaks, and reddish patches are sometimes evident. Both lavas are of a thick aa type. Both rocks are considerably evolved and associated with central volcanoes. They are comparatively rare.

Rhyolite (liparite)

Rhyolite is the most acidic eruptive rock and very similar to dacite. It is very light in colour, often cream coloured, microcrystalline and seldom contains phenocrysts. Flow-banding is common and the rock cleaves into thin slabs. It is very like dacite and the two rocks are difficult to distinguish in a hand specimen. However, dacite does have a better ring when struck with a hammer. Iron oxide precipitation is common and gives the rock a rusty-brown colour. Rusty streaks and tongues are common, lending rhyolite slabs a bright colour, and they are often used as a decorative material in buildings. Rhyolite is the most evolved rock and is associated with central volcanoes. It is fairly common and widely distributed, easily visible from a distance due to its bright colour among the surrounding basaltic rocks. The largest expanse occurs in the Torfajökull area (often referred to as Landmannalaugar). Close to Reykjavík rhyolite can be seen on the Móskarðshnúkar peaks at the eastern end of Mt. Esja.

The alkali basalt series is: ankaramite, alkali-olivine basalt (both are basalt), hawaiite, mugearite (two intermediate rocks), benmoreite, trachyte (both are acid rocks).

Ankaramite

This is the basic rock member of the alkali series. It is characterised by a high proportion of olivine and pyroxene (augite) phenocrysts. It is found in several places in the Eyjafjöll region, South Iceland.

Alkali-olivine basalt

This rock is characterised by noticeable phenocrysts of olivine and pyroxene (augite). It often occurs as pahoehoe lava. Alkali-olivine basalt lava was produced during the Surtsey eruption as pahoehoe lava. During the Heimaey eruption of 1973, on the other hand, mainly hawaiite was erupted.

The neovolcanism which began 2 million years ago on the Snæfellsnes peninsula is highly alkaline. Three volcanic systems belong to this lateral volcanic zone; from Snæfellsjökull to Grábrók in Borgarfjörður. Underlying these volcanic systems is much older tholeiite rock from a former rifting zone which became extinct about 6 million years ago. Examples of alkali-olivine basalt are Eldborgarhraun in Hnappadalur (pahoehoe lava), Berserkjahraun on the northwestern shore of the peninsula near Stykkishólmur (aa lava) and Búðahraun in the central

Minerals in acid eruptive
rocks commonly crystallise
in layers. Weathering splits
the rocks and the resulting
thin slices of rhyolite or
related rock types cover
many a mountain
slope. (RTH)

south of the peninsula (pahoehoe lava). The stratovolcano of Snæfellsjökull at the western extremity of the peninsula is an alkali central volcano which has been active for at least 700,000 years. All rocks of the
alkali basalt series can be found there. Snæfellsjökull last erupted just
under 2,000 years ago, producing both a violent Plinian eruption with
rhyolitic pumice and ash, and lava, probably including the Háahraun
lava (close to Dagverðará). This is trachyte lava, grey in colour, microcrystalline and free from phenocrysts, with strong flow-banding.

The transitional basalt series is: intermediate basalt, transitional basaltic Icelandite, transitional Icelandite, rhyolite.

The transitional basalt series is very like the tholeiite series and thus
it is difficult to distinguish between them. The eruptive rocks of some
of the best known Icelandic central volcanoes belong to this series.
These include Hekla, one of the most active volcanoes in the country.
Hekla's eruptive history and the variable composition of its tephra and
lava is a puzzle and various explanations have been suggested. Most
lavas are of basaltic Icelandite. The largest rhyolite central volcano in

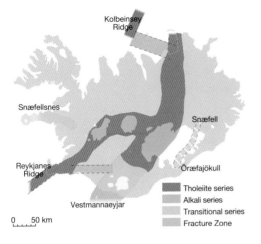

The established regional variation of the chemical composition of eruptive rocks belonging to three different series: the tholeiitic, transitional and alkali series. The rift zones contain tholeiitic rocks.

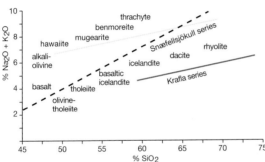

The diagram shows how the Icelandic magma archetypes relate to the ("Hawaiian") boundary line (stippled) between high-alkaline, nepheline-normative rocks and low-alkaline, quartz-normative rocks. The rift-zone basalts evolve from picrites and olivine tholeiites to rhyolite (e.g. the Krafla series, red), while the off-rift lateral-zone basalts evolve toward mugearite and trachyte (e.g. the Snæfellsjökull series, light blue). The "go-between" transitional series bridges the other two and is confined to the south Iceland region affected by a propagating rift (northern part of the SIVZ), shown in purple on the map.
(Main sources: S.P. Jakobsson 1972 and 1979, K. Sæmundsson 1978 and S. Arnórsson 1993).

the country is in the Torfajökull area close to Hekla. The Tindafjöll central volcano, also in this area, produced the youngest ignimbrite in the country. The large, active stratovolcano of Eyjafjallajökull is located much further south. Last but not least is Katla beneath Mýrdalsjökull, a large active central volcano with a caldera, eruptions from which are accompanied by major tephra falls and catastrophic meltwater floods or jökulhlaups.

Intrusive rocks

Iceland has been building up for the past 20 million years. New volcanic formations accumulate in the active volcanic zones and belts and their vicinities. The land subsides isostatically due to the overburden but does not rise again significantly, with the result that new volcanic formations are gradually buried under still newer ones. Spreading plate movements carries the crust laterally out of the volcanic rift zone, where erosion and weathering subsequently remove layer after layer. The land rises anew isostatically. Consequently, the now uncovered rocks show characteristics of having been buried at different depths. They have become altered and display different dyke densities. Since Iceland is young, the resulting erosion depth is not very great. It attains the highest values in the southeast, or about 1,800 m relative to sea level, while elsewhere the Tertiary rocks and the Older Ice Age formation has been eroded from several hundred metres up to just over one thousand metres. There is therefore no reason to expect gigantic intrusions at the surface, and indeed the largest have a surface area of about 15 km^2.

Thin intrusions such as dykes, sills, volcanic plugs and laccoliths generally solidify rapidly, as a result of which their rocks are similar in grain size to eruptive rocks, and the same terminology is used for these intrusions as for eruptives, as seen for example in the term basalt dykes.

The term intrusion is used if the rocks are fine to coarse grained (1 mm to a few cm) and they have special names.

Dolerite is used for fine-grained, basic intrusive rock. It is composed of feldspar and quartz as well as dark minerals, commonly pyroxene. It is light grey, often slightly beige, in colour.

- Basic intrusive rocks: dolerite (fine grained (1–2 mm)), gabbro (coarse grained (cm)).
- Intermediate intrusive rock: diorite.
- Acid intrusive rock: granophyre (fine grained (1–2 mm)), granite (coarse grained (cm)).

Hvítserkur is one of the many sea stacks found along the Icelandic coast. It is an eroded dyke, located on the eastern shore of Vatnsnes in Húnaflói bay. (RTH)

True coarse-grained granite with reddish feldspar is found only in the cores of the largest intrusions in Iceland, e.g. in the Slaufrudalur region between Hornafjörður and Lón in the southeast. In Mt. Ketillaugarfjall in Hornafjörður there is a granophyre intrusion with red-coloured feldspar.

Composite is the term used for an igneous intrusion composed of two or more rock types which intermingle without mixing. This may occur in large intrusions, dykes, cone sheets and even in lava and tephra. It is generally believed that two types of magma have solidified within each other. The reason for lack of mixing is the difference in composition (basic magma solidifies at around 1,100°C and acid

49

magma at around 800°C) and different viscosities (basic magma is very liquid, while acid magma is viscous).

The large intrusions of the southeast (revealed by large-scale erosion) originally formed at a depth of 1,000–1,800 m and some may in fact be shallow magma chambers. Most of them are composed of gabbro or partly of granophyre. In many of them basalt (gabbro) occurs intertwined with granophyre. On the one hand they contain rounded basalt (seldom gabbro) fragments, most of them ranging from tennis balls to footballs in size and surrounded by granophyre ("mixed vein complex"). This has been explained by hot basic lava intruding into colder acid magma, cooling rapidly to form fine-grained basalt in the surrounding acid magma, which then solidifies as granophyre. On the other hand there are veins of granophyre surrounding blocky basalt fragments. The veins may be very thin (in the order of mm), a so-called "net veined complex". Basalt magma has in this case heated the acid magma and reduced its viscosity, enabling it to easily intrude the finely fractured country rock and cause fragmentation. This phenomenon is most easily accessible on the Eystrahorn headland close to the farm of Hvalnes and in the mouth of the Hvaldalur valley.

Composite dykes occur mainly in the eastern fjords and the southeast, and over 50 are known. They share the fact that they consist of rhyolite in the middle and basalt at the edges. The most easily accessible site is south of Breiðdalsvík where there are good sections of a composite dyke at Streitishvarf, in sea cliffs, and also on the mountainside north of Breiðdalsvík. At its southern extremity the dyke is about 30 m wide, of which 12.5 m is rhyolite, and 7.5 and 9–12 m basalt. The rhyolite contains many rounded basalt xenoliths, most of them elongate and up to 45 cm in length. The formation of the dyke can be explained as follows: basalt magma forms a dyke which slices the top off a magma chamber containing rhyolite magma which is too viscous to intrude far into the country rock. On the other hand, the rhyolite magma can easily ascend through the centre of the basalt dyke which insulates it from the cold country rock and heats the acid magma, reducing its viscosity. The magma rips the half-solidified basalt along with it, the xenoliths being rounded closest to the magma chamber. Further away the basalt is colder and the xenoliths have sharper edges and corners.

Composite cone sheets are part of ancient (Tertiary) central volcanoes, e.g. those associated with the Setberg region on the northern
coast of the Snæfellsnes peninsula. In this area there are many thin basic (basalt and dolerite) cone sheets and thick acid (rhyolite and granophyre) cone sheets which dip 30° on average towards a magma chamber lying deep within the crust. In about 10 places, composite cone
sheets have been found with basalt edges and a rhyolite centre, containing sausage-shaped, rounded xenoliths. The largest dyke is about 15 m
thick and magnification shows evidence of the cooling of the basalt at
its junction with the acid centre. This suggests that liquid basic and acid
cone sheets have cut each other.

Composite lavas and tephra can be found in the largest rhyolite area
of Iceland, at Landmannalaugar. This rhyolite area is part of a volcanic
system named after Torfajökull. The magma belongs to the transitional rock series and the volcanic system is active, having erupted during
the Pleistocene and Holocene right up to historical times. The system is
part of the South Iceland Volcanic Belt where there is no plate rifting.
Northeast of the Torfajökull area another volcanic system, named after
Bárðarbunga in the west of Vatnajökull, contains rocks of the tholeiite
series and is one of the most active in the country, its centre being
directly above the mantle plume which lies under Iceland. Although
this system belongs to the South Iceland Volcanic Belt geographically
speaking, it forms part of an active rifting zone (see chapter 3). The
junction between these two volcanic systems follows the road running
towards Landmannalaugar.

It is noteworthy that the last three eruptions in the Torfajökull system
occurred at the same time as eruptions in the Bárðarbunga system. One
such eruption was about 1,800 years ago. This produced the Hnausa-
gígar basalt lava from a fissure in the south of the Bárðarbunga system,
while at the same time and in direct line with it the Dómadalshraun
lava erupted furthest north in the Torfajökull system. The latter is
composed of both basalt and rhyolite and also contains tephra fragments composed of welded light-coloured pumice and dark basic
scoria. The next eruption in both systems occurred in 871 AD. These
were large eruptions and in the Bárðarbunga system the unique ash-
crater row of Vatnaöldur was formed in a vigorous phreatic/hydrovol-

canic eruption that caused heavy ash fall throughout the country. In
the Torfajökull system, on the other hand, activity started with a brief
acid explosive eruption accompanied by a large amount of ash fall, so
that an easily identifiable tephra layer was formed, light at the bottom
and dark on top. This is the well-known Settlement Layer which overlies most remains from the Norse settlement of Iceland. There was also
some lava production, both intermediate and acid, including the Hrafn-
tinnuhraun lava. Finally there was an eruption in 1477 at Veiðivötn,
first a phreatic/hydrovolcanic eruption and later an effusive eruption.
The southernmost craters in the Bárðarbunga system are the triple
Ljótipollur craters and the crater Strútur from which the basaltic
Norðurnámshraun was produced. Just south of this are acid lavas of
equal age in the Torfajökull system: Suðurnámshraun and Laugahraun
directly above Landmannalaugar. In the Laugahraun lava there are
fragments of basalt. The black matt basalt is easily distinguishable from
the black high-shine lustre of the obsidian. This simultaneous volcanic
activity in two dissimilar but adjacent volcanic systems can be explained
if the fracturing which preceded volcanic activity in the very active
Bárðarbunga rifting system extended into the much less active but
non-rifting Torfajökull system and opened the way for the hotter basalt
magma to enter the top of the magma chamber and mobilise the colder
viscous rhyolite magma. Such an explanation is similar to that for the
composite dykes described earlier. This scenario has been explained by
distinguishing the Bárðarbunga Volcanic System as the tip of a propagating rift zone, advancing from northeast Iceland towards the south,
into the South Iceland Volcanic Belt.

Xenoliths are alien rock fragments of a different type from the main
rock which has solidified around them. They can be fragments of the
country rock but also of rocks which are found nowhere in the vicinity.
Thus gabbro fragments are quite common in basalt on the Reykjanes
peninsula, although gabbro is not found there as a surface rock. Sometimes there is evidence that the xenoliths have practically been
assimilated by the magma of the main rock. It is also common to find
a narrow dark cooling rim on the xenoliths but the junction may also
be very sharp. One of the best places to see this is at Hrólfsvík near

Festarfjall (Grindavík) on the Reykjanes peninsula. Cores of volcanic bombs are sometimes made of gabbro xenoliths. Examples of such bombs can be found around the maar Grænavatn near Krýsuvík.

Various visible properties of igneous rocks

Glassy volcanic rocks

Igneous rocks become glassy when solidification is so rapid that the magma is undercooled and no crystals can form. Such rocks have a glassy lustre and are usually black. Very liquid magma crystallises faster than viscous magma. Acid viscous magma crystallises more slowly than basic magma and tends to be rather glassy as a result. All dacite and rhyolitic lavas are therefore covered by thick black obsidian glass on top of much lighter-coloured acid rock. All tephra is glassy.

Obsidian

Obsidian is a compact glassy rock which forms fragments with a conchoidal fracture pattern, often black (though grey, green, brown and red obsidian are also found). Obsidian can be porphyritic, the phenocrysts being mainly white feldspar. Obsidian is always acid, glass being either fine-grained ash or vesicular scoria with fragment size from small pebbles up to quite large boulders. Good samples of obsidian are valued by collectors. When broken, obsidian produces thin slivers, as sharp as razors. Obsidian occurs widely but the best known localities are Hrafntinnusker in the Torfajökull area and Hrafntinnuhryggur at Krafla.

Water-rich glass has less lustre than obsidian, resembles pitch and is called pitchstone. It is usually black, but often green or grey. Perlite is a kind of pitchstone with about 3–5% water content which expands greatly. Perlite powder (grain size 1–2 mm) turns into finely vesicular grains of pea size when heated to 900°C. Perlite has very good insulation properties and is in demand as a building material. The name derives from the fact that it often consists of small light-grey welded spheres. Perlite occurs in Iceland (at Prestahnúkur in Langjökull and in Loðmundarfjörður in the east), but commercial extraction is not economically viable.

Very peculiar and rare are lava drops or tears (spherulites), which are hard spheres of soap-bubble size composed of grey or green acid glass, sometimes occurring singly but more often joined together in an unusual system, some empty and containing smaller spheres. They form in gas bubbles, from microscopic feldspar and quartz needles. Good localities include Hvalfjarðareyri, close to Reykjavík, and Álftavík eystri in the east.

Tephra

Tephra is generally glassy. Glass, basic in composition (tachylite), is black, down to the smallest grains. All basic tephra – scoria, pumice and ash – is therefore black, unless it is altered (cf. palagonite). Large consolidated fragments of basalt glass do not occur naturally, instead there are thin rinds (selvage) on dykes, sills and pillow lava, very vesicular scoria and frothy pumice and fine-grained ash. The latter two are very light in colour.

Scoria

Scoria (and volcanic slag) consists of large and small, highly vesicular fragments of basalt glass, usually black in colour. It is formed when magma blobs shoot into the air and solidify. It is usually black but can be red if the iron in the magma becomes oxidised by combining with oxygen from the air. This results in cryptocrystalline hematite (Fe_2O_3) which colours the scoria a bright and striking red. Scoria also forms on the surface of aa lava. It is usually black and denser. Scoria is in demand as a building material and has been used as such to a great extent. However, the resulting mining activity has had detrimental environmental effects, especially on shapely scoria craters.

Pumice

Pumice consists of frothy fragments which float on water. A basic variety is formed mainly in phreatic/hydrovolcanic eruptions in the sea or under glaciers. It is black in colour. The acid pumice is light coloured and forms, often in large quantities, in explosive (phreato-magmatic) plinian eruptions (Hekla, Askja, Snæfellsjökull, Öræfajökull). Pumice is in demand as a raw material for various purposes. Hekla pumice from the 1104 eruption is mined to some extent for export.

Tephra comes in different grain sizes, such as ash (very fine grained), pumice (or lapilli), scoria, lava spatter and more streamlined lava bombs. (RTH)

Ash

Ash is the finest-grained tephra, the basaltic variety being black, the intermediate grey and the acid light in colour. Ash is produced in almost every eruption. Large quantities of ash fall in plinian eruptions and form light ash layers in soil sections. Large amounts are also produced in basic or intermediate explosive eruptions which occur at the start of large lava eruptions (Hekla, Laki), and the resulting ash layers are black or dark grey. Ash layers of the type mentioned form the basis of tephrochronology which was pioneered in Iceland around the middle of the last century and later in other volcanic countries. The study of tephrochronology has proved to be of great value in earth science, ecology and archaeology. The ash layers are also found in lake sediments, on the sea floor, in glacier ice and even in the soils of neighbouring countries, all of which increases the value of this method of dating.

Palagonite tuff

Palagonite tuff or *móberg* is formed when basalt tephra, mainly ash, is cemented together and hardens. Large amounts of tephra, mostly ash, are produced in phreatic/hydrovolcanic eruptions under glaciers or in the sea. The tephra piles up at the volcanic centre, often producing an entire mountain, then hardens to form a rock resembling sandstone. The tuff is usually altered and brown but can be black and unaltered. The ash is composed of small vesicular spheres, splinters and mineral fragments (phenocrysts), and absorbs water well. The so-called palagonitisation process involves the ash, hot water, rapid absorption of the water and a resulting alteration. The glass is oxidised, iron hydroxide and clay minerals are formed, and some materials become dissolved and precipitate as amygdales, mainly various types of temperature-dependent zeolites. The newly formed minerals cement the grains together. This causes hardening of the rock. In addition to the tuff, scoria fragments, rock fragments and pillow fragments become cemented into volcanic breccia. Also present are basalt veins, dykes and sills.

Following the Surtsey eruption, the opportunity finally arose to study the formation of *móberg*. Two years after the close of the eruption, geothermal activity became evident in the tephra pile, the temperature being at 100°C just below the surface. It was clear that the tephra was beginning to harden as *móberg*. Ten years after the end of the eruption, a hole was drilled through the tephra pile to a depth of 181 m. Drillholes were also sunk through some scoria layers as well as one 10 m thick basalt intrusion. The water depth was 58 m. Above sea level the rock was saturated by 100°C hot steam and below sea level by hot sea water. The highest measured temperature was 141°C at a depth of 105 m, but the temperature fell below this depth. It was obvious that cold sea water flowed into the rock, was heated and rose, boiling when it reached sea level. It also became clear that the heat flux plays a key role in the formation of *móberg*. The heat sources are presumably cooling pillow lava and intrusions, and in addition the alteration reactions are exothermic: basalt glass + water = *móberg* + heat. The reactions themselves actually produce sufficient heat to support the alteration. It should also be mentioned that when the *móberg* was examined by electron microscope, certain strange features were observed, which proved to be bacteria. They occupied the holes and tunnels in the glass at the palagonite rinds. It appears that bacteria live in and on *móberg*, although probably they are of little significance in its formation, unless the tunnels and holes facilitate water absorption.

Since the hardening of the tephra proceeds so rapidly and begins immediately following its production, it can be regarded as a normal part of the final stages of the eruption and solidification of the lava.

Acid tuff also exists and is presumably formed in subglacial eruptions. The best-known example is Bláhnúkur in Landmannalaugar. A green-coloured tuff can be seen in the mountain, which is much less consolidated than the palagonite tuff. Within the tuff there are huge pillows composed of acid rock, several metres in diameter, with regular columnar jointing of pitchstone and a crust of basalt up to a metre thick.

Móberg is remarkable in many ways. It is often stratified, with graded bedding in which the lowermost coarser part consists of small scoria fragments and the uppermost part of fine-grained ash. Either part can be harder than the other and they weather differentially. The stratification is presumably the result of tephra fall from explosions in the crater. If the eruption is continuous, the tephra will be unstratified. Layers showing reversed graded bedding are also common. They are the result of cold, wet base surges which occur when the lowest part of the eruption cloud is so heavy that it collapses and the tephra surges down the mountainside. Very varied structures are widespread, including various kinds of folding, unconformities and faults, buried landscapes, etc. The rocks are also fairly easily eroded by water, wind and frost, although they vary in hardness. As a result they have often been eroded into sculptures, good examples of these being found in Þórsmörk in the south. Although *móberg* is a soft rock it is little fractured. This is very apparent in Surtsey. When the lava began to flow it was thought that the hard basalt would protect the island from ever being destroyed. However, it is clear that well-fractured hard lava is much less able to withstand undermining by the sea than soft dense *móberg*. The lava is therefore undergoing rapid erosion and after some thousands of years Surtsey will be reduced to a precipitous *móberg* cliff like the other nearby islands.

Ignimbrite

Ignimbrite layers are formed by hot, acid pumice flows in which pumice slivers and fragments have a different colour than the groundmass. The youngest ignimbrite in Iceland is found at Þórsmörk. It was formed in a pumice flow about 54,000 years ago when a stratovolcano in the Tind-fjöll region collapsed, accompanied by a catastrophic tephra eruption. The groundmass is grey while the pumice fragments are a darker grey. The largest ignimbrite layer in Iceland is the Skessulag layer which can most easily be studied on the northern side of Berufjörður. It is about 800 km^2 in area and about 15 m thick and has been altered to a greenish colour. There is another ignimbrite layer at Húsafell in Borgarfjörður.

Vesicles form when dissolved gases escape from the magma due to a lowering of pressure and temperature in a similar way to when a champagne bottle is opened. Most of the gas escapes immediately through the eruption vent and the extent of the gas largely decides the course of the eruption. Some of the gases, however, do not escape until lava flow and solidification commence. Gas bubbles then form and rise through the magma. Those which do not escape "freeze" as vesicles. In aa lava the vesicles are often spherical and 2–8 mm in size, or pea size, although there is great variation. The uppermost part of the lava solidifies first, blocking the gas bubbles so that most of the vesicles occur there, as well as the largest and most irregularly shaped examples. In the central part of the lava, which solidifies last, they are at a minimum, while some also occur at the bottom. In pahoehoe lava, on the other hand, the vesicles are small and evenly distributed throughout the lava. The bottom of this type of lava flow often contains gas "worm" pipes. The gas bubbles have formed at the very bottom and risen up through the magma and the lava is so cold and viscous here that the gas pipes have not closed. On occasion the vesicles are distributed unevenly throughout the lava. In some columnar lavas there is a rhythmic vesicle pattern in which finely vesicular layers alternate with vesicle-free layers of the same thickness. The vesicular layers weather more rapidly, producing hollows, while the non-vesicular layers stand out as ridges. As a result the surface becomes wavy, resembling corrugated iron. Small vesicles can also be unevenly distributed in the lava, especially in the case of

Different types of hyaloclastite (móberg);
brownish palagonite tuff and breccia. (RTH)

Ignimbrite (welded, clastic tuff) in Berufjörður, eastern Iceland is associated with an old Tertiary central volcano. (RTH)

pahoehoe lava. Weathering produces depressions in the vesicular part and ridges in between so that various patterns form on the surface, often resembling Japanese characters. The vesicles, as well as fractures, make recent lavas very porous. Secondary minerals form in vesicles during alteration to form amygdales, as will be discussed later. Vesicles also may contain trace elements important for studies of magma origin and composition.

Flow structures are common in more viscous lava. Basalt is usually very liquid and the main body solidifies as a single layer. More viscous lava, such as andesite, dacite and rhyolite, as well as some basalt lavas, is so viscous that laminar flow forms shear surfaces which do not completely heal when the lava solidifies. Lava of this type breaks down into slabs upon weathering or for other reasons. The same can be seen in lava domes and occasionally in dykes. Flow-banded lava does not form columns. Flow-banding can often be seen in obsidian lavas in which bands of black obsidian and light porous and pumice-like rhyolite lava alternate. Flat or elongate crystals lie parallel to the flow, indicating its direction.

Columns are common in basalt. When glowing hot lava solidifies and cools, it contracts and fractures. The joints thus formed are always at right angles to the cooling surface and therefore vertical in lava and sills, but horizontal in dykes. Joints in flowing lava are usually irregular and unremarkable. However, if the lava is stagnant, as in lava lakes, the joints form regular columns which should generally be six sided, although there are exceptions to this. This is known as columnar jointing. Chisel marks can often be seen on joint surfaces showing that they formed in small "bursts". Sills are also beautifully columnar whereas dykes are seldom so. Volcanic plugs often display fine columnar structures too and the cooling surfaces are often curved so that the columns bend into strange shapes.

If water flows over half-solidified lava, it percolates down into the lava, causing quenching and the rock fractures into many small columns to produce "cubic rock". Often, however, the water only cools the surface so that the lower part of the lava fractures into beautiful columns. Fine columnar basalt can be found on the west of the Reynisfjall mountain in Mýrdal (in the south), Svartifoss in Skaftafell, Litlanesfoss at Hengifoss in the Hérað region (eastern Iceland), Hljóðaklettar in Jökulsárgljúfur, Aldeyjarfoss in Bárðardalur (northern Iceland), Kálfshamarsvík in Skagi (northwestern Iceland) and Gerðuberg in Hnappadalur (western Iceland).

The world of minerals
Geothermal alteration
Iceland is a young country still in the making and as a result has almost no metamorphic rock at the surface. Within the active volcanic zones a large amount of new igneous rock is produced. This includes both lava flows and build-up of *móberg* mountains. However, the land height does not increase by the same amount because isostatic movement causes the land to sink almost to the same extent. The newly formed rock therefore sinks thousands of metres into the crust as younger rock is constantly added above. The lavas are very porous and water reaches far down into the crust where it heats up in accordance with the high temperature gradient (ca. 100°C/km). Hot water alters the rock in-

creasingly with greater depth and secondary minerals precipitate in the cavities. At the same time plate spreading carries the crustal rocks later- ally until they leave the active volcanic zones. New material is no long- er added on the surface, but instead erosion, especially glacial erosion, removes it. The overall land height changes little since isostatic equilib- rium ensures that the crust rises in proportion to the material removed by erosion. As more and more time passes the crust moves yet further laterally due to spreading and more erosion unveils still deeper and older rocks. Since the country is young, erosion and weathering have not succeeded in removing more than up to 1,800 m (relative to sea level) in the southeast.

In the uppermost 100–200 m of the bedrock the temperature is gen- erally below 30°C and therefore free of secondary minerals and amy- gdales. At above 30°C amygdales begin to form. The predominant min- erals are zeolites and the term zeolite facies is used for the crust down to a depth of about 1,700 m. At around 230°C clay minerals of the chlorite group (Greek *chloros* =green) are most conspicuous, in addi- tion to the secondary mineral epidote, and the rocks have a greenish appearance (propylitisation). This is known as the chlorite facies. Around former central volcanoes and large intrusions this zoning is upset and shifts towards the surface. Propylitisation is known to have occurred at a depth of only 500 m. At still greater depths metamorphic rock takes over, first greenschist, then amphibolite and finally granu- lite. None of the metamorphic facies is found at the surface.

Important clay minerals:
- Smectite (alumosilicate with water and Ca, Na, Mg and Fe): white, brownish or greenish.
- Kaolinite (alumosilicate with water): white, often coloured reddish, brownish or bluish.
- Celadonite (alumosilcate with K, Mg and Fe): blue-green.
- Illite (alumosilicate with K): white.
- Chlorite (alumosilicate with Mg and Fe): green, light green to almost black.

Secondary minerals are common in Iceland. Most of them are quartz, varieties of zeolite and calcite. Zeolites are shown here along with clear quartz and jasper. (RTH)

Clay minerals

The alteration of basalt leads to the formation of various clay minerals. Of these the most important is smectite which starts to form before the zeolites. Kaolinite is found where high-temperature alteration has taken place, mainly in acid rocks. There is some illite, mainly a variety known as celadonite, which occurs as a highly conspicuous blue-green coating inside cavities and often under other amygdales, giving them a very colourful appearance. In areas with ancient amygdales, the clay mineral chlorite colours the rock green.

Classification of the secondary minerals (amygdales):

- Quartzes. $SiO_2.H$ 7. Cannot be scratched by a knife point. Scratches glass easily.
- Calcite. $CaCO_3$. H 3. Easily scratched by a knife. Effervesces in diluted cold hydrochloric acid
- Zeolites. Scratched easily or poorly by a knife. No effervescence in hydrochloric acid.
- Metal ores. Obvious metallic lustre.

Secondary minerals (amygdales)

Almost all amygdales can be divided into groups depending on relationships and location. There are four main groups and it is quite easy to distinguish between them.

Quartz minerals

Composition SiO_2. H 7, glassy lustre, no cleavage. In practice one mineral but is found in many slight variations that all have the same basic composition. The mineral properties are therefore the same, except for opal which is the softest variety. Quartz is the hardest of the Icelandic amygdales, scratching glass easily, and this is a diagnostic property. The outward appearances of the quartz minerals differ and are varied, each variety having its own name. Quartz minerals are often very beautiful and in demand as ornamental minerals. The varieties are many and complex and just five are considered here. Icelandic quartz minerals are often beautiful but seldom outstanding:

Rock crystal

Very distinct, clear quartz crystals, usually six sided with a point. Often form a crystal system in cavities: chalcedony outermost in the cavity with rock crystal growing inwards. Known coloured varieties are amethyst (red-purple) and smoky quartz (brownish).

Chalcedony

Cryptocrystalline quartz (apparently amorphous), H 7. Semi-transparent, usually colourless, white or grey. Occasionally with white and grey bands. The surface sometimes consists of small curved protrusions. Found on beaches as white (sometimes coloured yellowish by iron oxide) pebbles. Many colour varieties: bluish, yellowish, brownish, greenish. In demand for polishing as a decorative mineral.

Jasper

Amorphous, matt, strongly coloured quartz. The most common colours are red, green, brown and yellow. These colours are often woven together in many forms, commonly along with chalcedony and rock crystal. Often occurs as large stones. Used to best effect if large surfaces are cut and polished.

Opal
Amorphous, hydrated silica, strong lustre, softer than quartz (H 5.5–6.5), can be scratched by a good knife. Many generally dull colour varieties: light, brown, green and red. Relatively rare; no precious opal has been found in Iceland.

Silicified wood
Opalised wood. Tree growth rings can often be seen when polished. Light in colour and much denser than wood.

Calcite and other salts
Apart from calcite, this group includes amygdales other than silicates and sulphides.

Calcite
Calcite $CaCO_3$ is one of the commonest amygdales in Iceland. Many different crystal forms are known. White or often coloured yellowish by iron hydroxide. Almost always opaque. H 3, can be scratched easily by a knife. Very good cleavage along three planes and the crystals are dice shaped but with slanting sides. Glassy lustre except for the shelly lustre on fracture surfaces. A sure test is effervescence in cold diluted hydrochloric acid. Two Icelandic varieties can be mentioned. One is the famous Iceland spar: large, clear, perfect calcite crystals which are very rare and for a long time were only found in Iceland where the largest and most beautiful examples originate. The best-known locality in the world is Helgustaðir in Reyðarfjörður (in the eastern fjords). The double diffraction of light was discovered and explained using Iceland spar from Helgustaðir. The nicol prisms of petrological microscopes were previously made from Iceland spar. Mining was carried out at Helgustaðir (the mine is closed to the public) and in Hoffellsdalur in Hornafjörður (southeast Iceland), but was discontinued around 1930. Iceland spar is, however, quite widespread in Iceland. Most major min-

eralogical museums own examples of Iceland spar from Iceland, while the largest crystal (230 kg) sits at the entrance to the mineralogy collection of the Natural History Museum in London.

Sugarstone
Sugarstone is amber-brown calcite and resembles candy-sugar. It is found in fossilised shells at Tjörnes (northern Iceland). Other coloured varieties also exist.

Aragonite
Aragonite $CaCO_3$ is the other variety; a high-temperature, high-pressure modification of calcium carbonate, which therefore has a different crystal form (orthorhombic) than calcite (hexagonal). Different conditions determine which variety precipitates in the cavities. At surface conditions calcite is stable but the difference in crystal form is so small that aragonite gradually changes to calcite. The outward crystal form of aragonite is, however, maintained after recrystallisation and the calcite is thus a pseudomorph of aragonite. One and the same crystal can even be partly calcite and partly aragonite, making identification difficult. Aragonite crystals are usually six sided and often radiate with coarse crystals (cf. scolesite). It is white or grey. H 3.5–4, harder than calcite. Glassy lustre. Poor cleavage.

Dolomite
Dolomite $CaMg(CO_3)_2$ is closely related and very like calcite. Rare.

Siderite
Siderite $FeCO_3$ has been found as an amygdale. It forms small spheres with a radiating inner structure. Yellow to brown in colour. H 4–4.5.

Fluorite
Fluorite CaF_2 has been found in Iceland in the highly altered rocks of ancient central volcanoes and within or at the edges of large intrusions. It crystallises as cubes and displays good cleavage into cubes. Clear or dull purple. Glassy lustre. H 4.

Zeolites

A group of minerals (about 25 species) which share the fact that they are Na, Ca, K network silicates with Al-exchange and poorly bound crystal water. When heated they lose their crystal water and retrieve it again in high humidity. They occur mainly as a secondary mineral/ amygdale in basalt. Very common in Iceland ("zeolite country"). Here some 18 types have been found as well as two minerals which resemble them. The best-known locality is Teigarhorn in Berufjörður (in the eastern fjords), where collecting is prohibited. Although the zeolites are regarded as a single group their crystal forms are very varied. They have been divided into three groups by appearance.

Zeolite classification:
- Fibrous: scolecite, mesolite, natrolite, thomsonite, mordenite, laumonite, phillipsite, garronite, gismondine.
- Platy: stilbite, heulandite, epistilbite, levyn, yugawaralite, erionite, cowlesite.
- Equant: chabazite, analcite.
- Similar minerals: apophyllite, gyrolite, okenite, thaumasite, reyerite, ilvaite.

Fibrous zeolites

Scolecite (Ca-Al silicate) is one of the commonest zeolites. Needle-like, four-sided crystals which grow radially outwards from a single point. Often 1–10 cm in length. White or semi-transparent. Glassy lustre. H 5.5.

Mesolite (Na-Ca-silicate) is common. Delicate, hair-like needles which radiate from a single point, very fragile. Much finer than scolecite. Sometimes several centimetres in length. White or grey. Glassy or silky lustre. H 5.5.

Natrolite (Na-Al-silicate) is closely related to scolecite and mesolite and resembles mesolite so strongly that distinction between them is almost impossible. Very rare.

Thomsonite (Na-Ca-Al-silicate) is very common. Dense hemispheres of extremely fine and dense crystal fibres, often about 0.5 cm long. White, but often bluish. H 5.

Mordenite (Na-K-Ca-Al-silicate) is common. Hair-like, flexible fibres which resemble mould or grow in tufts, often with a silky lustre. Usually white but also often red-brown and sometimes a reddish band lines the contact with the host rock. H 3–5.

Laumonite (Ca-Al-silicate) is common. Thin elongated fibres, horizontal lines and slanting points. Often grows irregularly and sometimes in bundles about 0.5 cm in length. Usually snow-white but sometimes red-brown. Good cleavage. Dull shelly lustre. Usually crumbles when broken. Crystal water is loosely bound so that the mineral also crumbles if kept in dry conditions. Forms at the highest temperature of all the zeolites, up to 200°C.

Phillipsite (Ca-Na-K-Al-silicate) is probably quite common but difficult to identify due to its small size. Very small (< 5 mm), four-sided crystals, often in radiating fans, but sometimes occurring singly. Clear or white. Glassy lustre. H 4.5.

Garronite (Na-Ca-Al-silicate) is rare. Radiating, densely packed groups, often 1–2 cm in length. White with a glassy lustre. Often intergrown with phillipsite.

Gismondine (Ca-Al-silicate) is rare. Small, radiating crystals resembling thomsonite. Clear or white. Glassy lustre. H 4–5.

Platy zeolites

Stilbite (Ca-Na-K-Al-silicate) is very common. Fairly thick, platy crystals which grow with a chisel-shaped end. Commonly a cluster of tightly packed crystals which widen at the ends. Often from 1–2 up to 6 cm in length. White, seldom red-brown. Good cleavage. Glassy lustre at the points but shelly lustre on the sides. H 3.5–4.

Heulandite (Ca-Na-Al-silicate) is common. Clusters of platy crystals, sometimes bent. Semi-transparent, seldom pink. Often from 0.5–1 cm up to 10 cm. Good cleavage. Strong shelly lustre on cleavage surfaces. Often occurs with stilbite.

Epistilbite (Ca-Al-silicate) is rare. Triangular, elongate, fairly thick crystals, cut at right angle at ends. Up to 1 cm in length. White or clear. Glassy lustre at the ends but shelly lustre on the sides. H 4–4.5.

Levyn (Ca-Al-silicate) is rather rare. Flat crystals with a hexagonal form, which often stand in an irregular row. Often several mm long. Clear or white. Glassy lustre. H 4.5.

Yugawaralite (Ca-Al-silicate) is very rare. Thin crystals with cut corners at the top. Several mm to 1 cm. Clear. Glassy lustre. H 4.5.

Erionite (Ca-Na-K-Al-silicate) is rare. Fibrous, flexible, soft crystals, usually forming intergrown groups. 2–3 cm in length. White. Shelly lustre. H 4.

Cowlesite (Ca-Al-silicate) is rare. Very small, sheet-like, very thin crystals which end in a point. Common length is about 1 mm. Most often occur as hemispherical protrusions. Grey or white. Glassy or shelly lustre. H 2.

Cubic-form zeolites

Chabazite (Ca-Al-silicate) is very common. Cubic crystals. Twin forms are common in which the corners of one crystal extrude from the face of the other. Often several mm up to 1 cm long. White or clear, occasionally slightly rosy. Glassy lustre. Poor cleavage. H 4.5.

Analcite (Na-Al-silicate) is common. Polymorphs. Crystals separate but often lie together and form a coating within cavities, which glitters and appears to be black. Often 0.2–0.5 up to 1 cm long. White or clear. Conspicuous glassy lustre. No cleavage. H 4.5–5.

Similar to zeolites

Apophyllite K-Ca-F-silicate. Four-sided crystals with truncated corners. 1–3 cm in size. Usually white or clear but blue-green, yellowish and reddish varieties also occur. Shelly lustre. Good cleavage. H 4.5–5.

Gyrolite (Ca-silicate). Thin, platy, often hexagonal crystals, usually in bunches which resemble a fan. White. Strong silky lustre. H 3–4.

Okenite (Ca-silicate) is rare. Fibrous crystals, usually dense amygdales with dull, radiating pattern, also small spheres with very fine protruding needles like cotton-wool balls. Several mm (spheres) to several cm long. White. Dull glassy or shelly lustre. H 4.5–5.

Thaumasite (Ca-Al-sulphate that belongs to the ettringite group) is rare. Fibrous crystals form poorly distinguishable radiating mass. White, colourless. Glassy or silky lustre. H 3.5.

Zeolite belts in olivine tholeiite in the eastern fjords

Zeolites	Temperature	Depth of formation
No zeolites	30°C	Up to 100–200 m
Chabazite-thomsonite zone	30–50°C	Up to 600 m
Analcime zone	Up to 70°C	Up to 800 m
Mesolite-scolecite zone	Up to 120°C	Up to 1,700 m
Laumonite zone	Up to 230°C	Above 1,700 m

Reyerite (Na-K-Ca-Al-silicate) is rare. Sheet-like crystals form small flakes. White. Matt, glassy or dull shelly lustre. H 3.5–4.5.

Ilvaite (Ca-Fe-silicate) is very rare. Elongate, slightly streaky strands or cube-shaped polymorphs. 2–4 mm. Black. Dull metallic lustre. H 5–6.

Zeolite belts

It is obvious that olivine-rich rock (olivine tholeiite) alters earlier and more rapidly than olivine-poor rock (tholeiite). Olivine is the least stable mineral and therefore the first to break down and change rapidly into other minerals. Initially it turns red ("iddingsite"). The early alteration minerals occupy a greater volume than the olivine so that the rock breaks down easily. They are followed by the zeolites, of which there are more in the olivine-rich rock. Tholeiite alters later and fewer zeolites form. It displays a higher degree of crystallisation and therefore quartz minerals become more conspicuous in this type of rock than in olivine-rich rocks, as well as silica-rich zeolites such as mordenite, stilbite, heulandite and epistilbite.

About 40 years ago geologists working in the eastern fjords under the guidance of G.P.L. Walker noticed that the amygdales, especially zeolites, were arranged in almost horizontal belts according to the depth of formation. The type of secondary minerals which form is thus dependent on the temperature and composition of the country rock. Central volcanoes and large intrusions upset this zonal distribution.

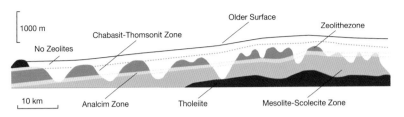

The classic presentation of zeolite zones in East Iceland. Local anomalies also occur close to extinct volcanic centres or dense dyke swarms. The zones reflect rock temperature at depth when the zeolites formed as secondary minerals.
(Modified after: G.P.L. Walker 1960)

Metal ores, sulphides

Metal ores are included here with amygdales. Only one sulphide type, pyrite, is fairly common in Iceland. Hydrothermal metal veins hardly exist in Iceland, being found only in one place to any degree (Svínahólar in the Lón area, southeast Iceland).

Pyrite FeS_2. In Iceland pyrite always crystallises as cubes, generally small (<1 mm), but in a few places cubes of 1–2 cm edge have been found. It can be recognised mainly by its gold colour and metallic lustre (Fool's gold). It occurs mainly in fractures in the highly heated rocks of central volcanoes and in rhyolite. The general environment around pyrite is usually reddish due to chemical weathering.

In the farmlands of Svínahólar near a large intrusion in the mountain Reyðarártindur there is a small outcrop of rhyolite breccia, where small amounts of metal ores can be found, especially:

Chalcopyrite $CuFeS_2$, which forms yellow patches in the breccia. Sometimes there is a thin weathering crust of green malachite on the copper pyrite.

Galena PbS, which forms silver-coloured cubes with a high metallic lustre.

Sphalerite ZnS, which forms slightly shiny, dark-brown flakes.

Gold, silver and other metas have been found at locationswhere very old high temperature geothermal areas were once active.

71

High temperature minerals

Epidote (Ca-Fe-Al-silicate) forms at temperatures above 230°C and is a common amygdale in highly altered (greenschist) rock. It forms minute crystals, seldom 0.2–0.5 cm long rods. Dark yellow-green. Usually seen as a very thin layer in cavities and fractures. Glassy lustre. H 6–7.

Chlorite (Fe-Mg-Al-silicate) is a green (fading to brown) clay mineral which forms in large quantities where the temperature has exceeded 200°C (propylitisation). Very common as an alteration mineral and amygdale.

Chlorophaeite (hydrated Ca-Mg-Fe silicate) is like chlorite in composition but amorphous and very soft and can be scratched with a finger nail. In fresh rock it is dark greenish in colour but becomes brown or black upon weathering. Waxy, with a greasy lustre. Common amygdale.

Surrounding large intrusions, evidence of thin contact metamorphic aureoles can be found. In these instances, the metamorphic rock is hornfels or skarn, and in both of these as well as in cavities in the intrusive rocks certain secondary minerals/amygdales are sometimes found.

Prehnite (Ca-Al-silicate) is found in basalt and gabbro. Small spherical crystal groups. Usually light green. Glassy lustre. Good cleavage. H 6–6.5.

Garnet (Ca-Mg-Fe-silicate) has been found in contact aureoles. Minute individual polymorphs, visible through a magnifying glass. Brown to reddish. H 7–7.5.

Actinolite (Ca-Mg-Fe-Fluorosilicate) is amphibolite which forms at or above 300°C. Small (up to 1 cm), fibrous or radiating crystals. Greenish. Glassy to silky lustre. H 5.5–6.

Hedenbergite (Ca-Fe-silicate) is pyroxene, forms at or above 400°C and is mainly found in gabbro. Slender rods of up to 0.5 cm in length. Dark green. Glassy lustre. H 5.5–6.

Minerals at hot springs

Very extensive environmental changes are evident on the surface of presently active geothermal areas, in particular high-temperature areas. From far underground, boiling water containing dissolved solids, steam and various gases comes into contact with cold rock (usually basalt), cold groundwater and the oxidising oxygen in the atmosphere. Varied precipitates, chemical reactions, oxidisation and reduction, etc. occur and a number of new minerals form. Some of the chief examples are dealt with here.

At the hottest water springs (>70°C) a silica crust precipitates. It is amorphous and water-rich, usually frothy and has a rough surface. The basic colour is white, but it is very often coloured by other materials, brown, reddish or grey to black. It can change to opal if it becomes buried. At the larger springs an apron of crust forms, which can be very beautiful. In Iceland, silica deposits at the main locations are unfortunately being damaged by a constant flow of visitors. If the water in the springs is still, it is usually blue-green due to microscopic silica chains. Around the smaller springs there is a crust of precipitate. Most of this is silica sinter around the water springs of high-temperature areas of which the best known are Hveravellir on Kjalvegur and the Geysir area. Krýsuvík and Reykjanes on the Reykjanes peninsula are also worth mentioning. Some silica sinter also precipitates in the hottest of the low-temperature areas.

A small minority of geothermal springs contain so much CO_2 that they bubble (mineral springs). Since carbon dioxide-rich water dissolves calcium fairly easily, in places there are aprons of white calcium precipitates. The water also easily dissolves iron so these aprons are usually coloured brown or reddish by iron oxide. By far the largest deposits were found at the hot mineral springs (Icel. *ölkelda*) at Lýsuhóll on the Snæfellsnes peninsula. However, when drilling for domestic hot water was carried out there the surface geothermal activity ceased and the springs and precipitates disappeared as a result.

Gypsum (hydrated calcium sulphate) is formed when sulphate ions combine with calcium ions. This mainly happens close to steam springs. The gypsum forms platy crystals which often grow together in large or small slabs to resemble silica sinter. Various materials also colour it brownish or grey. Gypsum has a hardness of 2 which gives it a softer surface than silica sinter and glitter from individual crystals can be seen.

Sulphur forms at steam springs by oxidation of hydrogen sulphide (H_2S). It is easily recognised by its yellow colour. In steam vents, beautiful yellow crystal needles of sulphur are often found, mainly underneath the rock surfaces where they are protected from the rain. The needles are highly susceptible to change and in time they fade, but nevertheless make excellent picture material. Further from the springs sulphur forms a spade-thick layer underneath a thin layer of gypsum sinter. In the 14th to 18th centuries, sulphur was mined for gunpowder production. It was collected, melted in a pot, cleaned with cod-liver oil and cast in moulds. Both the mining and cleaning were regarded as undesirable work, even by those used to hardship. The mines were a marvel of nature, for although they were exhausted at intervals, rejuvenation always ensured their future. The extent of mining largely depended on wars in Europe.

Pyrite (FeS) is formed when iron combines with hydrogen sulphide in a reducing environment. Although visible pyrite crystals are brass yellow in colour, their streak colour is black. The black streak colour of pyrite is often evident in the vents of steam springs. Sulphur goes through three oxidation stages: reduction in the vent (sulphide, S^-), neutral (sulphur, S^0) at a slightly greater distance and finally completely oxidised (gypsum, sulphate, SO_4^-) furthest away from the vent.

In boiling mud pools the clay generally ranges from dark grey to black due to the streak colour of pyrite. In the surrounding area it is usually brownish due to colouring by iron oxide and sometimes bright red from the streak colour of hematite (Fe_2O_3), the same oxidising stage of iron $Fe^{++} => Fe^{+++}$.

Sulphur deposits found at high-temperature
geothermal areas were mined in the past. (RTH)

Clay

In high-temperature areas the surface rocks are greatly altered. In
steaming hot clay pools the hydrogen sulphide (H_2S) is oxidised to sulphuric acid (H_2SO_4). The water is very acid, as low as pH 1–2, and hot
acid alters the rock, especially the tuff to clay. It alters first to smectite,
then to a mixture of smectite and kaolinite and finally completely to
kaolinite. These clay minerals usually occur together in a single mixture and can barely be distinguished. Geothermal clay has been used
mixed with sedimentary clay in ceramics but proved to be somewhat
problematical. On the other hand, it has proved excellent for baths at
health centres.

Various minerals, especially sulphates

Various other minerals occur in high-temperature geothermal areas, many of them soluble in water. These include:

Halotrichite (spring salt, Fe-Al-sulphate), which precipitates on the hot clay floor around steam springs but soon dissolves. Often beautiful, with white and yellowish rinds and tufts. Water soluble, very bitter taste.

Brochanite (hydrated copper sulphate), which forms green lumps and rinds.

Chalcanite (hydrated copper sulphate). Bluish, blue-green, greenish. Short rods or thick flat crystals. Water soluble.

Alunogen (hydrated aluminium sulphate). Colourless, white crusts of fibrous crystals (hair salt). Water soluble. Bitter taste.

Jarosite (hydrated K-Fe-sulphate). Yellow or brownish sheets, fibrous crusts or small knobs on altered rhyolite. Resembles sulphur or brown ironstone.

Solfataric hematite forms porous slabs up to 0.5 m thick. They are rust brown and resemble scoria but are much denser. The mineral occurs in both active and extinct high-temperature geothermal areas.

Precipitation in newly formed lavas

At the close of an eruption gases still escape from the craters and solidifying lava. They form colourful precipitates, generally easily soluble salts which are washed away by the rain. Some are well known, such as yellow sulphur and salt (NaCl), while others are less familiar. Considerable quantities of these short-lived salts have been collected and analysed. Some have not been found to occur naturally anywhere else.

Selected bibliography

Surnames are written in italics. The Icelandic letters é, ó, á, ú, í and ý should be written as e, o, a, u, i and y, ö as ö, oe or simply o, æ as æ or ae, ð as d and þ as th when searching for references and papers in most databases.

S. *Arnórsson* 1993. Inngangur að bergfræði storkubergs (Introduction to the petrology of magmatic rocks). *Náttúrufræðingurinn* 62, vol. 3.4., p. 181–205.

E. *Gunnlaugsson* and K. *Sæmundsson* 2002. *Icelandic rocks and minerals.* Reykjavík., 233p.

H. *Kjartansson* 1979. Holufyllingar (Secondary minerals). *Útivist* 5, p. 33–57.

N. *Óskarsson*, S. *Steinþórsson* and G. E. *Sigvaldason* 1985. Iceland Geochemical Anomaly: Origin, volcanotectonics, chemical fractionation and isotope evolution of the crust. *Journal of Geophysical Research* 90, p. 10,011–10,025.

S.P. *Jakobsson* 1979. Petrology of recent basalts of the Eastern Volcanic Zone, Iceland. *Acta Naturalia Islandica* 26. Reykjavík.

S.P. *Jakobsson* 1979. Outline of the petrology of Iceland. *Jökull* 29, p. 57–73.

G.P.L. *Walker* 1959. Geology of the Reyðarfjörður area, eastern Iceland. *Quart. Journal Geological Society London,* 114, p. 367–393.

G.P.L. *Walker* 1960. Zeolite zones and dyke distribution in relation to the structure of the basalts of eastern Iceland. *Journal of Geology* 68, p. 515–528.

Surtsey 1966 (SÞ)

3 The creation and evolution of Iceland

The creation and evolution of Iceland span a period of roughly 20 million years. The entire process is associated with, on the one hand, the interaction of a hot spot, emerging from underneath Greenland and the nearby rifting zones in the Icelandic region of the North Atlantic on the other. The rifting at divergent margins and the strong influence of the Icelandic hot spot control the present volcanic and tectonic activity. The hot spot changes its position relative to the island due to the very slow northwest drift of both major Atlantic plates across it. This accounts for the rather complex shifting of rift zones in Iceland and the presence of intraplate lateral volcanic zones. The topography of the adjacent sea floor is also explained by this interaction, as well as the accretion of the Icelandic crust which is now generally considered to be thick rather than resembling a thin oceanic crust. The present active tectonic and volcanic regions are divided into proper rift zones and intraplate lateral volcanic belts, each with different characteristics. The zones themselves are characterised by active fissure swarms, volcanic systems and central volcanoes (composite volcanoes or stratovolcanoes).

Key words

Plate tectonics • plate spreading • spreading ridges • hot spot • rift zone • rifting • fracture zone • leaky fracture zone • mantle plume • intraplate lateral volcanic belt (zone) • rift jump • inclination of rock layers/strata • volcanic system • central volcano • dyke • dyke swarm • cone sheet • intrusions • laccolith • stock (ancient magma chambers) • zeolite zones

Plate tectonics and hot spots

The plates which move on the Earth's surface comprise the crust and the upper part of the mantle (i.e. the lithosphere). They are thickest beneath the highest parts of continents, at 100–200 km. Here the crust reaches depths of 70–80 km, although its average continental thickness is around 35 km. The plates are much thinner beneath the oceans and are believed to be thinnest near the active ocean ridges. The average thickness of the oceanic crust is 7–8 km, although in many places it reaches 20–50 km and even 60–75 km in restricted areas where there are hot spots, or over 100 km at ocean trenches on plate margins. The plates are brittle except where there is increased heat (e.g. at spreading ridges and hot spots) which can soften the rock or cause partial or complete melting. Such localised areas can occur at shallow depths or within 12–15 km of the surface but often lie much deeper. The brittle uppermost part of the crust in Iceland is generally 5–12 km thick. Beneath this the plates are solid but plastic, and deform under stress without fracturing.

Underneath the plates there is a 100–200 km thick, rather ductile or plastic layer in the mantle (asthenosphere or low velocity layer). The plates can be regarded as floating on top of this layer. Movement of mantle material in this layer is slow and it yields by ductile flow with associated upward and downward isostatic movement or by horizontal movement which is believed to be the result of slow deep-rooted convection flow of material due to differential heat flow through the mantle.

The plate margins in the North Atlantic are raised up into a spreading ridge which is cut up into ridge segments with a northerly orientation, while those on east-west fracture zones are offset. Plate movement at the spreading ridges is characterised by rifting as the result of tensile stress in en-echelon fracture swarms, i.e. each swarm opens up to the side and somewhat in front of the one behind. Shear stress builds up on the transverse fracture zones and horizontal displacement of the plates takes place on surface fractures such as large transform faults or open fractures. Obvious signs of mixed rifting and transform fault movement suggest that in many cases these are "leaky" fracture zones.

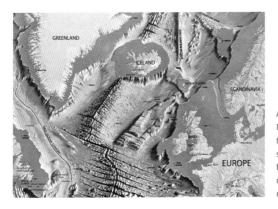

A schematic drawing of the North Atlantic Ridge. Note the Iceland shelf, the rift segments, transverse fracture zones and the ridges running between the main North Atlantic islands.

The oceanic crust forms by plate drifting (spreading) and upward movement of mantle material at the ridge segments. The upward movement of material causes volcanic eruption and intrusions in the crust. The crust is widely formed of sediment (the uppermost part), followed by eruptive rocks (including pillow lavas), then basic rocks lower down with high dyke concentration and finally gabbro with primitive cumulate rocks, i.e. basic plutonic rocks known as underplating. Uppermost in the mantle the rocks are classified as, for example, dunites and/or harzburgite, and the crustal rocks sit on top of a kind of mantle cap of such rocks.

The average rate of spreading of the plates beneath the northwestern Atlantic Ocean is 1.8–2.5 cm per year (0.9–1.25 cm in each direction). Plate spreading is intrinsically linked to intrusive and volcanic activity. Spreading occurs when tensile stress exceeds the strength of the rock and the plates fail (fracture). Magma frequently intrudes such fractures and widens them, but due to excess pressure it can also penetrate strata to actually cause fracturing with associated dyke formation. The basic causes of plate movement are complex but it is generally believed to be caused mainly by material flow in the mantle as a result of a heat flux from deep within, right down as far as the core. In places the mantle material rises to the lower surface of the plates, pushing them in opposite directions (under spreading areas), while at the same time cooled rock sinks at collision areas (convergent plate margins) and is heated anew when it reaches the mantle.

The rock under the spreading areas, for example the Mid-Atlantic Ridge, is hotter than the surrounding crust and is believed to rise slowly along the length of the plate margin. Magma separates from the rock, because it partially melts as the pressure drops, and moves upwards into the crust where it solidifies. A further part in this process is played by the upward movement of material at active hot spots which lie close to or beneath spreading areas. Another factor is slab pull by cold plates at convergent plate margins.

Hot spots occur over very long-lived mantle plumes. The plumes have either formed by continual flow of plastic and partially melted material from the lower mantle or else consist of gigantic heat pulses from the depths, rising as a large mass of expanding, partially melted material similar to an enlarging oil blob in water. Most mantle plumes are probably 100–400 km in width. The material they contain is probably 10–15% hotter than other mantle material at a corresponding depth and spreads out from the middle to the top of each plume. When an area of rising material lies close to or under a plate margin, the effects are considerable and may include encouraging magma production along part of the nearby spreading ridge, or lifting the crust immediately above and accelerating the build-up of volcanism there. Over 40 well-documented hot spots have been identified in the world.

The Icelandic hot spot already mentioned has played an important role in the opening out of the North Atlantic Ocean, the formation of basalt areas in Canada, Greenland and the Faroes, and in Scotland and Ireland. Iceland is the only large island to have risen on the plate margin. For the past 20–24 million years the mantle plume of the Icelandic hot spot has been situated below or just east of the plate margin in the vicinity of Iceland. The upper 600–700 km of the mantle plume are clearly revealed by the behaviour of P- and S-seismic waves. In this section it is 200–300 km in width but narrows at the top to 100–150 km. It has been called the "volcanic heart" of Iceland.

To a large extent the upward movement of mantle material under the spreading ridge only succeeds in producing ocean floor. In Iceland and vicinity, however, normal upwelling of mantle material associated

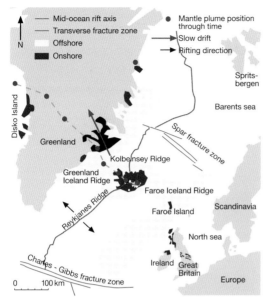

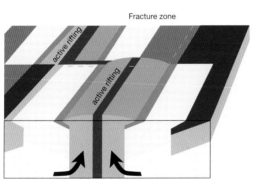

A general outline of the
large basalt formations in
the North Atlantic region,
the Greenland-Iceland-
Faroes Ridge and the
location of the North
Atlantic Ridge (as the
Reykjanes and Kolbeinsey
Ridges). Fracture zones are
also shown, as well as the
approximate spreading
(small) and sideways slide
vector (large). The circles
denote the location of the
centre of the Iceland hot
spot during the past
70 million years. The hot
spot is considered to be
stationary but the plates
and rift zones are moving
slowly in unison to the
northwest. (Modified after:
RS. White 1988 and 1989,
and A.D. Saunders, J.G.
Fitton et al 1997)

with the ocean ridge has combined with the additional material from
the fairly average-sized mantle plume which coincides with it to produce an island of 103,000 km² and just over 100,000 km² ofsubmarine,
basaltic rocks surrounding the island as a shelf or a platform.

This overall model is far from flawless and alternative volcano-tectonic models have been put forward. One alternative hypothesis for

83

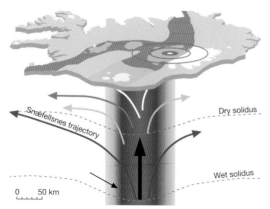

A stylised cross-section of Iceland and the abyssal depths beneath its central region. The "fiery heart" of the country consists of the main upflow of ductile mantle rock and magma beneath the North Atlantic Ridge as well as from the mantle plume of the Iceland hot spot. (Modified after I. P. Bjarnason, 1997 and Wolfe et al. 1997, Shen et al. 2002 and Ito 2002)

hot spot volcanic activity is the so-called Edge-Driven Convection, by which presumably cold down-wellings at the edges of continental land-masses create "shallow" hot spots or upwellings beneath the large oceans. It is not clear if this hypothesis applies to Iceland but further research may clarify the picture. Another theory points out the lack of high temperatures beneath Iceland and lack of seismic anomalies in the lower mantle, and proposes a new explanation. Enhanced melting occurs in the Icelandic region where the Mid-Atlantic spreading ridge coincides with the suture zone of the old Caledonian orogenic belt and a thick crust generates leaky microplate tectonics, which again enhances melting.

Wandering plates

The mantle plume for the Icelandic hot spot was once situated on the western edge of Greenland. Plates and plate margins can slowly wander (drift) together relative to the mantle plume while separating. The Eurasian plate and the North American plate are moving apart to the west-northwest and the east-southeast, the directions being N285°W and N105°E. At the same time both plates are slowly moving together towards the northwest over the mantle plume at a rate of about 0.3 cm per year. The hot spot thus appears to have moved to the southeast under the plates, or "wandered" from the ocean between Baffin Island

and western Greenland, under Greenland, to its present position beneath Iceland in about 65 million years. In fact the entire plate system is creeping northwest over the stationary plume. In the distant future the hot spot could emerge from under the east coast of Iceland just as it did from under the Greenland coast long ago. In fact it is uncertain how long upwelling lasts in a mantle plume of this nature. It must die out at some point.

The joint activity of the spreading zones and the nearby mantle plume can result in a changed distribution of spreading zones, with one segment becoming inactive while a new one opens laterally some 50–200 km from the old one. Upwelling at the plume has a considerable effect on the tectonics and volcanism for a radius of at least 500–1,000 km. When the plate margin approaches the hot spot due to slow sideways gliding of both plates, the plume begins to provide hot mantle material to the spreading zones and pushes under the plate, causing local uplift. This can cause both spreading and volcanism to increase and result in high-tensile stress towards the centre of the uplifted area/ dome. Sooner or later the plate fails and spreading begins nearer the plume than before. Lateral volcanic zones towards the edges of the uplift area/dome can also become active, both as intraplate volcanic zones and as embryonic rift zones. Eventually the hot spot coincides with the rift zone since the plates continue to wander relative to the mantle plume. At this point the crust can greatly thicken. Finally the wandering of the plates will cause the plate margin to move away from the hot spot and history will repeat itself at a new location. It is also thought likely that shifting of spreading zones can result if upwelling at the plume temporarily decreases, then maybe to increase again.

Shifts in the location of spreading zones of this kind are quite common, not least in Iceland, and must be taken into account when considering the country's geological history.

Once upon a time ...

Towards the end of the Permian period in geological history and at the beginning of the Mesozoic era, around 200 million years ago, there was increased upwelling of mantle material beneath the ancient Laurasian continent. The upwelling caused tensile forces and thinning in the landmass. Volcanism gradually increased and a large quantity of sediment and lava accumulated in the area. South of the equator, Africa separated from South America and a new ocean floor formed at a new ocean ridge. The southern part of the Atlantic Ocean widened rapidly over millions of years.

Volcanism to the north of the equator reached its height at the beginning of the Tertiary period, around 55–70 million years ago. In the early part of the period basaltic eruption commenced in the area between Baffin Island (Canada) and western Greenland. Some earth scientists believe that around this time there was a strong heat pulse under the crust near western Greenland (65 million years ago), which produced volcanism. Others think in terms of a constant flow in the plume, finally reaching the surface at this time. At the same time, and accompanied by volcanism, there was unrest within the continent in the area of the present-day North Atlantic, as can be seen in East Africa (the Great African Rift Valley). This development later led to the break-up of the continental landmass. The continental "Atlantic" landmass had separated in the northern hemisphere by 53–55 million years ago.

While volcanism was very active, and before the North Atlantic appeared, a widespread and thick pile of basalt lavas accumulated both in the west of Greenland and in an elongated area to its east. The volcanism occurred to some extent in shallow water, but much of it was on dry land. While the hot spot was active in the west and centrally beneath Greenland, a basalt area formed on Baffin Island and in the Disko vicinity of Greenland, around 58–64 million years ago. At around the same time basalt flooded out at the future plate margin east of Greenland (53–63 million years ago).

When the continental area to the east of Greenland finally broke up around 53 million years ago, part of the basalt lava pile accompanied it and drifted in a westerly direction (including the Blosseville coastal rocks which are 53–57 million years old). By that time the hot spot was much closer to the eastern edge of Greenland than before. The eastern basalt section, which broke away from its counterpart, became part of the northern British Isles area in the southeast. Basalt lava, intrusions and central volcanoes in the northwest of Scotland and Northern

The eastern edges of the Gjástykki rift valley (graben) in northeast Iceland. The fissure swarm was the scene of a volcano-tectonic episode in 1975–84. (OS)

Ireland are about 52–63 million years old, while the basalt of the Faroe Islands is 54–60 million years old.

After the continent broke up in the north, with the two basalt areas each accompanying their respective parts, a long period of volcanism followed, formation of the sea floor continued at the central spreading zone and the North Atlantic continued to grow in size. However, no large eruptive landmass emerged above sea level in the vicinity of present-day Iceland and the hot spot was still too far away beneath Greenland to have much impact on volcanic production to the east. Over the next few million years the plates and the plate margin continued their combined glide to the northwest and the hot spot appeared to approach the eastern edge of Greenland. Inland the crust is thick but the Greenland glacier prevents the observation of any direct evidence of volcanism associated with the hot spot.

Around 35–36 million years ago Greenland was so far to the northwest that the hot spot escaped from its confinement and continued its activity off the eastern edge of the country. Free of the overlying weight, it began to have a strong influence on plate movement outwards from the North-Atlantic Ridge, some way to the east of Greenland. Drifting ceased on the spreading ridge, which today lies to the east of Iceland (the Ægir Ridge), and a new ridge formed further west near Greenland (near the area of Iceland). Volcanism increased in the new spreading zone and at the plate margin generally with the approach of the mantle plume and upwelling. The majority of the hot spot volcanism remained, however, on the east coast of Greenland nearest its centre and the basalt rocks there are 28–35 million years old. At this time also, a sliver of continental crust broke away from the Greenland area and drifted eastwards with the sea floor from the new spreading zone. These rocks are believed to lie under the Jan Mayen area today and may extend all the way to the eastern part of Iceland.

Around 32–24 million years ago the hot spot was situated under the sea floor between Iceland and Greenland. This long-lived mantle plume steadily approached the active part of the spreading zone in the vicinity of Iceland. Volcanism from the hot spot itself was considerable at this time and presumably mostly occurred on the sea floor. Its proximity to the plate margin resulted in a slow but steady increase in volcanism in the eastern spreading zone, since mantle plumes can deliver magma horizontally or at an angle towards the ridge segment.

Evidence for the presence of the hot spot is obvious on the sea floor off Greenland. A 2–3 km thick unit of eruptive rocks extends as a submarine ridge between eastern Greenland and Iceland. Another similar ridge joins Iceland to the Faroe Islands. Together they are known as the Greenland-Iceland-Faroes Ridge (GIFR). Both are believed to be the product of the hot spot, i.e. an elongated thickening in the crust as a result of increased volcanism at the plate margin and gradual separation of the plates. Furthermore, since it is known that there was considerable volcanism on the sea floor at the hot spot, the Iceland-Greenland Ridge also indicates where the hot spot was located while the plate system slowly glidedto the northwest. Over the next few million years Greenland continued to move further away from the plume, while the Iceland area moved closer to it for the same reason.

The glaciated central volcano of Tungnafells-jökull (with caldera) in the foreground. The huge ice masses of the Vatnajökull ice cap in the background cover several volcanic centres.

The area between the ice caps, as well as the western part of Vatnajökull, are designated as the centre of the Iceland hot spot. (RTH)

Iceland emerges ... and grows

About 20–24 million years ago the hot spot was more or less in the location of present-day Iceland. The active spreading zone was close by to the east. The upwelling of mantle material in the plume, together with normal upward flow under the spreading zone, finally succeeded in producing sufficient magma to build up an island or islands above sea level; a primitive Iceland appeared. The main spreading zone (plate margin) may have lain off the present-day Vestfirðir area in the northwest; remains of central volcanoes have been found by gravity surveys on the sea floor off the northwest coast. But when Iceland's geological history began in earnest the spreading zone lay in an area still further east and within the present-day land area, including what is now the central axis of the Snæfellsnes peninsula, across Breiðafjörður, through Hvammsfjörður and northwestern to the Húnaflói inlet. Over the next few million years eruptive rocks accumulated on dry land in the Icelandic area along with steady plate drift. They can now be seen in the western and eastern parts of Iceland (Vestfirðir with Vesturland and Austfirðir) and are from 7 to 17 million years old; the oldest lying closest to the coast. The Tertiary rocks are dated by geomagnetic measurements and radioactive isotopes (mainly by K^{40}/Ar-dating). It may well be that a land bridge existed for a time between Iceland and one or other, or both of the continents to the east and west.

Active tectonic and volcanic areas

The volcanic acive regions are as follows:

- Two volcanic rift zones. These join in the centre of the country. They are the Southwestern Rift Zone or Western Rift Zone (WRZ) and the Northeastern Rift Zone (NRZ). The westernmost part of the WRZ has sometimes been defined as a separate volcanic zone or a leaky transverse fracture zone (the Reykjanes Volcanic Belt, RVB) but this definition will not be followed here. The characteristics of the rift zones are tension fractures, normal faults and grabens, basalt volcanism with a characteristic petrology and central volcanoes with calderas. Episodal rifting occurs within the rifting zones with or without volcanism.

- Two main lateral volcanic belts. These are the Snæfellsnes Volcanic Belt (SNVB) and the South Iceland Volcanic Belt (SIVB) which isoften referred to as the Eastern Volcanic Zone (EVZ). Here the term belt is used for lateral volcanic areas in preference to zone, which is also often used. The third volcanic area lies from Öræfajökull, through Esjufjöll to Snæfell, parallel to the SIVB and the NVZ, and is called the Öræfi Volcanic Belt (ÖVB). The characteristics of intraplate volcanic belts are normal faults, a wide variety of eruptive rocks with a different petrology from that of the rift zones and mainly intermediate and acid eruptive materials, as well as central volcanoes of stratovolcano type. Here typical rifting episodes do not occur.

In addition there are three seismic areas outside the active volcanic belt.

These are the:

• Tjörnes Fracture Zone (TFZ) off the northeast coast. This is an area of transform lineaments, grabens and remnants of volcanic activity.

• Borgarfjörður Seismic Zone (BSZ) which links the Snæfellsnes Volcanic Zone to the Western Rift Zone (WRZ). Fractures due to shearing and tension as well as transform faults are found in this area.

• South Iceland Seismic Zone (SISZ) or Fracture Zone (SIFZ). Shear-type fractures with lateral transform movements are common but there is no local volcanism which can be related to the tectonic movements.

The evolution continues

The mantle plume disappears under the new Iceland, the island grows and its oldest parts become eroded and disappear below sea level. By about 6 million years ago the middle of the hot spot is situated 50–100 km east of the plate margin. Spreading and volcanism then gradually cease in the old spreading zone (in the western half of Iceland) and begin anew closer to the hot spot in a spreading zone which runs through the country from the southwest (the present-day Reykjanes peninsula) to the northern part of Iceland, and then on northwards on the sea floor (the Kolbeinsey Ridge). Spreading and accumulation continue in this spreading zone for a long time. By then the hot spot has "moved" further still to the southeast (i.e. the country and the plate margin have wandereded to the northwest). Thus two new separate rifting zones gradually appear (WRZ and NRZ), which are joined in the centre of Iceland at the so-called mid-Icelandic zone. Here it is defined as a connecting sector for the spreading zones having the same characteristics. This is the conspicious "bend" in the center of the neovolcanic zone. A typical transform fracture zone joins the new spreading zone in the northeast with the Kolbeinsey Ridge on the sea floor to the north of the country (KRZ).

The next chapter in the geological history of Iceland starts with volcanism in two lateral belts; on Snæfellsnes (SNVB; 2–3 million years ago and still active) and in the central southern region of the country (SIVB; around 3 million years ago and still active). A third might be included: a narrow volcanic lateral belt between the Öræfajökull glacier and Snæfell, which runs parallel to the active zone in south and central Iceland. This Öræfajökull Volcanic Belt commenced activity 0.5– 1.0 million years ago. It may result from combined activity between the hot spot (the crust is uplifted above it) and stress within the nearby rifting zone which is in fact offset to the east in its course through central Iceland. The lateral volcanic zone or belt in the central south (SIVB) is the most active and largest of the three volcanic areas. One reason for this may be that in addition to opening due to the hot spot, the rifting zone in the northeast of the country (NRZ) is extending southwards and "eating" its way into the above-mentioned lateral zone. This feature is known as a propagating rift and in this instance, the very active Northeastern Rift Zone (NRZ) is attempting to form a single rift zone instead of the two which are now active. This will lead to the rift zone in the southwest (WRZ) becoming extinct. There are indications that the Snæfellsnes Volcanic Zone (SNVB) extends towards the Western Rift Zone, or in other words here we also have a lateral volcanic zone "following" the hot spot. The Öræfi Volcanic Belt (ÖVB) could at best be a nascent rifting zone, produced as the hot spot steadily approaches the east of Iceland as both plates wander to the northwest.

Finally, about 0.5–2.5 million years ago there was volcanism in the western part of northern Iceland in present-day Skagi, Skagafjörður and the heathlands north of the Langjökull ice cap. This area is either an old lateral volcanic belt (like the Snæfellsnes volcanic zone) or a short-lived and undeveloped rift zone which could be related to a lull in the mantle-plume activity. During this lull, rifting may have moved from the northeast to the west in a short-lived shift of the rift zone and formed a direct continuation of the Western Rift Zone (WRZ) northwards.

At the same time, rifting in the rift zones and the position of the hot spot laterally to them forced the formation of a very active transverse

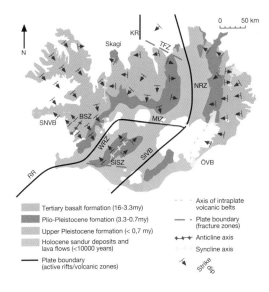

The present configuration of tectonic and/or volcanic zones and intraplate volcanic belts in Iceland. The broad or stippled lines denote the main axis of activity. Names used in the literature vary. RR: Reykjanes Ridge; WRZ: Western Rift Zone; BSZ: Borgarfjörður Seismic Zone (intraplate); SNVB: Snæfellsnes Volcanic Belt (intraplate); SISZ: South Iceland Seismic Zone (fracture zone); SIVB: South Iceland Volcanic Belt (intraplate, also known as the Eastern Volcanic Zone, EVZ); MIZ: Mid-Iceland Zone (defined here as a rift zone and included in the WRZ and NRZ which overlap); NRZ: Northeastern Rift Zone (propagating southward into the SIVB); ÖVB: Öræfajökull-Snæfell Volcanic Belt (an embryonic rift zone?); Skagi denotes a late Tertiary and early Quaternary volcanic area; TFZ: Tjörnes Fracture Zone; KR: Kolbeinsey Ridge. (Main source: K. Sæmundsson 1979)

fracture zone in the south, the South Iceland Seismic Zone (SISZ). This appears to be moving slowly to the south at the same time as the Southern Volcanic Zone (SIVB) is evolving into a rift zone. The southern part of the rift zone in the southwest appears simultaneously to be gradually changing into a leaky transverse fracture zone (the Reykjanes peninsula) where part of the tectonic movement is rifting due to tensile stress and volcanism, and part is transform movement due to shear stress.

What is down there?

The centre of the hot spot is at present situated near the northwestern part of the Vatnajökull ice cap. While the most active part on the surface is believed to be at least 100–150 km in diameter, the effects of the mantle plume are much greater, mainly towards the north and southwest along the plate margin. The affected area is probably 1,000 km wide, or more, and extends furthest from the plume below the rift zone.

Under the hot spot the mantle plume rises from a depth of at least 700 km beneath the crust, but its roots probably lie about 2,900 km deep at the junction with the Earth's core, from where it rose or rises still, slowly and perhaps by a winding path. Seismic evidence suggests that the mantle plume is about 200 km wide on average, but its most active part, below the hot spot, is only about 100 km wide. Towards the top of the plume, at a depth of 100–150 km, melting on a microscoping scale commences within the rising mantle rock. At around 60–80 km deep, magma veins probably form, which increase in size further up and reach the junction between the mantle and crust. In the overlying crust the veins are replaced by dykes and inclined sheets and magma chambers can develop. A similar situation exists beneath the rifting zone far from the mantle plume, but probably to a lesser degree.

Throughout the Earth at around 10–200 km deep within the mantle, temperature and pressure conditions result in the rocks being plastic, with only limited partial melting (1–5%). This is the previously mentioned asthenosphere or low velocity layer which allows the stiff overlying plates to drift horizontally and bend vertically. The lithosphere (the plates) comprises the crust and a thin layer of mantle rock, as explained earlier. Under Iceland's central axis the asthenosphere extends towards the surface due to a steady upward flow of material and anomalous temperature conditions. The asthenosphere is believed to lie at a depth of 70–75 km below the eastern fjords and 45 km below the volcanic belt in the northeast. One hypothesis is that remains of continental crust can be found under eastern Iceland. It must be emphasised that the overall picture of crustal thickness, plate thickness, the low velocity layer, magma formation and magma reservoirs under the country is still rather vague. It is only possible to peer this deep into the Earth using indirect measuring methods which merely give a rough idea of the main features. But technology advances rapidly and the picture is becoming gradually clearer.

From 1971 to 1993 scientists often described the crust in Iceland, i.e. that part of the lithosphere above the defined Moho discontinuity, as

8–16 km thick. In support of this they cited rather scanty seismic reflection and velocity measurements, gravity surveys of the distribution of rocks with different densities, and conductivity measurements. More detailed measurements, including seismic data, now suggest that Iceland is in fact a thickening above a mantle plume at a divergent plate margin. The crust is thought to be 10–45 km thick, being generally thinnest at the edge of the continental shelf and thickest under the centre of the country. Here too, the partially or completely melted material, which has separated out from the mantle rocks at still greater depth, lies at its shallowest depth. The upper part of the crust is a 6 km thick pile of lavas and intrusions, mainly dykes. The much thicker lower part of the crust consists for the most part of intrusions and solidified cumulates. The lithosphere, however, is composed of both the crust and the upper part of the mantle. So, when looking at the plates themselves, one has to define them as the rigid part above the ductile asthenosphere. In doing so, it appears as if this particular layer bulges up where the crust is thickest (in central Iceland), making the plates on both sides thin towards their margins; something which is both reasonable and attested in other localities.

The overall picture, according to the interpretation of new geophysical data, is thus as follows: the plates in the Iceland area are thickest out towards the edge of the country, except at the rift belts in the southwest and northeast. The plates thin towards the volcanic rift belt where they are about 40–45 km thick. The crust (not to be confused with the term "plate") is, on the other hand, thinnest out towards the edge of the island shelf (10–12 km) but thickens towards the centre. In other words, the low velocity layer or asthenosphere domes upwards to the bottom of the crust beneath the rifting and volcanic belts, even slicing a bit into the crust. Below these areas of activity, i.e. in the lower part of the crust and the upper part of the mantle, the temperature is sufficiently high and the pressure sufficiently low for partial melting to occur, which leads to the formation of magma. As a result the Moho discontinuity becomes indistinct or obscure in places. Localised seismic velocity anomalies also occur beneath very active volcanic areas which can be interpreted as limited areas of thin crust, or simply as strong upwellings of mantle and crustal material and magma. However, there are still

The Hekla central volcano in action in 2000.
(RTH)

further considerations to be taken into account. In short, different
models for the foundations of Iceland are still being debated.

Beneath the ocean ridges, including Iceland, and within localised
mantle plumes the temperature at a particular depth, for example 100–
200 km, is much higher than at the same depth in the mantle beneath
the plates elsewhere. Furthermore the mantle mass is moving upwards
towards lower pressure (decreasing overlying rock mass). The rock

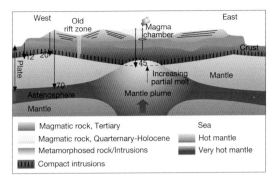

A simplified and schematic cross-section of Iceland, showing the general structure of the crust and mantle at Snæfellsnes, Borgarfjörður, across the rift zones to the eastern fjords. Opinions on crustal thickness vary. Spreading axis (rift zones) create broad "synclines". (Modified after H. Jóhannesson 1980)

starts to melt at great depth, starting with the materials with a lower melting point. This results in magma formation which increases rapidly higher up. The magma gradually separates from the rising rock mass and moves towards the surface in small cavities or veins, much more rapidly than the parent rock. Magma does not always reach the surface and indeed most of it probably solidifies at shallow depths within the crust as intrusions of various types (see chapter 5 for more detail). Partial melting under Iceland leads to the formation of basalt magma. There are indications that much of the magma appears in heatwaves of varied intensity, which move upwards within the plumes (in magma pulses).

Dykes feed eruptions in periods, episodes and events

If we assume that the present rate of volcanic eruption applies to Iceland's entire geological history then the number of events – at least 4–5 million eruptions – is staggering. We can also reasonably assume that volcanism and plate movement have remainedsimilar to that of the present time. If this is correct, then from the very beginning volcanic systems have been active, producing central volcanoes and shield volcanoes, while countless tectonic fractures and eruptive fissures dissected the crust within each system. Lava and tephra layers from all these volcanic systems, which cooled as they moved sideways away from the supply of magma within the Earth, succeeded in forming a pile of eruptive rock many hundreds of metres in diameter. Like the volcanoes, this

A set of vertical, basaltic dykes in an eroded fissure swarm that belongs to the Setberg

Volcanic Centre on the Snæfellsnes peninsula. (RTH)

pile was eroded and weathered in addition to drifting while lavas flowed over them from more active volcanoes on the plate margin. At the same time, the eruptive pile dipped towards the rifting plate margin from opposite directions. At the margin the plates gave way and sank under the overlying weight of the volcanic pile, thus forming a huge elongated trench resembling a syncline. With each lateral shift of the rifting zone a new trench was formed, while between the old and new trenches the strata are tilted upwards in the form of an anticline.

Dykes may withstand erosion and jut out like horizontal joints (Trékyllisvík). (RTH)
this one, and can be recognised by their

Based on a knowledge of plate movement and volcanism in the country we can assume that the general picture is as follows: the rift zones
were typified by periods of activity in each volcanic system. In by far
the majority of cases eruptions occurred as well as rifting, so that the
term volcano-tectonic periods is applicable. Within each period a tectonic rifting episode occurred when plate movement had succeeded in
building up sufficient tensile stress in the Earth's crust. Localised rifting, i.e. widening of the crust at weak lines, then began, accompanied

by earthquakes. Each rifting episode lasted for several days, weeks or even decades. During these episodes, tectonic events occurred at intervals, leaving open fractures or faults which resulted in swarms of earthquakes. In some or all of the rifting events occurring in each episode, magma intruded via fractures, often as almost vertical dykes or inclined sheets. The magma rose almost vertically from a depth of more than 10–15 km (primitive magma) or at an angle from the shallow magma chambers of central volcanoes within the volcanic systems (evolved magma). This occurred in so-called lateral magma injections. The magma usually solidified either as dykes or sheets in the crustal rocks or else reached the surface, resulting in a volcanic eruption (volcanic event). Subsequently, the volcano and its materials remained along with feeder dykes in the volcanic vent. Such periods of unrest represented not solely the common (tectonic) rifting episodes but rather what is called volcano-tectonic episodes. The same periodic process, divided into periods, made up of episodes, each containing so and so many events (only tectonic or volcano-tectonic), still continues today.

The possibly excess pressure of the magma, combined with the eruptive strength of the rock, controls whether or not the dyke reaches the surface. As already mentioned, we can assume two scenarios: release of stress causes fracture formation with resulting magma intrusion or sufficient excess magma pressure itself results in fracture formation with associated extension of the dykes.

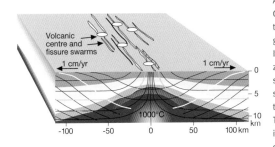

A calculated model by G. Pálmason (1981) depicts the main features of the generation of crust in Iceland, within the rift zones. The yellow trace shows the path followed by surface lavas with time and the spreading of the plates. The white example indicates the position of equally old lava flows formed at a given time. The shadings from red (close to magma temperature) to blue indicate the temperature gradient.

A difference in style

The above-mentioned rifting sequence is applicable within the rifting and volcanic belt on every occasion, such as in the WRZ and NRZ at the present time., However, lateral volcanic zones in the intraplate differ to some extent from what has been described. No real rifting occurs there. The period of time elapsing between eruptions is not as regular, except in the case of active magma chambers under large volcanoes.

Open tension fractures and even normal faults which are observed in lateral intraplate belts result from tension in the crust when magma pushes its way up through it. The excess pressure of the magma mass in the magma chamber or at greater depths beneath the volcanic system (maybe in magma reservoirs) is the controlling factor, although uplift at the hot spot and the associated stress field can also favour fracturing.

Excess pressure in the magma chamber commonly initiates fracturing in the crust, since there is a considerable difference between volcanic systems in the rifting zones and the lateral volcanic zones. Volcanic systems within the lateral zones are not as regularly arranged en echelon as in the rifting zones, with the exception of the Snæfellsnes peninsula, and the fracture orientation is frequently different to the normal southwest-northeast direction of tectonic lineations, which dominates in the rift zones. The appearance of central volcanoes is also different in the rifting zones and lateral zones; shield-like massifs with calderas are commonest in the rift zones as opposed to stratovolcanoes

Krafla: an enlightening episode

The Krafla Fires are an excellent example of the process which takes place at divergent plate margins when rifting occurs with associated volcanism. Krafla is a very active volcanic system in the Northeastern Rift Zone (NRZ). Two rifting periods have occurred there in Recent Time with a roughly 5,000-year interval. The latest began 2,000 years ago and is known as the Hverfjall period. Within this there is evidence for at least six volcano-tectonic episodes: the Hverfjall Fires, the former Hólseldar Fires, the later Hólseldar Fires, the Dalseldar Fires, the Mývatnseldar Fires and the Kröflueldar or Krafla Fires. About 250– 1,000 years elapsed between episodes, the shortest intervals being between the Mývatnseldar and the Krafla Fires, and between the Hverfjall and first Hólseldar Fires. In each rifting and/or volcanic event within these episodes, the land spread apart in the fracture swarms by many metres and some eruption accompanied the intrusion process. The most recent, as well as the best recorded and monitored example, was the Krafla Fires of 1975–84. The total spreading was about 8 m in 22 tectonic events. In most or all cases the magma pushed its way only into the crustal fractures, either to the north or south, but in nine volcanic events (volcano-tectonic events) it reached the surface and initiated basalt eruptions. The vents were moved further north as the events progressed and produced increasingly more material. The total area of lava extruded was 60 km² or 0.25 km³ in volume.

Main source: Kristján Sæmundsson 1991: Jarðfræði Kröflusvæðisins. In: Náttúra Mývatns (eds. A. Garðarson and Á. Einarson), Reykjavík.

in the lateral zones. Long volcanic fissures are almost absent in the lateral volcanic belts where, in general, crater rows tend to be shorter and less productive.

Looking into the past

Land areas older than 3.2 to 17 million years in age are heavily eroded and dissected by geomorphological forces. Pleistocene (i.e. the last Ice

A typical rift-zone fissure eruption (Krafla, January 1981). Lava fountains, fluid basalt lava and semi-parallel, en-echelon fissure segments characterise the event. (ÓR)

Age) glaciers were especially effective. Mountains, valleys and fjords in the west and northwestern parts of the country and in the east have been formed over millions of years, largely by glacial erosion. Over large areas strata some 1,000–2,000 m thick have been stripped away.

The central parts of the active Krafla Volcanic System in northeast Iceland, with a somewhat obscure caldera. Gjástykki is the central graben of the northern fissure swarm. Note the Gæsafjöll table mountain (left, partly formed subglacially). (OS)

However, isostatic rebound ensures that a high-relief landscape has formed, as impressive as before, the mountains reaching up to 1,000–1,500 m high.

The total thickness of the late Tertiary rock layers (strata from mid and upper Miocene and Pleiocene) is 4–6 km and they are mainly composed of 5–15 m thick lavas. In this upper part of the crust the density of the rocks increases with depth from around 2 g/cm^3 to 3 g/cm^3 and the temperature increases to 600–650°C, but porosity decreases from about 20–30% of the volume to 1%. The lavas form thick sequences in which several hundred metres may represent several hundred thousand years of volcanic activity or more. The general structure of the pile resembles a fan of many stacks of cards, forming lens-like units that intermingle or overlap each other and they all generally plunge with an inclination of 0–15° towards the rift zones. Locally the inclination may be as much as 15–45°, representing flanks of large volcanoes. Tephra layers and sediments appear between the lavas, as ancient soils, lacustrian and fluvial sediment, or other mechanically produced sediment,

Basalt lava flows, 5–6 million years old, intercalated with red interbeds (soils).

The Hengifoss waterfall, close to Lake Lögurinn in northeast Iceland, is 118 m high. (RTH)

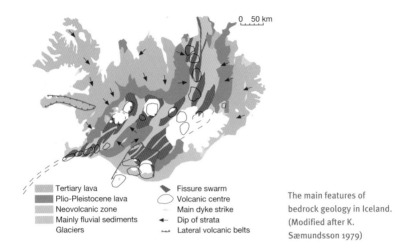

0   50 km

Tertiary lava
Plio-Pleistocene lava
Neovolcanic zone
Mainly fluvial sediments
Glaciers

Fissure swarm
Volcanic centre
Main dyke strike
Dip of strata
Lateral volcanic belts

The main features of
bedrock geology in Iceland.
(Modified after K.
Sæmundsson 1979)

and lignite and fossils are widespread. Intermediate or acid rocks are
noticeable in places.

Intrusions can easily be seen in many places. They are usually composed of gabbro but also of acid plutonic rocks, often solely of one of
these rock types or as a composite intrusion of acid and basic rocks. In
some cases, the intrusions classify as sills or laccoliths, but the majority
of plutonic masses are thought to be the tops of complex ancient magma chambers. The largest plutonic stocks or batholiths of this type
occur in the southeast and measure 10–20 km^2 on the surface. At their
edges there is evidence of mixing between the country rock and the
magma, and dykes and veins extend from them.

Acid and plutonic rocks can be seen mainly where remains of ancient
central volcanoes have been revealed in the landscape by geological
mapping. The rock is clearly altered near the centres of old high-temperature geothermal systems. Between 15 and 20 Tertiary central volcanoes are to be found in the eastern fjords and there are more such
structures in the west of Iceland, in the western fjords and the western
part of north Iceland. Most of these are associated with dyke swarms
which stand out in the landscape as approximately vertical features
(outside the central volcanoes), or as dipping cone dyke sheets (within
the central volcanoes). The dykes are commonly 0.5–10 m thick and

A part of an old volcanic centre in Slaufrudalur (Southeast-Iceland), characterized by gabbro and acid plutonic rocks (6–7 million years old). RTH

narrowly spaced within the swarms, displaying horizontal columnar jointing. They can be seen in mountainsides or in lowland areas where they resemble walls or wall fragments. Closer examination reveals glassy cooling surfaces at opposite ends of the columns. The vast majority of dykes are made of basalt or diabase, but some acid or intermediate examples are also known. Cone sheets which occur near large intrusions are believed to be evidence of caldera collapse and magma intrusions in the roots of central volcanoes. The vertical dykes form clearly visible groups which extend in opposite directions from the remains of the central volcanoes. They lie at right angles to the minimum compressive (maximum tensile) principle stress. They are regarded as being a cross-sectional view of the contents of the 5–15 km broad and 30–100 km long fracture swarms of ancient volcanic systems. The number of dykes in a particular swarm can be in the order of 2–10% of the surface rocks. The density of the dykes increases towards the centre of the central volcano and as far down as they are visible. Most common is a density of 5–6% and the total thickness of dykes in each fracture swarm represents the rifting which has occurred during the lifetime of the volcanic system (0.5–1.0 million years). Feeder dykes from the volcano represent only a small proportion.

The alteration of the rocks and types of amygdales present, especially zeolites, can provide information on the amount of erosion and weathering that have taken place. Zeolites precipitate from geothermal solutions in the deeper strata, at different temperature and pressure conditions. At the top of the thick Tertiary lava pile is a belt free of zeolites but underneath it, in order, are a chabazite-thomsonite belt, an anacime belt and a mesolite-scolesite belt, while at the bottom high-temperature zeolites are found in the form of the laumonite belt, which once lay up to 2,000 m under the Earth's surface. This belt is commonest in the westernmost section of the Tertiary part of the eastern fjords, furthest from the coast. Its lowest margin should be close to 3,000 m under the old surface but below this the crust is typified by increasing amounts of epidote with depth. At a depth of 5–6 km the lower crust shows indications of the temperature increasing with depth until it reaches 1,000–1,200°C in the base layer, outside the active volcanic zones. In the lower crust the density appears to remain unchanged with depth and the seismic P-wave velocity is almost constant (about 7.0 km/s in general, but 7.3–7.4 km/s in places). In the upper crust, in comparison, this velocity increases from 2–3 km/s at the top to 6.3–6.7 km/s at the junction with the lower crust.

Where to go?

The following list directs readers to some of the more typical study sites.

For more information refer to scientific papers or the road guide by T. Thordarson and A. Höskuldsson: *Iceland, Classical Geology in Europe 3*, Terra 2002.

1. *Reykjanes.* Active normal faults, grabens, eruptive fissures, lava shields (WRZ).
2. *Þingvellir.* Active normal faults, graben, tension fractures (WRZ).
3. *Hvalfjörður, Brekkukambur.* An eroded central volcano (2.5–3 million years old).

0   50 km

4. *Hafnarfjall-Skarðsheiði.* An eroded central volcano (4–6 m. yrs).
5. *Baula, Borgarfjörður.* A laccolith of rhyolitic rock, part of the Reykjadalur central volcano (4.5–7 m. yrs).
6. *Lake Hreðavatn.* Unconformity, fossils (8 m. yrs).
7. *Norðurárdalur.* Inclining strata; axis of rift zone "anticline".
8. *Grundarfjörður, Snæfellsnes.* The eroded Setberg central volcano (7–8 m. yrs).
9. *Kolgrafarfjörður.* Dyke swarms of the ancient Setberg Volcanic System.
10. *Álftafjörður, Northern Snæfellsnes and Garðar, Southern Snæfells- nes.* Inclining strata; axis of a "syncline" (old rift zone). In Bers- erkjahraun and Hnappadalur, active volcanic fissures line the Ljósufjöll Volcanic System and the Snæfellsjökull Volcanic System is an active part of the Snæfellsnes Intraplate Volcanic Belt (SNVB).
11. *Hvammsfjörður.* An eroded central volcano (7–8 m. yrs).
12. *Króksfjörður and Berufjörður.* An eroded central volcano (10– 11 m. yrs).

13. *Álftafjörður, Ísafjarðardjúp.* An eroded central volcano (Lamba-dalur central volcano 14 m. yrs).

14. *Reykjafjörður, Strandir.* An eroded central volcano (Árnes central volcano, 11–12 m. yrs).

15. *Víðidalur.* Inclining strata; axis of a "syncline" (old rift zone). Two eroded central volcanoes east and west of the axis (about 7 m. yrs).

16. *Öxnadalur.* An eroded central volcano (8 m. yrs).

17. *Krafla-Gjástykki.* Active normal faults, rifts, graben, eruptive fissures. Active rift zone (NRZ), central volcano.

18. *Melrakkaslétta.* Active normal faults, graben (NRZ).

19. *Borgarfjörður eystri.* The eroded Njarðvík central volcano (about 12 m. yrs) and the Dyrfjöll complex. The Breiðuvík central volcano (about 12 m. yrs).

20. *Hvítserkur.* Basaltic veins and dykes set in rhyolitic rock.

21. *Skriðdalur.* The eroded Þingmúli central volcano (8–9 m. yrs).

22. *Reyðarfjörður.* The eroded Reyðarfjörður central volcano (11 m. yrs).

23. *Skessa, Reyðarfjörður or Tinnudalur, Fáskrúðsfjörður or Breiðdalur.* Thick ignimbrite, the Skessa tuff (8 m. yrs).

24. *Sandfell, Fáskrúðsfjörður.* A laccolith of rhyolitic rock.

25. *Fáskrúðsfjörður and Stöðvarfjörður.* Dyke swarms in the ancient Reyðarfjörður Volcanic System.

26. *Breiðdalur.* A typical Tertiary central volcano (8–9 m. yrs).

27. *Berufjörður, north coast.* Ignimbrite at sea level.

28. *Berufjörður/Breiðdalur.* Composite rhyolitic centre peaks (Rönd-ólfur, Smátindar, Slöttur and Stöng) in the core of the Breiðdalur central volcano.

29. *Berufjörður (eastern part).* Dyke swarm in the ancient Álftafjörður Volcanic System (7–8 m. yrs).

30. *Streiti – Streitishvarf.* A rhyolitic, composite dyke.

31. *Eystrahorn and Vestrahorn.* Large stocks of gabbro/granophyre (parts of ancient magma chambers, 6 m. yrs).

32. *Slaufrudalur.* Granophyric stock (part of an ancient magma chamber, maybe about 8 m. yrs).

33. *Geitafell.* Gabbro intrusion and cone sheets (6 m. yrs).

34. *Öræfajökull.* Active central volcano in an intraplate volcanic belt (ÖVB).

35. *Eyjafjallajökull.* Active central volcano in an intraplate volcanic belt (SIVB).

36. *Hekla.* Active central volcano at the junction of a propagating rift, an intraplate volcanic belt (SIVB) and a fracture zone (SISZ).

37. *Þjórsárdalur.* An eroded Plio-Pleistocene central volcano.

38. *Stóri-Núpur – Hæll.* The Hreppar syncline (old rift axis).

39. *Landsveit – Skeið, Southern Lowlands.* Open fissures and transform faults of the South Iceland Seismic Zone (a transverse fracture zone).

40. *Heiðmörk – Grafarholt.* Active open fissures and faults within a fissure swarm of the Holocene Trölladyngja Volcanic System.

Selected bibliography

Surnames are written in italics. The Icelandic letters é, ó, á, ú, í and ý should be written as e, o, a, u, i and y, ö as ö, oe or simply o, æ as æ or ae, ð as d and þ as th when searching for references and papers in most databases.

R. M. *Allen*, G. *Nolet*, W.J. *Morgan*, K. *Vogfjörð* and B. H. *Bergsson* et al. 1999. The thin hot plume beneath Iceland. *International Geophysical Journal* 137: 51–63.

R. M. *Allen* 2001. The mantle plume beneath Iceland and its interaction with the North–Atlantic Ridge: a seismological investigation. Princeton University.

M. *Beblo* and A. *Björnsson* 1980. A model of electrical resistivity beneath NE–Iceland, correlation with temperature. *Journal of Geophysics* 47: 184–190.

I. Þ. *Bjarnason*, W. H. *Menke*, Ó. G. *Flóvenz* and D. *Caress* 1993. Tomographic image of the Mid–Atlantic plate boundary in Southwestern Iceland. *Journal of Geophysical Research* 98: 6,607–6,622.

A. *Björnsson.* K. *Sæmundsson*, P. *Einarsson*, E. *Tryggvason* and K. *Grönvold* 1977. Current rifting episode in North Iceland. *Nature* 266: 318–323.

S. *Björnsson* 1983. Crust and upper mantle beneath Iceland. In: *Structure and development of the Greenland–Scotland Ridge.* Eds. Bott et al. Plenum Press, New York, 31–61.

D.H. *Blake* 1966. The net–veined complex of the Austurhorn intrusion, Southeast Iceland. *Journal of Geology* 74: 891–907.

B. *Brandsdóttir*, P. *Einarsson* and W. H. *Menke* 2001. Axial Magma Chambers in Iceland 2001. Abstract. Spring Symposium, The Geoscience Society of Iceland. 24 Apr. Reykjavík.

P. *Einarsson* 1991. Earthquakes and present-day tectonism in Iceland. *Tectonophysics* 189: 261–279.

P. *Einarsson.*, B. *Brandsdóttir*, M. T. *Guðmundsson*, H. *Björnsson* and K. *Grönvold* 1997. Center of the Iceland Hotspot Experiences Volcanic Unrest. *Eos, Transactions.* American Geophysical Union, vol. 78, no. 35: 374–375.

H. *Eysteinsson* and J. F. *Hermance* 1985. Magnetotelluric measurements across the eastern volcanic zone in South Iceland. *Journal of Geophysical Research* 87: 10,093–10,103.

Ó. G. *Flóvenz* and K. *Gunnarsson* 1991. Seismic crustal structure in Iceland and surrounding area. *Tectonophysics* 189: 1–17.

Ó. G. *Flóvenz* and K. *Sæmundsson* 1993. Heat flow and geothermal processes in Iceland. *Tectonophysics* 225: 123–138.

G.R. *Foulger* and D.L. *Anderson* 2005. A cool model for the Iceland hotspot. *Journal of Volcanological and Geothermal Research*, 141: 1–22.

G.R. *Foulger*, J.H. *Natland*, D.C. *Presnall* and D.L. *Anderson* (eds) 2005. Plates, Plumes and Paradigms. *Geological Soc. of America Special*, vol. 388, 861 pp.

G. R. *Foulger* et al 2001. Seismic tomography shows that upwelling beneath Iceland is confined to the upper mantle. *Geophysical Journal Int.*, 146: 504–530.

Á. *Guðmundsson* 1995. Ocean-ridge discontinuities in Iceland. *Journal of the Geological Society* 152: 1,011–1,015.

Á. *Guðmundsson* 1995. Infrastructure and mechanics of volcanic systems in Iceland. *Journal of Volcanological and Geothermal Research* 64: 1–22.

Á. *Guðmundsson* 1998. Magma chambers modeled as cavities explain the formation of rift zone central volcanoes and their eruption and intrusion statistics. *Journal of Geophysical Research* 103: 7,401–7,412.

Á. *Guðmundsson* and C. *Homberg* 1999. Evolution of stress fields and faulting in seismic zones. *Pure Applied Geophysics* 154: 257–280

Á. *Guðmundsson* 2000. Dynamics of Volcanic Systems in Iceland: Example of Tectonism and Volcanism in Juxtaposed Hot Spot and Mid-ocean Ridge Systems. *Annual Review of the Earth and Planetary Sciences.* 28: 107–140.

Á. *Guðmundsson* and L.B. *Marinoni* 2001. Geometry, emplacement and arrest of dykes. *Annales Tectonicae* 13: 71–92

Á. *Guðmundsson* 2002. Emplacements and arrest of sheets and dykes in central volcanoes. *Journal of Volcanological and Geothermal Research* 116: 279–298.

Á *Guðmundsson* and I.F. *Loetveit* 2005. Dyke emplacement in a layered and faulted rift zone. *Journal of Volcanology and Geothermal Research* 144, 311–328.

Á *Guðmundsson* and S.L. *Brenner* 2005. On the conditions of sheet injections and eruptions in stratovolcanoes. *Bulletin of Volcanology* 67, 768–782.

Ó. *Guðmundsson* 2003. The dense root of the Iceland crust. *Earth and Planteary Science Letters* 206: 427–440.

H. *Jóhannesson* 1980. Jarðlagaskipan og þróun rekbelta á Vesturlandi (The bedrock strata and evolution of rift systems in Western Iceland). *Náttúrufræðingurinn* 50: 13–31.

H. *Jóhannesson* 2005. Ages of different large intrusions (personal communication).

M.K. *Kaban*, Ó.G. *Flóvenz* and G. *Pálmason* 2002. Nature of the crust-mantle transition zone and the thermal state of the upper mantle beneath Iceland from gravity modeling. *Geophysical Journal. Int.* 149: 281–299.

S. D. *King* and D. L. *Anderson* 1998. Edge driven convection, *Earth and Planetary Science Letters,* 160, 289–296.

A.L. *Lawver* and R.D. *Müller* 1994. Iceland hot spot track. *Geology* 22: 311–314.

J. C. *MacLennan* 2000. Melt generation and movement under N-Iceland. University of Cambridge.

W. *Menke* 1999. Crustal isostacy indicates anomalous densities beneath Iceland. *Geophysical Research Letters* 26: 1,215–1,218.

N. *Óskarsson*, S. *Steinþórsson* and G. E. *Sigvaldason* 1985. Iceland Geochemical Anomaly: Origin, volcanotectonics, chemical fractionation and isotope evolution of the crust. *Journal of Geophysical Research* 90: 10,011–10,025.

G. *Pálmason* and K. *Sæmundsson* 1974. Iceland in relation to the Mid-Atlantic Ridge. *Annual Review of the Earth and Planetary Sciences* no. 2: 25–50.

G. *Pálmason* 1986. Model of crustal formation in Iceland and application to submarine mid-ocean ridges. In: The Geology of North America Vol. M: the Western North-Atlantic Region. Eds. Vogt and Tucholke. *Geological Society of America*, 87–97.

A.D. *Sanders*, J.G. *Fitton* et al 1997. North Atlantic Province. In: Large igneous provinces: continental, oceanic and planetary flood volcanism. Eds. J. J. Mahoney and M.F. Coffin. *Geophysical Monograph* 100, American Geophysical Union, Washington DC, 44–93.

R. C. *Searle*, J.A., *Keaton* et al. 1998. The Reykjanes Ridge: structure and tectonics of a hot-spot-influenced, slow-spreading ridge, from multibeam bathymetry, gravity and magnetic investigations. *Earth and Planetary Science Letters* 160: 463–478.

F. *Sigmundsson* 1991. Postglacial rebound and asthenosphere viscosity in Iceland. *Geophysical Research Letters* 18: 1,131–1,134.

F. *Sigmundsson* 2006. *Iceland Geodynamics – Crustal deformation and divergent plate tectonics.* Springer-Praxis, Chichester, UK. 209 pp.

H. *Sigurðsson* and R.S.J. *Sparks* 1978. Lateral magma flow within rifted Icelandic crust. *Nature* 274: 126–130.

H. *Soosalu* and P. *Einarsson* 2004. Seismic constraints on magma chambers at Hekla and Torfajökull volcanoes, Iceland. *Bulletin of Volcanology* 66: 276–286.

R.K. *Staples*, R.S. *White*, B. *Brandsdóttir*, W. *Menke* et al. 1997. Faroe-Iceland Experiment 1. Crustal structure of northeastern Iceland. *Journal of Geophysical Research* 102: 7,849–7,866.

E. *Sturkell*, F. *Sigmundsson* et al 1994: Strain accumulation 1986–1992 across the Reykjanes plate boundary, Iceland, determined from GPS-measurements. *Geophysical Research Letters* 21: 125–128.

K. *Sæmundsson* 1979. Outline of the geology of Iceland. *Jökull* 29.

F. *Þórarinsson*, S. G. *Magnússon*, P. *Einarsson*, L. *Kristjánsson* et al. 1989. Gravity, aeromagnetism and earthquakes in SW-Iceland. *Jökull* 39.

G. E. *Vink* 1984. A hotspot model for Iceland and the Vöring Plateau. *Journal of Geophysical Research* 89: 9,949–9.959.

Peter R. *Vogt* 1983. The Iceland Mantle Plume: Status of the hypothesis after a decade of work. In: *Structure and development of the Greenland-Scotland Ridge.* Eds. Bott et al. Plenum Press. 191–213.

G. P. L. *Walker* 1974. The structure of Eastern Iceland. In: (Ed.) S. Kristánsson. *Geodynamics of Iceland and the North Atlantic area.* 177–188.

R.S. *White* 1988. A hot-spot model for early Tertiary volcanism in the N.-Atlantic. In: (Eds.) A.C. Morton and L.M. Parson, Early Tertiary Volcanism and the Opening of the NE.-Atlantic. *Geological Society Special Publication* 39: 3–13.

R.S. *White* 1992: Crustal structure and magmatism of North Atlantic continental margins. *Journal of the Geological Society*, London, 149: 841–854.

C.J. *Wolfe*, I. Þ. *Bjarnason* et al. 1997. Seismic structure of the Iceland mantle plume. *Nature* 385: 245–47

4 The restless Earth

Because of Iceland's situation on a divergent plate margin and on top of a mantle plume, earthquakes can be expected to occur frequently. And they certainly do. Earthquakes are registered in thousands every year, most of a magnitude in the region of Ms =1–4.0, and sometimes enough to startle people, though they do not cause any noteworthy damage. A few may exceed Ms = 4 and reach Ms = 5.5, causing only minor damage if close enough to inhabited areas. Every decade a few more can top Ms = 6, while each century the "big ones" of between Ms = 6 and Ms = 7.2 may occasionally occur. These are serious events and have caused local damage or even proved fatal to people during the past 1,100 years. Most earthquakes have a purely tectonic origin, even when magma is on the move deep down in the Earth. Other earthquakes accompany volcanic eruptions but these rarely exceed Ms = 4.0–4.5. Open fractures, fissures and faults mark old and new earthquake areas or zones. An elaborate monitoring system is operated, based on seismometers, GPS-positioning systems, strain-meters, gravity measurements, radon measurements and InSAR image interpretations.

Key words

Tensile stress • compressive stress • shear stress • earthquakes • tectonic movements • earthquake waves • earthquake magnitudes • seismic fractures • fissures • faults • tectonic lineations • fissure swarm • graben • fracture zone • isostatic movements • seismic monitoring

Rifts and faults. Rifting Zone at Þingvellir. (RTH)

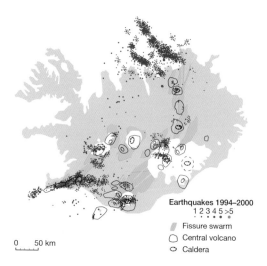

Epicentres (red dots) of earthquakes with magnitude equal to or greater than 1 in the period 1994–2000. Earthquakes of magnitude greater than 5 are marked by green hexagonals. Note the epicentres of two large earthquakes in the SISZ. Volcanic systems are shown in yellow. (Source: S.S. Jakobsdottir et al. 2002)

Earthquakes and tectonic movements

Large-scale but slow movements in the lithosphere (e.g. plate movement/spreading) or movement of material in the asthenosphere result in stress in the brittle upper part of the crust. The lower layers tend to behave in an aseismic manner under stress. The stress is either tensile or compressive, but shear stress can also occur. Tensile stress is characteristic of the Icelandic rifting zone. Pure compressive stress is mainly associated with subsidence in central volcanoes. Shear stress occurs mainly on fracture zones between rifting zones.

Tensile and/or shear stress steadily builds up and increases in certain places within active areas. Sooner or later stress approaches the fracture strength of the rock. The rock fails and huge slabs of crust are displaced, with fracturing and differential movement. In general each fracture surface is vertical at the top but dips further down, except for strike-slip faults which are usually vertical. A particular tectonic movement begins at a specific point on the fracture surface and in a split second or over a period of several seconds the crustal slabs are displaced and the tectonic movement itself is completed. The energy released is in proportion to the accumulated stress and size of the fracture surface. Part of this energy causes heating of the rock while another part takes the

Widening and subsidence at an old normal fault (Tóveggur, Öxarfjörður) during a volcano- tectonic episode in the Krafla Volcanic System in late 1975. (RTH)

form of kinetic energy, evident as a shockwave which spreads outwards through the crust in all directions from the fracture surface and results in deformation of the strata and the rocks within them. Since the crust is layered, and for the most part composed of crystalline, solid materials, seismic waves are apparent as separate wave sets which move and shake the rock in different ways. An earthquake can last for tens of seconds; the larger the earthquake, the longer it will last.

The origin of an earthquake is known as the earthquake focus. These can occur at depths of 1–35 km in Iceland but most commonly occur 3–12 km deep. Within a split second after the energy release, the pressure waves (primary or P-waves, like sound waves in air) and shear waves (secondary or S-waves) have separated in the rock mass, the P-waves travelling faster than the S-waves. The wave velocity in rock is of the order of a few kilometres per second and increases with greater rock density. The waves die down with time and so do the effects with increasing distance from the focus. Hot plastic or ductile rock, not to mention magma, retard the P-waves or stop them. The surface waves (R- and L-waves also spread outwards from the earthquake epicentre (directly above the focus) and travel at the lowest velocity, while the earth rises and falls. Digital seismometers detect and record the waves. Important information is collected: focus depth, and distance from the seismograph, earthquake location and magnitude, as well as fault plane solutions and data for calculations of, for example, fracture surfaces and stress changes in the area surrounding the focus. The magnitude is calculated from the movement of the seismometer (from its trace or what is termed as the seismograph). The magnitude is a measure of the energy of the earthquake; i.e. the energy released at the focus per time. Three different values of magnitude can be obtained, depending on the method used. A particular magnitude is represented by the Richter scale (in whole numbers from 0 to 10, with an accuracy of one decimal place) and each step represents a roughly thirtyfold increase in energy (two intervals represent a roughly 30 x 30 increase or approximately 900 x increase). Each half step represents around a fivefold increase in energy. In this chapter magnitude is based on calculations of the surface waves (Ms).

The effects of earthquakes on people, manmade structures and the landscape rely to some extent on their distance from the focus. The strength of an earthquake, i.e. how it is felt at a particular place, can be expressed on the Mercalli scale (from I up to XII). According to this the same earthquake has different effects with increasing distance from the focus, with the highest values being closest to the focus.

Fractures, fissures and faults

Fracture planes commonly occur on the Earth's surface as tectonic cracks, fractures and open fissures, i.e. tectonic lineations. In Iceland they range from fine fractures up to the largest which form gaping sores in the crust. They measure from a few centimetres wide and tens of metres long to several metres wide and hundreds of metres long. They are usually displaced laterally in an en-echelon or sideways-shifting fashion. Thus the total length of many fracture sections can reach many kilometres. The fractures are open at the top but for the most part closed a few metres or tens of metres down. The fracture walls or planes

Normal faults (40 m total throw within the last 10,000 years) mark the central part of the Western Rift Zone at Lake Þingvallavatn,

A view towards the Hengill central volcano. The American plate is on the right-hand side and the Eurasian on the left. (OS)

are usually nearly vertical, whereas at depth they dip at 45–90°. The vast majority of tectonic surface lineations in Iceland are tensile fractures and fissures, formed when the bedrock splits as a result of accumulated stress in the rifting zone. Flosagjá and Nikulásargjá (Peningagjá) at Þingvellir are typical examples of this fracture type. These tensile fractures are usually orientated in a north-south or southwest-north-east direction.

When there is upward, downward or lateral movement of the rock slabs on either side of a fracture, it is referred to as a fault. There are many faults in the Icelandic fracture swarms. Reverse faults are mostly the result of compressive stress. They are common abroad where plates collide and strata are pushed together. This type of fault is rare in Iceland, although it occurs in Borgarfjörður and at Tjörnes. In comparison, normal faults and transform faults (or strike-slip/lateral faults) or hybrids of these two types are very common in Iceland. The best known example of a normal fault is the Almannagjá at Þingvellir. It is about 7.7 km long, in several en-echelon sections. In normal faulting one of the crustal blocks subsides relative to the other. At Almannagjá the subsidence measures up to 40 m in the last 10,000 years. In the case of transform faults the displacement is on a horizontal plane with one block sliding past the other. Transform faults are termed either right lateral or left lateral, depending on whether movement is to the right or left when viewed from the opposite side of the fracture. A transform fault can be seen from the north-south fractures in southern Iceland, within the southern Iceland seismic zone. Fault solutions for earthquakes suggest stress release and the kind of movement that occurs on particular faults. For existing faults it is necessary to investigate the surrounding rocks in order to estimate the type of fault involved.

The present rifting – fissure swarms

As described in chapter 3, rifting and the associated volcanic activity commence in bursts or episodes, which consist of a series of events. The episodes are both due to the fact that local stress alternately accumulates and releases within the rift zones and also because magma production beneath Iceland is not constant. Upwelling under the rift zone of the Mid-Atlantic Ridge appears to occur with intervals and the same can be said of upwelling of partially melted mantle rock under hot spots. In addition, there are weak areas throughout the rift zone in the form of the en-echelon fracture swarms of volcanic systems. In some of these the crust is weaker than in others, and consequently rifting episodes tend to be more frequent there than elsewhere.

The interaction between plate movement and rising magma can take two forms. In one, the magma forces its way through the rock due to excess pressure and directly results in fracturing and dyke formation, with corresponding rifting on the surface. In the other, accumulated tensile stress causes the rock to fail and existing magma simultaneously intrudes the crust. The result is the same: a rifting episode, formation of intrusions and perhaps eruption. It must be assumed that in some rifting episodes no magma is involved.

Open tension cracks and fissures line the floor of the Þingvellir down-faulted valley (graben). This is Peningagjá (the Money Chasm). (RTH)

As well as comprising en-echelon fracture groups, the commonest tectonic lineations in Iceland, i.e. tensile fractures and normal faults, form long, rather narrow arrays of tectonic-fault areas known as fissure zones or fissure swarms. Along with volcanoes, the fissure swarms are arranged in the previously mentioned (around 30) independent volcanic systems in the neovolcanic zone. The most common orientation of active tensile fractures in this zone is northerly or northeasterly. Generally there is subsidence within the fracture zones, mainly in the most active (often central) part of the swarms. Here we can see broad down-faulted valleys several kilometres wide, also known as graben which are a kind of mirror image of what we see below sea level on the ridge crest. Normal faults and grabens are very common in the rift zones and volcanic zones, for example on the Reykjanes peninsula, in the Þingvellir area and Kaldidalur valley and in the northeast. There are many stepped faults, i.e. several normal faults with different degrees of down-throw have occurred on parallel fractures. This type of formation can be clearly traced in the Vogar fracture swarm close to the Reykjanes highway near the Grindavík junction. Each normal fault is the result of repeated stress release and associated earthquakes. Well-known graben include the Þingvellir graben, the valley Blikalónsdalur in the Melrakkaslétta area, Heljargjá in central Iceland and Gjástykki north of Krafla.

The Reykjanes peninsula is unique. Here the spreading ocean ridge emerges on dry land while the plate margin bends to the east towards the South Iceland Seismic Zone (SISZ). The bend is due to the strong influence of the transform fault zone stress field on drifting and rifting on the peninsula. The shifting of the transform zone to the south further contributes to this deformation of the plate margin. The plate margin can be easily traced by the distribution of earthquakes along it in a 2–5 km belt. Four volcanic fracture swarms, which form part of the Western Rift Zone (WRZ), are arranged en-echelon along this bent plate margin. Furthest east in the Hengill area a triple point is formed where the westernmost fracture swarm on the Reykjanes peninsula, the SISZ, and the bent plate margin meet. Two types of fracture system occur on the peninsula. The large fissure swarms are oriented to the northeast (about 40°N). They are characterised by tensile normal faults

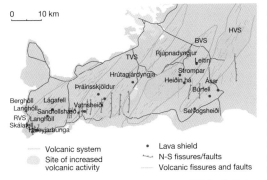

A presentation of the main tectonic and volcanic features of the Reykjanes peninsula, southwest Iceland. Volcanic fissures, fractures and normal faults line the four volcanic systems and lava shields are found within them or bordering on them. RVS: Reykjanes Volcanic System; TVS: Trölladyngja Volcanic System; BVS: Brennisteinsfjöll Volcanic System and HVS: Hengill Volcanic System. The HVS, the SISZ fracture zone, and the axis of seismic activity at Reykjanesskagi form a triple point in the Hengill area. Note the N-S-trending strike-slip faults.
(Main source: H. Jóhannesson and K. Sæmundsson 1998)

as well as eruptive fissures and extend right across the peninsula. On the bent plate margin towards the south of the peninsula there are shorter, elongated fracture zones with northerly fractures which exhibit transform movement. The maximum compressive stress in the peninsula bedrock seems to vary with time and place. After a period of maximum horizontal compressive stress, the resulting tectonic activity is in the form of transform movement on northerly fractures (westerly fractures exist but are rare). The largest earthquakes may reach Ms = 5–6.2 (exemplified by an event in the Bláfjöll mountains in 1929). The last major earthquake episode of this type occurred following the south Iceland earthquake of 2000 (Ms = ca. 5.5). On other occasions the maximum compressive stress is vertical and stress release occurs with rifting and subsidence on northeasterly fractures. The associated earthquakes are weaker (Ms = 4–5). At intervals of 500–1,000 years there are periods when sufficient magma is present under the plate margin for volcano-tectonic episodes to occur with rifting, earthquakes and eruptions within the four volcanic systems. Such episodes probably last for decades or a few centuries until activity returns to its previous level. The last eruptive episodes on the Reykjanes peninsula occurred about 2,000 years ago and again from late in the 10th century until the end of the 13th century.

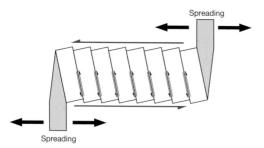

The South Iceland Seismic zone behaves as shown here in a schematic illustration. The top transform fault (in the north) is a left-lateral fault, as is the bottom one (in the south). They are not evident on the surface, however. Instead, an array of old and new north-trending fissures appear, most of which show a right-lateral fault motion. This has been called "bookshelf" faulting and rotation (counter-clockwise). (Based on P. Einarsson 1991)

Fracture zones

A fracture zone is a block-like elongated area in which rift zones are placed offset to each other. In Iceland the fracture zones form east-west tending zones. There, plate sections move laterally past each other as they are pushed apart along the nearby rift segments. The plates within the zone literally deform because one boundary part of the block is pushed to the left while the other boundary part is subjected to a right-wardpush. High stress builds up within the block (fracture zone) before the forced slip-fashion movement can occur, thereby causing still larger earthquakes than found in the rift zones.

Fracture zones are found along the whole Mid-Atlantic Ridge, many at right angles to the rift segments; one in south Iceland (the South Iceland Seismic Zone, SISZ), another immediately off the northeast coast, roughly between Grímsey island and the bays of Öxarfjörður and Skjálfandaflói (Tjörnes Fracture Zone, TFZ). All earthquakes around or above Ms = 6.5 in the south of Iceland (SISZ) have caused quite extensive damage on land. According to written sources, houses collapsed and a number of people died in earthquakes in South Iceland during the period 1164–1896. However, large shocks off the northeast coast are easier to cope with as the seismicity originates on the sea floor.

The SISZ stretches from the town of Hveragerði in the west to the volcano Hekla in the east. It is some 15–20 km wide and 70–80 km long. This flat block-like crustal section is wrenched, tugged and pulled

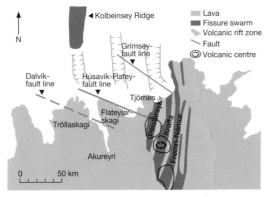

The Tjörnes Fracture Zone (TFZ) links the inland North-eastern Rift Zone (NRZ) with the offshore Kolbeinsey (rifting) Ridge. Note the offset graben-like structures. Unlike the fracture zone in southern Iceland, the TFZ not only produces strong earthquakes (like the SISZ) but also displays volcanic activity. (Map modified from: E. Sturkell, B. Brandsdóttir et al. 1992 and Á. Guðmundsson et al. 1993)

at by the adjacent sections of the crust, as the plates, each containing half of Iceland, are pushed apart. A westward motion tears at the northern side of the block while an eastward motion occurs at the southern side. For thousands of years a system of north/northwest-tending major cracks and fissures has developed in the area (like the spaces between books standing on a shelf). Most of them are hard to spot because thick soils in this fertile, rural area quickly cover the earthquake marks. During tectonic events, however, an array of en-echelon fissures, cracks and pressure mounds forms on top of some of the major fissures. The smaller fissures and cracks commonly have a more northeasterly trend than the bigger ones and are easily detected, even decades after each major episode. In historical times, more than 30 earthquake episodes have hit southern Iceland, about twice a century on average. There are many records of damage and land distortion but it should be borne in mind that houses in those days were built of timber, turf and stone. The last seismic events of any significance occurred in 1784 (estimated Ms = 7+), 1896 (lasted for almost 3 weeks), 1912 (only in the far eastern part of the zone) and in 2000 (two quakes on one major fissure each, Ms = 6.5–6.6). There are some clues pointing to a slow southward migration of the whole fracture zone. The explanation could be found in the propagating rift (NRZ), extending into the South Iceland Volcanic Belt, to the east of the fracture zone.

Two earthquakes (magnitude 6.5) occurred in the South Iceland Fracture Zone in 2000. Divergent plate movements cause lateral pull at the edges of a microplate. Over 30 earthquakes were recorded in the SIFZ during the last millennium, with magnitudes of up to around 7. (RTH)

The Borgarfjörður Seismic Zone (BSZ) is a narrow earthquake belt or block that stretches from the southeastern end of the Ljósufjöll Volcanic System (in the intraplate Snæfellsnes Volcanic Belt) inland to the upper reaches of the Borgarfjörður rural area. Recent episodes have involved earthquakes of up to Ms = 5–6 and young fissures show extension (e.g. from 1974). The tectonic pattern is, however, complicated, with six different groups of fractures, some very old. The pattern indicates a long history of fracturing and can be attributed to different causes such as the migration of a fracture zone, with shifts in the major rift fissure location, or the extension of the SNVB into the wake of the hot spot.

The Tjörnes Fracture Zone (TFZ) consists of two main fault lineaments, both subject to shear stresses and transform movements. The northerly Grímsey fault line stretches from the island of Grímsey, southeast into the bay of Öxarfjörður. There it connects to the fissure swarm of the Krafla Volcanic System (in the NRZ). At least two prominent graben-like tectonic structures straddle the Grímsey fault line. Volcanic structures have been revealed on the ocean floor within them and the earthquake activity is very lively. Volcanic submarine eruptions have been recorded and geothermal activity is evident. The similarity between this area and Reykjanesskagi is clear to some extent.

The southerly Húsavík-Flatey fault has approximately the same trend as the Grímsey fault line. It barely touches the island of Flatey and runs ashore in the vicinity of Húsavík, where it connects to the Þeistareykir fissure swarm (in the NRZ). The northwestern end dies out in a graben-like structure which runs due north from the mouth of Eyjafjörður towards the Kolbeinsey Ridge, without apparent volcanic activity, the same being true of the Húsavík-Flatey fault itself. Bursts of earthquakes (up to Ms = 6–7) occur on both these main tectonic lineaments, the last having taken place in 1872 (Húsavík-Flatey fault) and 1976 (Grímsey fault line). A third northwest-tending fault line can be traced, still further to the south, from the mouth of Skagafjörður through the northernmost part of the Tröllaskagi peninsula into Eyjafjörður (the Dalvík fault line). A large earthquake occurred here in 1934 (Ms = 6.3) and another was felt in 1963, with an epicentre off the mouth of the Skagafjörður fjord (Ms = 7). There seems to be a subsequent age difference between the three lines, the southernmost (Dalvík fault line) being the oldest and the Grímsey line the youngest. This could be attributed to a slow migration of the main fracture zone towards the north and east in cohesion with the apparent eastward shift of the hot spot.

Isostatic movements

When travelling in the coastal lowland areas of Iceland it is obvious that the sea level has very recently been higher than it is at present. Raised beaches, wave-eroded surfaces, shell remains in loose deposits, old sea cliffs and other evidence are all indications of a considerably higher sea level, by more than 100 m in places. There is also evidence that the sea level has been considerably lower than it is at present. This can be seen from peat and tree remains at the present-day low-tide mark (Kjalarnes, Seltjarnarnes) and from lava which clearly extended further out than the present coastline (Þjórsárhraun at Stokkseyri) about 7,800 years ago. The higher strandline can be explained to some extent by rapid transgression following sudden warming at the end of the last glacial period and beginning of the present era. However, the strandline is too high to be entirely explained in this way. An additional factor is the buoyant movement of the crust. The plates bend downwards or upwards depending on whether the overlying weight increases or decreases. This results in slow isostatic movements. At the same time material changes occur in the underlying asthenosphere, involving compression or extension, corresponding to subsidence or uplift respectively. This can be the result of the accumulation of crustal layers or growth of large glaciers (subsidence), or rapid ablation of glaciers and crustal rifting outwards from the upwelling of hot material beneath rift zones or hot spots (uplift).

The thick Pleistocene ice cap which covered Iceland at the close of the last glacial period had pushed the land downwards to a large extent, with the greatest deflection at the centre. When the sea level suddenly rose, the water reached far inland as a result of the land's original subsidence. This high position was, however, short-lived, since as soon as the ice cover decreased, uplift began. It took the land only about 1,000 years to "spring" back again to its original position, a much shorter response time than in mainland Scandinavia. This is not surprising, since the mantle material is about 100 times less mobile under the continents. The sea now receded rapidly (regression) and when the land had completely recovered, about 8,000 years ago, the strandline was lower than at present. Since then transgression has reoccurred, partly

The Northeastern Rift Zone is characterised by normal faults, open fissures, hyaloclastite ridges from the late Ice Age and Holocene volcanoes in four volcanic systems. (RTH)

Peat on the coast at Kjalarnes near Reykjavík tells the tale of a rising sea level. The peat is about 3,000–9,000 years old. The marine transgression is partly due to isostatic, crustal movements. The landmass in the Southwest is subjected to a downflexing movement. (RTH)

because of the rising sea level due to melting glaciers and warming up of the seas, and partly because of land subsidence for various reasons.

Minor isostatic movements also occur. Exact measurements of the Langisjór lake show that it moved steadily away from the Vatnajökull ice cap in the period 1959–91, accompanied by uplift of the land close to Vatnajökull. These changes and uplift at Höfn in Hornafjörður can be explained by material movement in the asthenosphere beneath the ice cap. As the latter thickened during the "Little Ice Age", the underlying land sank, but after the end of the cold period around 1900 the glacier shrank fairly rapidly for most of the 20th century and uplift began.

Isostacy affects more than just Pleistocene geology. Rising hot, light material in the mantle keeps the country, especially the central area, further above sea level than would otherwise be the case. Iceland

Trölladyngja counts as one of the largest postglacial lava shields. The volcano and the lava flow have a volume of several dozen cubic kilometres. Rapid isostatic uplift in the wake of the sudden regression of the Weichselian ice cap created favourable conditions for large effusive lava eruptions of primitive magma. (RTH)

"floats" on a hot mantle cushion. On the other hand, accumulation of volcanic rocks in the rifting and volcanic zones "pushes" the land downwards. As the land drifts away from the rising magma area below, the crust cools and sinks. Thus the surface rocks are carried down to a considerable depth and drift in opposite directions. Some descend deep down to the hottest area and melt ("recycled magma").

Erosion and weathering also denude the surface of the land and sediments are carried away. This causes uplift and maintains the high profile of the Tertiary areas. Finally it is thought that subsidence and uplift associated with the receding Pleistocene glaciers affect the frequency of volcanic eruption and the quantity of eruptive materials, in particular primitive (unevolved) basalt lavas. Rapid uplift encourages volcanic eruption and huge flood eruptions with the associated build-up of large shield volcanoes (see chapter 5). A period of numerous shield-volcano formations thus occurred from around 11,000 to 5,000–6,000 years ago.

Langisjór is a long, narrow lake at the western margin of the Vatnajökull ice cap. The lake bottom, close to the ice cap, is raised as the glacier retreats, due to isostatic lifting, and the strandline is tilted. Note the long hyaloclastic ridges *(móberg)* from subglacial fissure eruptions. (OS)

Earthquake monitoring in Iceland

In Iceland earthquakes reach up to Ms = 5–6.5 in the rifting zones, largely due to tensile stress build-up but also due to shearing stresses. In the lateral volcanic zones the earthquakes are smaller and mainly related to magma pressure and movement. In the main transform fracture zones, i.e. in the southern coastal plains (SISZ) and on the sea floor off the northeast (TFZ), earthquakes of Ms = 5–7+ can occur, mainly due to higher shear stress. On the Reykjanes peninsula earthquakes are caused by the release of tensile stress but stronger earthquakes also occur (Ms = 6+) because shear stresses can build up and cause fracturing. Deformation on the peninsula due to plate movement has been monitored using GPS and InSAR measurements. In 2001, for example, a total of 14,000 earthquakes was recorded in Iceland, and 160,000 between 1991 and 2000.

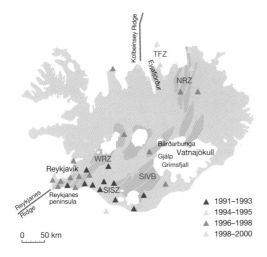

The location of SIL-stations and other monitoring stations designed to monitor active volcanic systems and seismic zones. New stations have been added.

An elaborate and automated volcano-tectonic monitoring system is operated in Iceland. It is a multi-purpose, multi-instrumental network based mainly on seismometers and a GPS positioning system, but also on strain-meters, gravity measurements, gas-emission measurements and InSAR image interpretations. Although largely based on the original SIL monitoring system which was initiated in the 1980s as an inter-Nordic project, it has now been enlarged and updated (to more than 40 stations in 2005). Information from dozens of widely distributed instruments is continuously collected at a central station in Reykjavík where analysis is carried out and active zones are monitored in order to be able to provide warnings of earthquakes and/or eruptions. Icelandic building construction in seismic areas is subject to strict regulations as regards foundations, iron reinforcement and other safety factors.

Earth scientists also use seismic data from both natural and man-made earthquakes to obtain knowledge about the interior of the Earth, the extent of magma chambers and the size of mantle plumes and other features. Seismic measurements also form part of research which can be used to forecast volcanic eruption and tectonic movement, and this has been successful in some cases. For example, magma intrusion in the Krafla Fires and Hekla eruptions have been forecast with from halfan-hour to an hour's warning. The second of two large earthquakes in southern Iceland in 2000 was forecast and alerts can be organised when measurements suggest eruption is imminent, as for instance in the case of the Gjálp (Vatnajökull) eruption in 1996 and Grímsvötn in 2004. It is also possible to follow the progress of an eruption from beginning to end by monitoring low frequency earthquakes and tremors which accompany such events. For example, the commencement of the eruption beneath the glacier at Gjálp could be observed 48 hours before it broke through the 500–600 m thick ice cover and became visible from a considerable distance. In the case of Katla it is important to be able to forecast eruptions as well as to pinpoint where eruption has started, so that the location of the expected jökulhlaup flood can be predicted.

In all cases, scientist have to get aquainted with the character of each volcanic system and each central volcano. The volcanic systems tend to develop a pattern of behaviour that can be deduced from a 10,000–20,000-year-long history. Rifting systems tend to behave differently from off-riff systems and some systems go through quite regular periods of unrest while others behave more erraticly. A number of systems are productive and show short times of repose. Others tend to the opposite. Each of the larger volcanic centres also behave like individuals with a certain character which, however, is subject to sudden changes. Hekla is a good example. The large tephra-producing eruptions have been absent for almost a millennium. For centuries the long, mixed eruptions occurred once or twice each century until after 1948. Then the volcano suddenly went into a phase where it erupts every decade or so and the unrest is rather short-lived, albeit forceful. The Grímsvötn volcano, on the other hand, erupts every 5–10 years in rather long periods that are spaced apart by a number of decades. While Hekla seems to start erupting at a very short notice (1–2 hours), Katla has a slower approach and somewhat longer time elapses between telltale earthquakes and the start of an eruption.

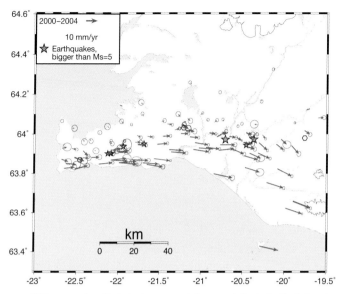

GPS-surveys show the tectonic movements in southwest and south Iceland 2000–2004, relative to the North-American plate (From Þ. Árnadóttir, Nord. Volc. Inst. 2005)

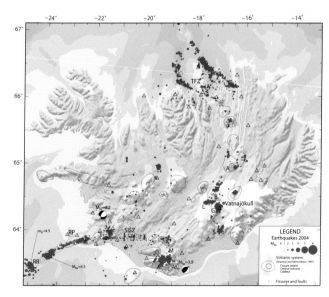

Earthquakes in Iceland 2004.
(S. Hjaltadóttir, H. Geirsson and Þ. Skaftadóttir,
Jökull 55 (107 119), 2005)

135

Where to go?

A description of typical localities and cases serves to promote further studies.

The following list directs readers to some of the more typical study sites in the active tectonic areas. For more detailed information refer to scientific papers or the road guide by T. Thordarson and A. Höskuldsson: *Iceland, Classical Geology in Europe 3*, Terra 2002.

1. *Reykjanes.* Reykjanes is the southwestern tip of the Reykjanes peninsula where the Reykjanes rifting ridge meets Iceland. The area is covered with volcanic fissures, small lava shields (one made of picrite), geothermal vents and large normal faults, open rifts and a graben. A footbridge crosses large, parallel fractures at an interesting road-side educational site close to Sandvík and Kinn.

2. *Vogar fissure swarm.* Vogar is a small town en route from Reykjavík to the Keflavík International Airport. North of the road at Stapi hill, there is a fine view across an array of normal faults which create a graben. Postglacial dilation amounts to at least 15 m.

3. *Grindavík – Blue Lagoon.* Faults and fissures cut through recent lava flows northeast of the Blue Lagoon. The summit of the mountain Þorbjörn (243 m), close to the Svartsengi Geothermal Power Station, is cut by two large parallel normal faults, forming a narrow graben.

4. *Þingvellir.* The area displays a prominent graben. It cuts through many Holocene lava flows over a distance of at least 40 km from the slopes of the Hengill volcano to the Skjaldbreiður lava shield. It is 10–15 km wide in the southwest, narrowing to 5–7 km in the northeast and bordered by Holocene or subglacial volcanic formations. The central Þingvellir lava (9,000 years old) is dissected by about 100 fractures and faults. Their average length is 620 m. The maximum is reached at Almannagjá (7.7 km), which borders the graben to the west. The maximum width of this famous normal fault is 68 m and the largest throw 40 m. The 11 km long Hrafnagjá (30 m throw) forms the eastern boundary fault. The measurable crustal dilation and sinking of the main graben floor (about

0 ___ 50 km

5 km wide) is in the order of 1–2 mm a year but tectonic episodes occur a few times each millennium. They are accompanied by earthquakes, and crustal movements in the order of >1–2 m occur; the most recent in 1789.

5. *Hengill.* Hengill (808 m) is a volcanic centre southwest of Lake Þingvallavatn. The mountain rises above the Nesjavellir Geothermal Power Plant. Faulting is evident and volcanic fissures stretch along the fissure swarm associated with the volcano. In the 1990s the Hengill area was subjected to a long period of unrest, including thousands of earthquakes (up to Ms = 5.5) and magma injections (into the satellite Hrómundartindur Volcanic System).

6. *Heiðmörk – Búrfell crater – Helgafell.* Heiðmörk is a large recreational area southeast of Reykjavík, part of the capital's "green belt". It consists of glacially denuded lava, Holocene lavas and large patches of low-profile forest and heath vegetation. In the Hjallar area, large faults and fissures form a series of parallel, narrow grabens. Further to the south and east, the Holocene craters and

crater rows of the Trölladyngja Volcanic System (e.g. Búrfell) intermingle with subglacial, volcanic formations (small mountains, e.g. Helgafell). An interesting short hiking trail links Búrfell with the main Heiðmörk road, while a seven-day-long hike would take a medium-grade hiker from the Nesjavellir Geothermal Power Plant to Reykjanes, along the whole crest of the Reykjanesskagi peninsula (the Reykjavegur Trail). One of the trail bases is at Kaldársel, close to Helgafell.

7. *Suðurland.* The SISZ is a fracture zone in the so-called Southern Lowlands. The main road (Ring Road, National Route 1) cuts right through this very active seismic area. Faults and tectonic fractures and mounds are evident at many locations, commonly on farm-land. For study sites, refer to scientific papers and ask locally for permission if necessary. The earthquake activity is periodic. Usually, earthquakes start occurring in the eastern part of the fracture zone but subsequently the epicentres "move" westwards and an episode can last for a few weeks. The hardest shocks may attain a magnitude of Ms = 7–7.2, and large earthquakes of magnitude Ms = 6.0–6.5 are common. The last incident of this kind occurred after a few foreshocks with a magnitude 6.6 earth-quake on 17 June 2000, close to the town of Hella. The best-fitting fissure model for the quake is a 16 km long and 10 km deep right-lateral strike-slip fissure striking almost due north and with a maximum slip of 2.25 m. On the surface, the fault appears as a long system of rifts, mounds and strike-slip faults. Another main fault further to the west (Hestfjall) slipped on 21 June 2000, again with similar consequences. At least 2,500 buildings were damaged, many of them very seriously, but there were no fatalities and only seven people were injured, none of them badly. It is likely that the seismic activity will continue still further to the west in the Selfoss-Ölfus area in the near future.

8. *Borgarfjörður.* The active tectonic area in Borgarfjörður is located in the inland valleys, such as Reykholtsdalur. For locations, refer to scientific papers (e.g. M. Kohdayar 1999). Most of the geothermal activity in the valleys is confined to the active fissures and faults.

9. *Kópasker.* Located on the eastern shores of Öxarfjörður, Kópasker is a town at the junction of the Grímsey tectonic line and the Krafla fissure swarm. It is very close to the site of a magnitude 6.2 earthquake that occurred in 1976 after the strong initiation of the Krafla Fires volcano-tectonic (rifting) episode in 1975.

10. *Húsavík.* Húsavík is a large town by Icelandic standards, located on Skjálfandaflói bay and famous for its whale-watching tours. In this area, the Flatey strike-slip fault connects to the Northeastern Rift Zone (fig. 4.4).

11. *Krafla-Mývatn.* This area is world renowned for its rich natural displays of volcanic and tectonic activity. It stretches from the Gjástykki graben in the north, through the Leirhnjúkur and Víti crater area at the volcanic centre, onwards to Lake Mývatn. At Bjarnarflag and in the vicinity of Reykjahlíð village, fine examples of normal faults, open fissures, geothermal areas and crater rows bear witness to the rifting processes and plate tectonics at play in Northeast Iceland. As in the Þingvellir and Vogar fissure swarms, many open fractures contain groundwater, with the exception at Mývatn that the water is warm.

12. *Öxarfjörður (inland).* The broad bay of Öxarfjörður was strongly affected by the volcano-tectonic episode in 1975–84 (the Krafla Fires). Inland, many open fractures showed strong dilation and faulting and have done so during all similar episodes in the past. There are some good examples of open fissures and normal faults at the roadside in an area to the west of the Jökulsárgljúfur National Park. Faults and fissures also cut the Jökulsárgljúfur Canyon in the vicinity of the mighty Dettifoss waterfall, including the Randarhólar eruptive fissure. A feeder dyke connects to the crater Sjónarnípa 1 km downstream from Dettifoss (see also 9. Kópasker).

Selected bibliography

Surnames are written in italics. The Icelandic letters é, ó, á, ú, í and ý should be written as e, o, a, u, i and y, ö as ö, oe or simply o, æ as æ or ae, ð as d and þ as th when searching for references and papers in most databases.

F. *Bergerat*, A. *Guðmundsson*, J. *Angelier* and S. *Rögnvaldsson* 1998. Seismotectonics of the central part of the South Iceland Seismic Zone. *Tectonophysics* 298:319–335.

R. *Böðvarsson*, S. *Rögnvaldsson*, S. *Jakobsdóttir*, R. *Slunga* and R. *Stefánsson* 1996. The SIL data acquisition and monitoring system. *Seismic Research Letters* 67: 35–46.

A. *Björnsson* 1985. Dynamics of crustal rifting in NE Iceland. *Journal of Geophysical Research* 90:10,151–10,162.

A. *Clifton* and P. *Einarsson* 2005. Styles of surface rupture accompanying the June 17 and 21, 2000 earthquakes in the South Iceland Seismic Zone. *Tectonophysics* 396: 141–159.

A. *Clifton*, C. *Pagli*, J. F. *Jónsdóttir*, K. *Eyþórsdóttir* and K. *Vogfjörð* 2003. Surface effects of triggered fault slip on Reykjanes Peninsula, SW_Iceland. *Tectonophysics* 369: 145–154.

P. *Einarsson* 1979, Earthquakes in Iceland. *Jökull* 29: 37–43.

P. *Einarsson* 1991. Earthquakes and present-day tectonism in Iceland. *Tectonophysics* 189: 261–279.

K.L. *Feigl*, J. *Gasperi*, F. *Sigmundsson* and A. *Rigo* 2000. Crustal deformation near Hengill volcano, Iceland 1993–1998: Coupling between magmatic activity and faulting inferred from elastic modeling of satellite radar interferograms. *Journal of Geophysical Research* 105: 25,655–25,670.

Á. *Guðmundsson* 1987. Geometry, formation and development of tectonic fractures on the Reykjanes Peninsula, Southwest Iceland. *Tectonophysics* 139: 295–308.

Á. *Guðmundsson* 1987. Tectonics of the Thingvellir fissure swarm, SW Iceland. *Journal of Structural Geology* 9: 61–69.

Á. *Guðmundsson* 1990: Dyke emplacements at divergent plate boundaries. In (eds.): A.J. Parker et al: *Mafic dykes and emplacement mechanism*. Balkema, Rotterdam: 47–62.

Á. *Guðmundsson* and S. *Brynjólfsson* 1993. Overlapping rift-zone segments and the evolution of the South Iceland seismic zone. *Geophysical Research Letters* 20: 1,902–1,906.

Á. *Guðmundsson*, S. *Brynjólfsson* and M.Þ. *Jónsson* 1993. Structural analysis of transform fault-rift zone junction in North Iceland. *Tectonophysics* 220:205–221.

S. *Hreinsdóttir*, P. *Einarsson* and F. *Sigmundsson* 2001. Crustal deformation at the oblique spreading Reykjanes Peninsula, SW-Iceland: GPS-measurements from 1993–1998. *Journal of Geophysical Research* 106: 13,803–13,816.

S. *Jakobsdóttir*. G.B. *Gunnarsson* and R. *Stefánsson* 2002. Seismicity in Iceland 1991–2000 monitored by the SIL-system. *Jökull* 51: 87–94.

M. *Khodayar* 1999. On the pattern of faults and dykes in Borgarfjörður, W-Iceland. *Jökull* 47: 21–44.

B.O. *Långbacka* and Á. *Guðmundsson* 1995. Extensional tectonics in the vicinity of a transform fault in North Iceland. *Tectonics* 14: 294–306.

J. *Maclennan*, M. *Jull*, D. *Mackenzie*, L. *Slater* and K. *Grönvold* 2002. The link between volcanism and deglaciation in Iceland. *Geochem. Geophys. Geosyst.*, 3(11), 1062, doi:10.1029/2001GC000282.

S. *Rögnvaldsson*, Á *Guðmundsson* and R. *Slunga* 1998: Seismotectonic analysis of the Tjörnes Fracture Zone; an active transform fault in North Iceland. *Journal of Geophysical Research* 103; 30,117–30,129.

F. *Sigmundsson* 1991. Postglacial rebound and asthenosphere viscosity in Iceland. *Geophysical Research Letters* 18., bls. 1,131–1,134.

F. *Sigmundsson* and P. *Einarsson* 1992. Glacio-isostatic movements caused by historical volume change of the Vatnajökull ice cap, Iceland. *Geophysical Research Letters* 19: 2,123–2,126.

F. *Sigmundsson* et al 1995. Rift-transform kinematics in South Iceland. Deformation from Global Positioning System measurements 1986 to 1992. *Journal of Geophysical Research* 100: 6,235–6,248.

F. *Sigmundsson* 2006. *Iceland Geodynamics – Crustal deformation and divergent plate tectonics.* Springer-Praxis, Chichester, UK. 209 pp.

R. *Sigurbjörnsson*, B. *Bessason*, Þ.I. *Sigfússon*, Þ. *Sigfússon* and S. *Þorvaldsdóttir* 1998. Earthquake risk mitigation in South Iceland. In (eds.): P. Bisch et al.: *Proceedings of the 11th European Conference on Earthquake Engineering.* Balkema. Rotterdam.

G. E. *Sigvaldason*, K. *Annertz* and M. *Nilsson* 1992. Effect of glacier loading/deloading on volcanism: postglacial volcanic production rate of the Dyngjufjöll area, Central Iceland. *Bulletin of Volcanology* 54: 385–192.

R. *Stefánsson* et al. 1993. Earthquake prediction research in South Iceland seismic zone and the SIL project. Seismology Society of America Bulletin 83: 696–716.

E. Sturkell, B. *Brandsdóttir*, H. *Shimamura* and M. *Mochizuki* 1992. Seismic crustal structure along the Öxarfjörður trough at the eastern margin of the Tjörnes Fracture Zone. *Jökull* 42: 13–25.

E. *Sturkell* et al. 1994. Strain accumulation 1986–1992 across the Reykjanes Peninsula plate boundary, Iceland, determined from GPS measurements. *Geophysical Research Letters* 21: 125–128.

K. *Sæmundsson* 1992. Geology of the Þingvallavatn area. *OIKOS*, Copenhagen: 40–68.

E. *Tryggvason* 1982: Recent ground deformation in continental and oceanic rift zones. In (ed.): G. Pálmason: Continental and oceanic rifts. *American Geophysical Union. Geodyn.* Series 8: 17–29.

Lakagígar 1783–1784. (OS)

5 The volcanic activity

Contrary to common belief, the earth cannot split open anywhere in Iceland and spout lava or tephra. The present rift zone, along with at least two intraplate volcanic belts, forms the active volcanic region of Iceland. In most of the areas outside this branched zone, the earthly fires have been extinguished for hundreds of thousands or millions of years, as these parts of Iceland drifted away from the magma sources. Within the active zone, volcanoes and volcanic fissures do not appear at random, but are confined within elongated areas bounded by fissures, faults and volcanic formations. These areas form about 30 volcanic systems with hundreds of eruption sites and craters. Many volcanic systems are partly or wholly covered by ice caps and the highest volcanoes are glaciated. Submarine volcanic activity is quite common. The types of volcanoes and craters are varied and so are the different eruptive rocks and modes of eruption. All in all, Iceland has such a wealth of volcanic formations that it is almost unparalleled in the world. The occurrence of a volcanic eruption every fourth year on average also makes Iceland one of the liveliest places in the world of volcanoes.

Key words

Neovolcanic zone • volcanic system • Tertiary • Quaternary • Plio-Pleistocene • Holocene formation • dating of eruptives • magma generation • types of magmatic rocks • types of eruptives • magma chamber • magma reservoir • lava • tephra • types of eruptions • classification of volcanoes

The appearance of eruptives according to age

Igneous rocks from the Tertiary era (3.2–17 million years old) form the oldest parts of the country. The lavas in these areas are characterised by amygdales and are also widely altered by geothermal heat. Tephra is generally found compressed as baked, red-coloured sediments between the lavas. Intrusions are common and varied, from dykes up to large plutonic intrusions which are believed to be the remains of magma chambers. Rocks younger than 3.2 million years old (Plio-Pleistocene) are generally amygdaloidal or altered, although the younger they are, the less this is true. In general the Quaternary era is defined as starting 1.8 million years ago (divided into the Pleistocene, or Ice Age, and the Holocene). At this time glaciation had already started and bare rock surfaces of up to 3.2 million years old bear testimony to this. For this reason the age classification of rocks is based on this point in time and known as the Plio-Pleistocene. Interglacial formations from the Plio-Pleistocene are for the most part glacially eroded lavas, while glacial rocks are mainly represented by pillow lavas and tuffs *(móberg)*. The youngest formations, from the last two to three glacial periods (late Pleistocene), are best preserved. Most substantial hyaloclastic *(móberg)* mountains which cannot be classified as central volcanoes probably date from the last glacial period.

The age of Holocene eruptives

Prehistoric volcanic remains from the Holocene (younger than 10,000–12,000 years) are usually not glacially smoothed but they can appear to be quite old because of erosion and weathering which are rapid processes in Iceland. Age can be determined using radioactive materials with a short half life. Radiocarbon (C^{14}) has been commonly used. The accuracy of such age-determination methods is typically in the order of 20–100 years. To be able to use radiocarbon, there must be organic remains either overlying or underlying the volcanic deposit and the age must be corrected to give an absolute date. In recent years, age determinations have been developed using other radioactive materials which enable direct dating.

Herðubreið (northeast Iceland) is an archetypical subglacial formation, formed in one or more effusive eruptions but affected by thick, overlying glacier ice during a recent glacial period of the Ice Age. It rises about 1,100 m above its surroundings. The rock is basalt but deposited as pillow lava, breccia and tuff. Basaltic glass turns into palagonite with time and tephra grains become cemented together. The formation is capped by a small lava shield. Formations of this kind are termed table mountains, tuyas or *stapis* (in Icelandic). (RTH)

If a widespread and easily identifiable tephra layer can be successfully dated by some means or other, it will provide a marker layer which can in turn be used to date other neighbouring layers, for example lava which has flowed over soil containing tephra layers or lava underlying soil containing marker layers. This type of tephrochronology was pioneered in Iceland. Marker layers include acid ash layers from Hekla

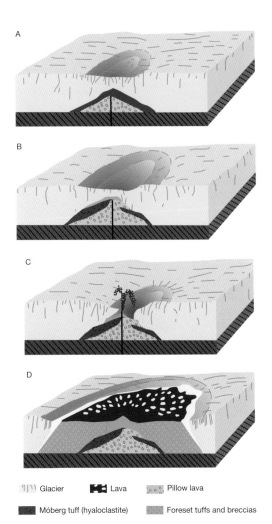

A
B
C
D

A schematic representation of the last two stages of a large-volume, sub-glacial (or submarine) eruption. If the eruption stops before entering the final, effusive stage, a tuff cone will be preserved (e.g. Keilir, Reykjanes or Stapafell, Snæfellsnes). The final stage allows a lava cap to form on top of dipping tephra and breccia layers. The volcano is called a table mountain, tuya or stapi (móberg). Examples include Gæsafjöll in NE Iceland or Hlöðufell and Hrafnabjörg in SW Iceland. (From: G. Kjartansson 1961, G. J. Jones 1969 and E. Sturkell 1998 et al.)

Glacier   Lava   Pillow lava

Móberg tuff (hyaloclastite)   Foreset tuffs and breccias

(e.g. 900 BC and 1104 AD) and Öræfajökull (1364), a double tephra layer from Vatnaöldur (the settlement layer from 871 AD) and basalt tephra layers from Katla and Reykjanes (the medieval layer, 1226). Tephrochronology and chemical analysis have been used to date unknown tephra layers in the broad outlet glaciers of Vatnajökull and connect them to particular volcanoes. It appears that each central vol-

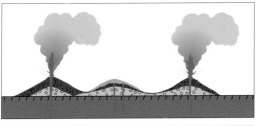
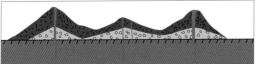

A schematic explanation of the formation of a typical multi-summit tuff or hyaloclastite ridge during an eruption on a long, subglacial, eruptive fissure (e.g. ridges east of Þingvellir, Sveifluháls on Reykjanes and Jarlhettur, central Iceland). In both cases pillow lava may occur and the resulting structures will differ according to the length of the eruption and the external conditions. (ATG)

cano produces tephra with its own compositional properties which can be used to trace tephra layers to particular eruptions or volcanoes.

In the historical period, from the middle of the 12th century, written sources make dating of volcanic remains easier, especially after 1500. In ice cores from the glaciers of Greenland and Iceland there is evidence of eruptions in Iceland (sulphuric acid from the atmosphere or tephra), which can be chronologically dated in the ice core. Marine sediments underneath or overlying the eruptive remains can also assist with dating. Tephra on the sea floor is well preserved and can often be dated.

The making of magma

Molten rock, magma, does not occur everywhere in the Earth's mantle or deep within the crust. Most of the crustal and mantle rocks are solid but where the viscosity is lowest the mantle rock can deform extremely slowly. The melting point of rocks increases with increasing pressure. Below Iceland the crustal temperature increases by about 50–100°C for every kilometre and in three areas the increase reaches up to and above 150° C/km. This temperature gradient is very high compared to that of the continents lying to the east and west.

Beneath ocean ridges, under Iceland and in mantle plumes, the temperature at a particular depth, for example 100–200 km, is generally much higher than at the same depth in the mantle under the centre of

Katla erupts in 1918. The tephra-producing, subglacial eruption was powerful and lasted for about three weeks. Huge meltwater floods or glacier bursts *(jökulhlaups)* have accompanied eruptions of Katla about 20 times since the settlement of Iceland. (KG)

the plates. The difference is probably 100–200°C. In addition, the mantle material is rising towards lower pressure (rock overburden). The rock melts at a great depth, up to 120 km below the surface, at 1,400°C to 1,500°C. The part of the rock with a lower melting point

Rapid degassing of pahoehoe lava creates
a beautiful show in Krafla, 1981. (SP)

melts first, melting more with increasing temperature in proportion to
depth (or overburden pressure). This partial melting results in magma
formation. The proportion of partial melt in the rock increases rapidly
with decreasing depth, in the depth range 30–80 km. The magma separates gradually from the rising rock mass and travels towards the surface. It is thought that a thin magma coating forms on the crystals of
the mantle rocks during partial melting and the "liquid" detaches and
rises. Thus a magma coating forms which coalesces as small liquid
drops within the solid mantle material. Coalescence continues and
leads to rising small magma lenses and veins in the porous rock; the
initial stage can be compared to a fine sponge containing water or
slush. The process is widespread and continuous. The magma is hot
and lighter than the surrounding crust. It contains dissolved gases and
rises within the rising mother rock, but faster. Newly formed fractures
often absorb magma fed from small lenses and veins below. Some of
the magma which moves upwards in expanding lenses or fractures in
this way solidifies when the magma or mother rock is carried laterally

in huge currents and cools. Some of the magma pushes its way periodically into the crust to form intrusions and solidifies there. It never reaches the surface as eruptions and probably represents the greater part of the magma.

Partial melting of mantle rock or melting of crustal rocks produces various types of magma. Under Iceland partial melting produces primitive basalt magma. It probably forms at a depth range of 30–120 km. Locally, however, the formation depth of evolved basalt magma or intermediate and acid magma can be less. It can form at only a few kilometres' depth in the case of intermediate or acid magma, in magma chambers with melting of the surrounding country rock. Where there is a high temperature at shallow depths, i.e. in rift zones, tholeiite magma is produced, while alkaline magma is produced at the greatest depth in adjacent areas, i.e. within the lateral volcanic areas (Snæfellsnes and the Westman Islands). Magma in the transitional zone is produced at a depth intermediate to these (Southern Iceland).

It is believed that partial melting uppermost in the mantle plume, such as occurs in the Icelandic plume, is around 5–10% of the volume of the rock, but can reach 20%. The magma which separates during the melting process in mantle plumes can rise at a rate of 50–500 m per year, based on strong mantle plumes such as that beneath the Hawaiian islands. The latter is stronger than its Icelandic counterpart where the figure is closer to 200–300 m per year. The rising rock velocity within the plume in general is much lower or around 0.1–2 m per year. There is considerable evidence that much of the magma rises in heat waves of varying strength which move upwards through the plume (in "magma pulses"). They could perhaps be the result of a hiatus between the heat production deep within the plume and the ability of the mantle rock above to conduct the heat away. Also, the mantle rock may heat up a great deal at a certain depth, causing more rapid rising. A "heat pulse" results, followed by magma rising within the mantle.

A fine example, albeit a small one, of a lava ring
made of spatter during the final phase of the
Surtsey eruption (in 1967). (SP)

Magma becomes rock

Solidified magma becomes rock, which in turn is composed of minerals. During solidification the elements are bonded according to certain
physical laws, forming crystals of various sizes (see chapter 2). Igneous
rocks are divided into plutonic and volcanic. On the whole, the crust of
Iceland is composed more of intrusions and plutonic rocks than of volcanic rocks. On the other hand, the visible bedrock is mainly composed
of volcanic rocks (around 85–90%). Other materials are sediments or
intrusions.

When magma solidifies, crystallisation of the rock-forming minerals
begins in a particular sequence, related to their melting point. A good
example is the crystallisation of olivine-rich tholeiitic basalt in the

Hawaiian islands. The flowing lava has a temperature of 1,250°C. While it is cooling to 1,190°C, green olivine crystallises. Black pyroxene then follows as the temperature falls to 1,180°C. Light-coloured plagioclase feldspar crystallises at 1,170° to 1,169°C, and the lava is already half solidified by 1,065°C. Other minerals are added until the basalt is nine-tenths solid at 1,030°C. The remaining melt solidifies as glass containing various trace elements. The glass often accumulates in segregation veins in volcanic rocks. They contain materials which provide varied information about the magma. If a rock mass composed of basic magma solidifies as a plutonic rock (gabbro), the cooling will be slower, the minerals form generally larger crystals than in volcanic rocks and glass is insignificant.

In volcanic rocks, the first-forming crystals can be considerably larger than the others, and the rock is known as porphyritic if they are present in large numbers. As well as crystallised rock-forming minerals, which occur in different proportions according to rock type, part of the magma solidifies as amorphous glass, as mentioned earlier, the amount increasing with the rate of cooling. Only a few dozen minerals account for the basic composition of Icelandic igneous rocks, frequently three to five main minerals in each type (see chapter 2). Igneous rocks are divided into acid, intermediate and basic depending on the total amount of silica oxide. The acid rocks contain most and the basic rocks least. Igneous rocks are also divided into three series depending on the total amount of potassium and sodium oxide, relative to the amount of silica oxide. Each series is comprised of acid, intermediate and basic rocks with different names. The smallest quantity of these alkali metals occurs in the tholeiitic series and the largest in the alkaline series. The transitional series falls in between, representing a transitional phase in the magma generation (see also chapter 2).

Tholeiite rocks are characteristic of the rifting zone and of several well-known mantle plumes around the world. The term basalt is in fact an umbrella name for several basalt types of which tholeiite and olivine tholeiite are the most common in Iceland. The rock is dark coloured, ranging from an almost pure-black dense variety to a grey, coarser-grained type. The intermediate rock is either dark or grey-brown in colour, while the acid rock, which has generally been known as liparite

The tuff (tephra) ring Hverfjall, close to Lake
Mývatn is about 2,800 years old. The diameter is
1,050 m. (RTH)

or rhyolite, is light coloured. Obsidian is a rapidly cooled, acid rock
(mainly glass), while a dark basalt glassy rock is called sideromelane or
trachyte.

Magma can reach the surface of the Earth after spending a very short
period at greater depths. On the other hand, erupting magma may have
paused on its way to the surface for decades or even centuries and
evolved as a result. Evolution may have taken place as a result of internal changes, for example partial solidification and differentiation of
minerals with different densities, or because the surrounding rocks
have melted to a greater or lesser degree and polluted the magma. The
picture may be even more complicated. For instance, different magma
types can mix and in addition water-rich crustal rocks, which become
buried by subsidence and move outwards laterally from the rift zone,
can be remelted. All these processes are examples of evolution. It
requires variable conditions at depth (temperature, pressure and surrounding country rock) and restriction of space or other factors which
delay the magma on its way to the surface.

Storing of magma

Ideas about magma chambers under the Earth's surface are not yet fully developed. One hypothesis envisages considerable amounts of magma from the mantle forming large temporary magma traps or reservoirs, possibly at the junction of the crust and mantle, or very deep within the crust. These may exist under the main areas of weakness (the volcanic systems) produced by rifting/plate movement. The reservoirs are thought to be tens of kilometres long and 5–10 km wide, but shallow. According to this hypothesis, part of the magma which forms under Iceland is believed to collect in and form these huge, elongate, relatively narrow reservoirs. The magma may evolve there, for example as a result of differentiation and a large part of it may cool, never to surface. So far no direct measurements have proved the existence of these reservoirs. Rather they indicate a very large and dense rock mass under at least three volcanic systems, where the seismic wave velocity is high. This could indicate a solidified magma mass in a reservoir, but other explanations are also possible, such as intrusions or crystallised high-temperature "precipitation" from important magma chambers at lesser depth than a reservoir beneath centres in the three volcanic systems.

Whether or not large deep-lying magma reservoirs play an important part in volcanism, the stress conditions in the crust and the jerky plate movements largely determine the path of magma into the upper part of the crust. Part of the magma rising under Iceland or pooling in magma reservoirs, if they exist, finds its way into the upper layers of the crust through tectonic fractures. The magma pressure may be sufficient, together with stress conditions in the crust, for the magma to erupt without hindrance from tens of kilometres deep. This will result in a flood eruption of primitive or poorly evolved magma. However, it is also fairly clear that part of the magma pauses for a longer or shorter time locally within the crust, at not very great depth. Single dykes are probably formed as a first stage, followed by dyke swarms and/or sills until eventually the intrusions become so numerous and dense that a mass of molten and hot rock forms a magma chamber. There is evidence of lens-shaped magma chambers under, for example, Krafla, Grímsvötn

Öræfajökull is Iceland's largest composite cone volcano and highest mountain (2,114 m). The last eruptions occurred there in 1362 and 1727. The small but 700 m deep summit caldera overflows with glacier ice and is lined with small lava domes.
(RTH und OS)

155

and Katla, but also a similar rather large storage system of magma-chamber type at a greater depth, for example under Hekla. The magma chambers are thought to be much smaller than the previously mentioned magma reservoirs and possibly of the size range 10–100 km^3, if compared to known plutons in Iceland, and are probably located at a minimum depth of 3–8 km. Magma can escape from such reservoirs and reach the surface as a result of internal pressure or contemporary rifting which facilitates the flow of melt into the crust. The question of how far lateral dyke-forming magma surges can extend from the magma chamber is a matter of debate. It could be that sudden rifting of the crust opens the way for a temporary flow of magma to the magma chamber, causing the pressure to increase until lateral dyke injections, or a commence eruption occurs. It is also thought that basalt dykes sometimes break their way into magma chambers, setting off a process which can result in eruption.

Magma chambers must inevitably change, for example by increasing in size. On top of them central volcanoes build up during relatively frequent eruptions, parallel to the development of the magma chamber. Caldera formation is a common part of the development, especially where the crust is faulted and hot, such as in rifting zones. Colder and less faulted crust encourages the formation of high volcanoes such as occur in the lateral volcanic zones. Intermediate and acid magma also erupt as long as magma chambers and central volcanoes are active, for up to 0.5–1 million years and in a few cases for up to 2 million years.

It is not known for certain what magma chambers actually look like while they are active or to what extent they are molten at a particular time or for how long the molten fraction exists. It is possible that only a small part of the total volume of the magma chamber needs to be molten at any time in order to explain, for example, the behaviour of seismic waves or geodetic measurements which form the basis of understanding the nature and activity of magma chambers and their connection with magma influx or other magma reservoirs. It appears that large intrusions (e.g. in the southeast) which could be the uppermost part of magma chambers are in fact a complex system of variously aged laccoliths and dykes. Perhaps it is common that independent, relatively

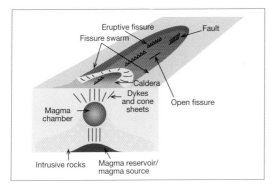

The concept of magma reservoirs and magma chambers is shown here by a simplified cross-section of a volcanic system. A magma chamber evolves within the densest part of a dyke swarm. Most known Icelandic chambers seem to rest on a large, mostly solidified, high-density mass. This fact may contradict this model to some extent, or simply indicate that a magma reservoir lies immediately below the solidified bulk of a magma chamber. In this case, only a relatively small amount of molten magma, if any, is found at the top of each plutonic mass at any given time, until magma injections activate the chamber. In general, volcanic eruptions draw melt from magma chambers as well as directly from deeper sources, as deduced from the chemistry of the magma. (Based on: Á. Guðmundsson 1990, 1995 and 1999)

small magma intrusions in magma chambers or in the crust only "live" for a few decades and cause more than one eruption in this period. Magma can evolve in such a relatively small intrusions.

The most fruitful way to study large magma sources and to reveal their behaviour is to do research into the various intrusive bodies that are found in the northwest of Iceland an in the area between Höfn in the southeast and Dyrfjöll in the northeast. Geophysical modelling of such sources while buried deep in the bedrock hardly yields a picture with high enough resolution to show construction details, and possibly, to show the way these magma chambers, multiple dykes, sills and even magma reservoirs really work. The geophysical studies, combined with geochemical studies may, however, tell us much about the rougher outlines of magma stores, the ongoing proccess in them ,while functioning, and about how they evolve, chemically and physically, and how the connect with the deeper levels of the crust and mantle.

Eruptives are not just lava

Eruption takes place when magma forces its way to the surface via fractures. When magma containing dissolved gases (up to 5% by weight) reaches the surface, the surrounding decreasing pressure causes the gases to rapidly expand and escape. The magma "boils" and part of it becomes frothy, either deep within the feeder conduit or even towards the top of the magma chamber or near the surface. Finally, in the eruption crater, the gas largely separates from the lava and tephra (unconsolidated eruptives). Some of the gases escape from the lava at a considerable distance from the eruption site and in some eruptions there is no lava flow due to vigorous gas escape or ingress of water. The latter can be groundwater, lake water, sea water or melted glacier ice. Tephra formation and explosive activity are then dominant. There is a relationship between the gas content of the magma and its chemical composition, temperature, degassing and viscosity. Acid magma is the "coldest", most viscous and has the highest gas pressure, while primitive basalt magma is the hottest, least viscous and has a relatively low gas pressure.

Water vapour from within the Earth is the commonest magma gas (60–75%), but also present in considerable amounts are sulphur dioxide and hydrochloric acid. Others include carbon compounds such as poisonous carbon monoxide and hydrogen fluoride. Sometimes pure hydrogen is released and burns. Sulphur- and chlorine gas frequently form small acid drops with water from the atmosphere. Acid aerosol and fine ash dust can prevent the sun's radiation from reaching the Earth's surface, thus causing changes to the weather for many months or even years. Cooling of this kind as a result of Icelandic eruptions has occurred, for instance following Skaftáreldar/the Laki eruption in the 18th century. Hydrogen fluoride poisons grazing land and causes disease in sheep and cows, affecting limbs and teeth, and causing swelling joints and abnormal growths in bone tissue. Carbon monoxide is poisonous and can kill organisms. Sulphur dioxide is also a poisonous gas.

Surtsey: tephra-producing explosions in November 1963. A submarine eruption in 1963–67 created a new island, Surtsey, off the south coast in the Vestmannaeyjar island group. The interaction of sea and magma caused an explosive (phreatic) eruption. The magma is olivine tholeiite. The island was already visible on the second day of the eruption, rising from a depth of 130 m. (SÞ)

As soon as the sea stopped entering the volcanic vent in Surtsey, the eruption mode changed from phreatic to effusive. A lava shield formed on top of the tuff cone during the period from April 1964 to 1967. (SÞ)

Eldgjá is a prominent feature of the Katla Volcanic System. It is an eruptive fissure with different types of crater, stretching for 70 km through the area between the ice caps of Mýrdalsjökull and Vatnajökull. It formed around 934–938 AD. The lava flow is the most voluminous to erupt in Iceland in historical times at 16–18 km³. It even surpasses the Laki Fires lava of 1783–1784. (RTH)

The Eldgjá Fires and Laki (or Skaftár) Fires

Several catastrophic eruptions have occurred in Iceland in the historical period. Outstanding tephra eruptions include the Hekla eruption of 1104 and the Öræfajökull eruption of 1362 which can be compared to the Pinatubo eruption in the Philippines in 1991. Two lava eruptions belong to this group: the eruption in Eldgjá around 934–938 AD and the Skaftáreldar 1783–1784 (Skaftáreldar, the Skaftá Fires, is the Icelandic term for what is known as the Laki eruption or Laki Fires in the English literature). The former eruption occurred in the fissure swarm of the Katla Volcanic System in approx. 934 AD. The eruptive fissure is discontinuous but 75 km long, extending from Katla northeast towards Vatnajökull. On it are large tephra craters, spatter cones and sinter craters and grabens. In its centre, Eldgjá (8 km) resembles a graben with lava and sinter craters. It is thought likely that the eruption episode lasted for 5–6 years with 10–15 events which produced a large amount of tephra both outside and inside the Mýrdalsjökull ice cap, and even more lava. The quantity of tephra measures 1.4 km³ while the lava measures about 18 km³ and covers 780–800 km². If it formed a 5 m thick and 10 m wide lane, the lava would extend for a distance of 360,000 km, or nine times the circumference of the Earth. It flowed south, destroying settlements. The pseudocraters at Álftaver and Landbrot were also formed during this most productive eruption in Icelandic history. The latter eruption occurred in the Grímsvötn fissure swarm, southwest of Vatnajökull.

Lakagígar. The volcano-tectonic episode we call the Laki Fires (*Skaftáreldar* in Icelandic) was a major eruption in 1783–84. About 130 craters line a 27 km long eruptive fissure in the southern highlands and the lava covers an area close to 600 km². The episode had widespread effects in Iceland and Europe. (RTH)

It started at the beginning of June 1783 and lasted for eight months. This episode consisted of ten volcanic events with lava discharge of up to 5,000 m³ per second and 1,000 m high lava fountains, while many events began with explosive, tephra-producing activity (totalling 0.4 km³). There was also eruption in Grímsvötn. The crater row is 27 km long and is composed of a side-shifted (en-echelon), displaced section with about 140 craters, with the small móberg mountain Laki near the fissure centre. The lava flowed to the south, partly covering the Eldgjá lava. It engulfed vegetated land, completely destroying 17 farms and damaging more. The volume is 14.7 km³ and the area about 600 km². Both eruptions had a major impact on the weather pattern in the northern hemisphere. The climate turned cooler for several years as a result of large amounts of sulphuric acid aerosol spreading through the stratosphere. The Laki eruption produced about 122 million tons of sulphur dioxide and more than twice that amount of aerosol, more than ten times that produced by Pinatubo in 1991. The SO_2 gas in the Eldgjá eruption exceeded 200 million tonnes (forming 450 million tonnes of aerosol along with atmospheric water) but the effect on climate was less obvious than during the Laki eruption because the Eldgjá eruption lasted much longer so that the concentration of gases in the air never reached the Laki eruption level.

Main sources: Þ. Þórðarson (T. Thordarson) and S. Self 1993, T. Thordarson et al. (2001) and G. Larsen et al. (2000).

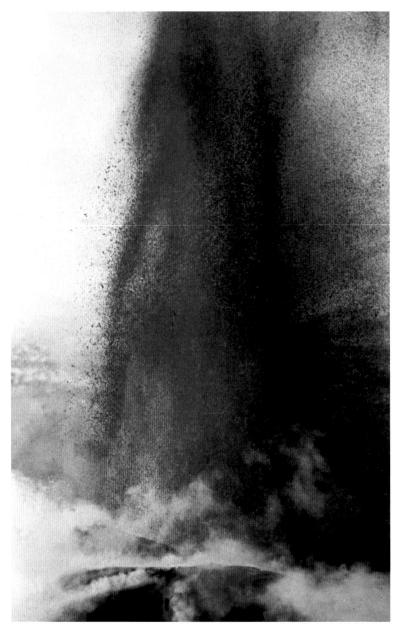

Spatter, lava bombs, scoria and pumice rain
down from a high lava fountain in the early
stages of the Askja eruption in 1961. (JJ)

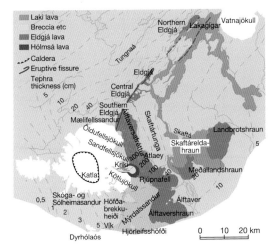

Simplified map showing
two large eruptive fissures
and lava flows: The Eldgjá
Fires in 934–38 AD and the
Laki eruption (Skaftá Fires)
in 1783–84. The Eldgjá
Fires relate to the Katla
volcanic centre (bottom-left
corner) and the Skaftá Fires
to Grímsvötn (top-right
corner, outside frame).
(Source: G. Larsen 2000,
maps redrawn and
simplified)

Tephra is classified into ash, pumice, scoria and spatter, the ash being the finest material. The grains of the latter are finer than 2 mm in diameter. The pumice is low in density, the grains reaching up to 64 mm in diameter, while larger fragments are called scoria and are usually denser. Spatter denotes lumps and pieces of dense lava, commonly larger than scoria fragments and more consolidated. Rounded spatter lumps are known as lava bombs. They can be cylindrical, spherical or twisted and are formed when pieces of magma are thrown for some distance through the air. Tephra has a tendency to become altered to the pelagonite tuff or hyaloclastites that are called *móberg* in Icelandic and also forms breccia made of lava and pillow-lava fragments mixed with ash and pumice. In time the tephra fragments can become cemented together through the effects of water, heat and the overlying weight of the eruptive pile. Chemical changes result in precipitation of zeolite minerals between the fragments and the tephra glass is altered. The tephra acquires a brown shade instead of black. This process is called palagonitisation and starts as soon as the eruptive materials build up and after a few years or decades large amounts of the tephra have become layered, glassy, brownish tuff interspersed with small lava lumps and bits of pillow (*móberg* and breccia, the latter known as *þursaberg* in Icelandic, see chapter 2).

163

Icelandic lavas are of three main types, classified by flow behaviour and/or appearance. *Apalhraun* or scoria lava (aa lava) is relatively thick and flows rather like a slow-moving landslide. It has a rough surface covered in scoria and sinter. Examples of this type are intermediate and acid lavas and evolved basalt lava. Strictly speaking there is another variety known as block lava, the surface of which is covered by sharply edged blocks. *Apalhraun* can flow for tens of kilometres from its source. *Helluhraun* or plate lava (pahoehoe lava) flows like a very viscous liquid in tongues, closed channels and thin expanses. Its surface is generally composed of a ropey wave-like pattern or large smooth plates, but it can also be fractured and undulating (with tumuli). Primitive basalt magma generally forms *helluhraun* and can also solidify as *apalhraun*. In some fissure eruptions apalhraun is produced first, but is followed by *helluhraun* if the magma changes its composition as the eruption proceeds. *Helluhraun* can flow for long distances or more than 100 km from its source.

Pillow lava is a special variety of lava. It extrudes in rounded shapes, resembling small, filled sacks with a glassy skin and columns which radiate outwards from the middle. The pillows are generally 20 cm to 2 m in diameter, although larger examples are found. For pillow lava to form, there must be magma flow at a high external pressure with rapid cooling or lava flow with rapid degassing and cooling in water. The bulk of pillow lava is therefore thought to have formed at considerable depth in the sea, in lakes or in water underneath glaciers, or where gas-impoverished lava has come into contact with water. When the external pressure falls, as the water depth or glacier thickness becomes less, the eruptive production becomes breccia (a mixture of broken pillows, lava fragments and tephra) and finally tephra. If the eruptive vent is protected from water ingress, lava flow can take place. This was clearly seen in the Surtsey eruption. Pillow-lava formations can reach hundreds of metres in thickness.

Pillow lava forms while the overburden pressure is high in relation to the magma gas content. The pillows grow like "toothpaste blobs", mostly without being disconnected. Most pillows have a glassy crust and radial joints. (RTH)

Types of eruption

Volcanic eruptions in Iceland are traditionally classified using an alternative nomenclature to that normally used (hawaiian, strombolian, vulcanian, plinian, etc.):

1. Explosive eruption. Magmatic eruptions that may range from vulcanian to plinian or very powerful pélean type. The magma shoots out of the vent as fragments due to high gas pressure. The eruptive materials are mainly gas-rich tephra which can be mixed with breccia. The eruptive material sometimes consists mainly of volatiles. The amount of material calculated as solid material can, in such cases, be small, as well as containing fragments from the country rock.

2. Hydromagmatic tephra eruption. Magma shoots in fragments from the vent due to the effect of external water in the surrounding rocks or on the surface (lakes, the sea and glaciers). Rapid cooling, flash boiling and steam formation fragmentise the magma and the result is an explosive, phreatic type of eruption which is often quite violent. The

The Krafla Fires

No.	Deflation cm	Magma surge	Location	Length km	Volume Mill. m³	Lava km²
1. Dec. '75 –Feb. '76	230*	to the north and south	at Leirhnjúkur	›0.5	0.4	0.036
2. Sept. '76	17	to the north	–	–	–	–
3. Nov. '76	51	to the north	–	–	–	–
4. Jan. 77	32	to the north	–	–	–	–
5. April '77	81*	to the south	north of Leirhnjúkur	›0.5	0.01	0.001
6. Sept. '77	24*	to the south	north of Leirhnjúkur	0.9	1–2	0.5
7. Nov. '77	3	to the north	–	–	–	–
8. Jan. '78	119	to the north	–	–	–	–
9. July '78	64	to the north	–	–	–	–
10. Nov. '78	72	to the north	–	–	–	–
11. May '79	88	to the north	–	–	–	–
12. Dec. '79	3	?	–	–	–	–
13. Feb. '80	11	to the south	–	–	–	–
14. Mars '80	53*	to the north and south	at Sandmúli	3–4	2–3	1.3
15. June '80	2	?	–	–	–	–
16. July '80	43*	to the north	Snagaborgir	4–5	20–30	5.3
17. Oct. '80	29*	to the north	at Sandmúli	7	30–40	11.5
18 Dec. '80	16	to the north	–	–	–	–
19. Jan. '81	44*	to the north	Éthólaborgir	2	30	6.3
20. Nov. '81	47*	to the north	south weast of Sandmúli	8	50	17
21. Sept. '84	55*	to the north	Éthólar	8.5	70–90	24

* eruption, inflation and rifting

Main sources: Páll Einarsson 1991: Umbrotin við Kröflu 1975–1984, In: Náttúra Mývatns (eds. A. Garðarsson and Á. Einarsson), Reykjavík.

eruptive materials are glassy tephra and lava or various types of breccia of different sizes and variety.

3. Mixed eruption. Strombolian or Vulcanian activity. Gas and magma pressure are sufficient to cause continuous or discontinuous magma fountains which are a mixture of glass-rich fragments and glowing lava spatter, forming intermittent magma ejecta. Some of the eruptive materials cool rapidly, immediately forming tephra, while others fall to earth close to the crater and may join the lava flow emerging directly from the vent. Eruptive materials are lava and tephra come in various proportions.

A Krafla fissure (November 1981) erupting
fast-flowing tholeiitic basalt lava. (PI)

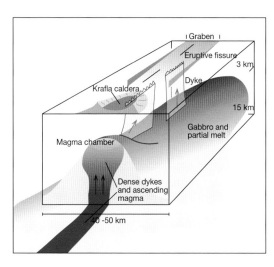

The nine eruptions of the
Krafla Fires volcano-tectonic
episode (1975–84) produced
60 km² (0.25 km³) of
overlapping lava flows. This
schematic model of the
magma chamber is based on
new seismic data. It reveals a
small magma chamber on top
of a high-density pillar. The
magma chamber inflated until
a magma injection was
released into the crust
causing the volcanic centre to
deflate, only to start inflating
again immediately (over 20
times). (Main source:
K. Sæmundsson 1991 and
B. Brandsdóttir et al 1995)

167

A large meltwater flood followed the 1996 Gjálp subglacial eruption in the Vatnajökull ice cap. It emerged at the margin of the Skeiðarárjökull outlet glacier. The murky discharge was 48,000 m³ per second and the sediment load, dissolved chemicals and icebergs swept across the old outwash plain of Skeiðarársandur. (OS)

4. Effusive eruption. Hawaiian activity. Magma fountains are continuous (usually low) or lacking. Relatively vigorous degassing can occur far from the eruption site. Eruptive materials are almost entirely lava.

5. Lava doming. No continuous magma fountains but may display limited ejecta. Thick lava builds up over the eruption conduit or extrudes for a short distance from it. There is a considerable flow of hot material from the dome. Behaviour like this is typical of acid eruptions in which internal gas pressure is low.

6. Cataclysmic, explosive eruptions. Very violent explosive eruptions are cataclysmic ultraplinian events. In this type, explosions and pyroclastic flows containing large amounts of rock fragments or red-hot nuées ardents can change the appearance of the volcano and ignimbrite layers may form.

Eruptions in glacier-covered volcanoes are accompanied by meltwater floods (jökulhlaup). These are catastrophic events caused by rapid ice melting. The rate of melting in the Gjálp eruption in Vatnajökull in 1996 reached about 5,000 tonnes of ice per second. In Katla eruptions

This ice canyon opened up during the subglacial Gjálp eruption in the Vatnajökull ice cap in 1996. Prior to the eruption the ice was 500–700 m thick. (RTH)

it is probably many times greater. Flood discharge from the accumulated meltwater in Grímsvötn reached 45,000–50,000 m^3/s for a time. There have been many greater floods than this and jökulhlaup floods associated with Katla eruptions are commonly thought to discharge 100,000–300,000 m^3/s. The jökulhlaup floods carry an enormous amount of tephra and/or eroded material from the bedrock down to sand deposits in front of the glaciers, such as the outwash plains (or sandurs) of Mýrdalssandur and Skeiðarársandur (500–700 km^2), as well as dissolved materials and chemical compounds on the surface of the tephra grains.

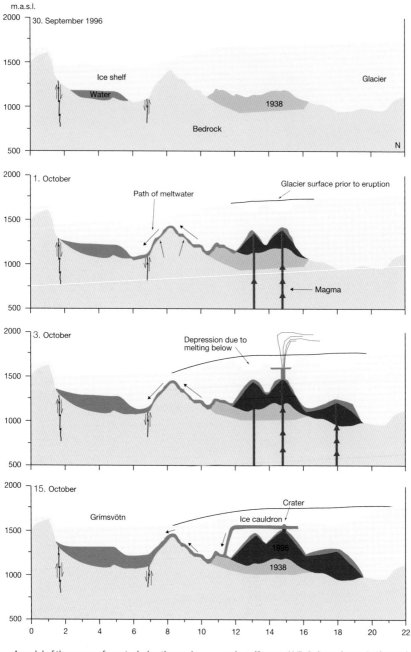

A model of the course of events during the 1996 Gjálp eruption north of Grímsvötn. The yellow hyaloclastite mountain piled up during an eruption in 1938. The eruptive volume was estimated at 0.7 km³. (Source: M.T. Guðmundsson, F. Sigmundsson and H. Björnsson 1997 and M.T.Guðmundsson, F. Sigmundsson, H. Björnsson and Th. Högnadóttir 2004).

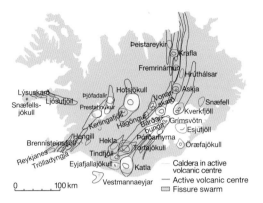

About 30 volcanic systems line the active neovolcanic zones in Iceland. A few volcanic centres east of the main zones add to the variety. For a more detailed description, see the last section of this chapter. (Main source: H. Jóhannesson and K. Sæmundsson 1998 and S.P. Jakobsson 1979)

Volcanic systems and classifications of volcanoes

Volcanism in Iceland occurs mainly within the volcanic systems. Most of them are a kind of tectonic hinge on the divergent plate margin within the rifting zone. The systems lie en echelon and orientated north or northeast on the plate margin; five in the southwest, four in the central axis (between Langjökull and Tungnafellsjökull) and nine under Vatnajökull and in the northeast. In the lateral volcanic belts which are formed adjacent to the rifting zone, similar tectonic hinges occur, but the orientation of volcanic systems is northwesterly on Snæfellsnes (three systems that lie en echelon). In the south there are seven systems, two of which have a westerly fissure orientation and the other five a northeasterly fissure orientation. A few small volcanic systems also occur in the volcanic zone and on the sea-floor continuation of the Reykjanes peninsula, while others occur within the transform fracture zones off the northeast and on the Kolbeinsey Ridge. In all there appear to be about 30 volcanic systems in Iceland, of which all except five have a clear central volcano or developing volcanic centre. In addition there are a few hundred volcanic structures lined up on fissures that have been active, if single craters or crater rows are counted individually, bearing in mind that it is common for a volcanic fissure to consist of displaced en-echelon segments, each with a number of volcanic vents. The central volcanoes erupt frequently within a limited area, while in the surrounding volcanic system, eruption fissures usually open at new

Main volcanic eruptions 1700–1900

year	location	volcanic activity
1892	Grímsvötn	no estimate
1887	Grímsvötn	no estimate
1878	Near Hekla	small
1875	Askja, Sveinagjá	vigorous
1867	Grímsvötn/Þórðarhyrna	no estimate
1862–´64	Tröllagígar	medium (›2 events)
1860	Katla	small
1854	Grímsvötn	no estimate
1845	Hekla	large lava volume
1838	Grímsvötn	no estimate
1821–´23	Eyjafjallajökull	small
1823	Katla	medium
1823	Grímsvötn/Þórðarhyrna	medium
1783–´85	Lakagígar, Grímsvötn	tremendous
1774	Grímsvötn	no estimate
1766	Hekla	large
1755	Katla	large
1753	Grímsvötn	no estimate
1727	Öræfajökull	medium
1725–´26	Grímsvötn	no estimate
1725	Near Hekla	small
1724–´29	Krafla	medium (5 events)
1721–´40	Dyngjujökull/Dyngjuháls	medium (4 events)
1721	Katla	large
1702–´20	Dyngjuökull/Dyngjuháls	medium (›3 events)
1702–´06	Grímsvötn	no estimate

locations during each volcanic episode or event, although this is not always the case. Some eruption fissures spout eruptives more than once as indicated by multiple-sheeted dykes observed in the Tertiary lava pile. Many shield volcanoes have built up, not only within the volcanic systems of the rifting zone, but also at their edges. They are much rarer in the lateral volcanic belts.

Within the rifting zone the central volcanoes appear in the landscape as irregular-shaped or shield-like mountain ranges, such as Krafla,

Skjaldbreiður is one of many postglacial lava shields in Iceland, made of rather primitive basalt. Unlike the composite Hawaiian shield volcanoes, the Icelandic lava shields formed during one long-lasting voluminous effusive eruption, in this case producing at least 25 km³ of lava. (RTH)

Grímsvötn and Hofsjökull. In the lateral volcanic belts there are several high volcanoes of the stratovolcano type, for instance Eyjafjallajökull and Hekla, but highland areas or what might be called mountain massifs, with calderas also occur, such as the Torfajökull area and Katla, which is shield-like in appearance. On the Reykjanes peninsula central volcanoes appear not to have developed because of the thin crust, although there is always an active upland centre within each system. Active centres of this type also occur on Snæfellsnes, along with the high stratovolcano of Snæfellsjökull. Hengill is a young central volcano and in the Westman Islands (Vestmannaeyjar) there are indications of a central volcano slowly being built up in the Heimaey area.

Volcanic rocks from the Holocene (past 10,000 years) account for probably 450–500 km³, originating from all the volcanic systems. In the historical period there have been more than 200 eruptions if individual eruption bursts within longer episodes are included, or in other words an eruption every four years on average. The eruption frequency in the 20th century is rather higher, which is almost certainly due to better record keeping than previously. About 70% of the rocks from the Holocene are basalt from the tholeiitic series (by volume), about half being tholeiite and half olivine tholeiite. Of the remaining 30% the acid part is rather

The Dyngjufjöll massif is the volcanic centre of the Askja Volcanic System. A smaller, more recent, water-filled crater (from 1875) has been superimposed on a large caldera. The last eruption was in 1961. (OS)

The principal lava shields in NE Iceland

Name	Elevation	Crater diam.	Age	Volume of shield
	m	m	year	km³
Þeistareykjabunga	564(140)	600	5,500 –6,000	5
Stóravítisdyngja	551	700	7,000 (or older))	
Ketildyngja	939(220)	700	3,000 –4,000	6
Kerlingardyngja	963(200)		‹4,000	6
Kollóttadyngja	1,117(260)	800	7,000 –8,000	?
Trölladyngja	1,460(440)	1,200	‹7,000	8

The higher elevation figure denotes altitude above sea level and the lower one indicates the elevation of the crater rim above the lava apron (Rossi, 1996). (Sources: Ó. Jónsson 1945, G. Gíslason et al. 1984 and M.J. Rossi 1996)

The main lava shields on Reykjanesskagi

Name	Height	Area of eruptives	Age	Volume of lava
	m	m	years	km³
Skálafell	(40)		›5	0.17
Sandfellshæð	(45)	120	ca. 13,000	4.8
Langhóll	(12)	20		0.8
Þráinsskjöldur	(45)	130	ca. 13,000	5.2
Hrútagjárdyngja		›100	at least 5,000	3.2
Heiðin há	516(90)	170	at least 7,000	6.8
Selvogsheiði	195(50)	50		1–2
Leitin		100	4,700	›3.0

Altogether there are 26 lava shields and associated lava flows on the peninsula (4,500–13,500 years old). According to calculations by Ágúst Guðmundsson (1986) the mean lava shield volume is 1.1 km³ and the total volume 29 km³. The first height value is relative to sea level and the latter figure is the height of the shield top above the lava apron closest to the volcano (Sources: M. Rossi, 1996 and J. Jónsson, 1978).

larger than the intermediate. About 85% of the volcanic rocks have erupted in the rift zone and the rest in the lateral volcanic belts.

Activity in most of the volcanic systems occurs in episodes which can be explained partly by the release of accumulated stress in the crust as a result of plate movement. Decades, centuries and even thousands of years can pass between episodes of stress release in an active period within a particular system. But sooner or later an episode commences. Mostly these are "pure" rifting episodes (i.e. without eruptions) but very often they are accompanied by one or more eruptions and are then known as volcano-tectonic episodes. In each episode there is a wave of eruptive events and earthquakes such as, for example, the 20 events which occurred in the Krafla volcano-rifting episode of the Hverfjall period, each spaced by a few days, weeks, months, even a few years.

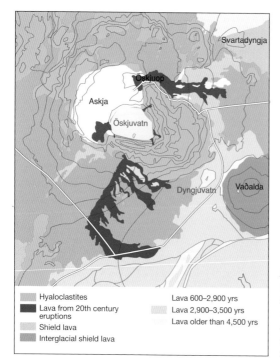

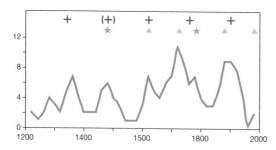

Hyaloclastites	Lava 600–2,900 yrs
Lava from 20th century eruptions	Lava 2,900–3,500 yrs
Shield lava	Lava older than 4,500 yrs
Interglacial shield lava	

A bedrock map of Askja. Lake Öskjuvatn formed as a small caldera within the main caldera structure after a series of eruptions in 1875. (Source: G. E. Sigvaldason)

+ Peaks in strain release in SISZ (Stefánsson and Halldórsson, 1988)
▲ Episodes of rifting in the Northern Rift Zone
★ Major fissure eruption in the South Iceland Volcanic Belt

Forty years running average of the number of volcanic eruptions in Vatnajökull. A period of 130–140 years clearly emerges. A strong correlation with peaks of strain release in South Iceland seems evident. High volcanic activity in other parts of Iceland also seems to have been influenced by the Vatnajökull unrest which is commonly attributed to "hot spot pulses". (From: G. Larsen, M.T. Guðmundsson and H. Björnsson, 1998)

A view across the Mýrdalssandur outwash plain and the Kötlujökull outlet glacier to the expanses of the Mýrdalsjökull ice cap under which the volcano Katla lurks. Iceland's second largest caldera is barely visible as a slight but broad dent in the ice dome. (RTH)

Rifting in the volcano-tectonic episodes opens the way for magma injections, either from magma chambers or reservoirs. There is evidence for such events, but hypotheses which assume magma intrusion long distances from the source are controversial. It is likely that intrusion has occurred where the fissure eruptions were no more than 5–25 km from the magma chamber, as in the case of the Sveinagjá Fires in 1875 and Krafla Fires in the 20th century. However, when the distance from a magma chamber is greater, or the eruption is very productive (cf. Eldgjá and Laki Fires) then a continuous but evolved magma supply originating from a greater depth is a more likely explanation than lateral magma injection from a central source. The magma in such eruptions may originate in the lower part of the crust or the upper mantle, or stem from a magma reservoir which extends the length of each volcanic system.

Another element of episodal activity can be explained by other factors than rifting due to plate drift. As previously mentioned, magma production under hot spots seems to be periodic (both short and long periods). This type of mantle-plume behaviour is known, for example, from the Hawaiian islands. The first indications of this in Iceland are beginning to emerge from observations of volcanic systems (e.g. the Reykjanes peninsula) and the chronology of over 100 eruptions in Vatnajökull over the past few thousand years. The same is true when the eruptive history of the country as a whole is considered. In the former case decades-long periods are involved, but much longer peri-

Eruptions of Katla in historical times

Year	Duration days	Dormant years	Remark
9th century			
920			
934 +/- 4 years			Large eruption concurrent with Eldgjá eruption
11th century			
1179			
1245			Probably a jökulhlaup flood on Sólheimasandur
1262			
1357			Year uncertain, eruption in western part of glacier
1416			
1440			
15th century			
1500			
1580		80	
1612		32	Concurrent with eruption in Eyjafjallajökull?
1625	13	13	Shortest known quiescent period
1660	›60	35	
1721	›100	61	
1755	120	34	Largest eruption since 934
1823	28	68	Concurrent with eruption in Eyjafjallajökull
1860	20	37	Small eruption
1918	24	58	
1955	?	37?	Probably small subglacial eruption

(Main Source: Guðrún Larsen 2000)

ods can be deduced from the eruptive history. It is thought that furthest from the hot spot, plate spreading (rifting) is the key to volcanism, while closer to the mantle plume its direct effects are increasingly felt and account for about half the activity in the centre of the country.

In the lateral volcanic belts, volcanism is mainly caused by magma intrusion and gradually increasing magma pressure until the crust fails in volcanic systems. Periodic magma production in the Icelandic mantle plume can doubtless also have an effect.

In addition to subglacial volcanic vents and central volcanoes, an attempt is made here to further develop existing classifications of basaltic eruption vents/structures according to appearance and eruptive behaviour.

Volcanology and the monitoring of volcanoes

Volcanological research has been carried out in Iceland since the 19th century, but tracing this is outside the scope of this book. Research dealing with volcano monitoring and eruption forecasting is a relatively new study. It is closely related to research on the interior and underlying strata of volcanoes as well as plate movement and hot spots.

Up until 1970 or so, volcanological research was directed mainly at features on the surface of the Earth, volcanic centres, igneous rocks,

---

Classification: Central volcanoes/volcanic centres

1. Complex, multi-vent massif (20–30 km wide) with caldera. Rhyolite predominant. Torfajökull, Kerlingarfjöll.

2. Complex, multi-vent massif (at least 20 km wide) with caldera. Basalt predominant. Krafla, Grímsvötn, Bárðarbunga, Kverkfjöll.

3. Complex, multi-vent massif (⋯≯20 km wide) without caldera. Strong influx of acid eruptives. Ljósufjöll.

4. Complex, multi-vent massif (⋯≯20 km wide) without caldera. Small or no influx of acid eruptives. Centres of Trölladyngja, Fremrinámur and Þeistreykir volcanic systems.

5. Composite shield volcanoes with caldera (24–38 km wide). Many linear vents. Basalt predominant but influx of acid eruptives. Hofsjökull, Katla volcano, Dyngjufjöll (Askja).

6. Stratovolcano (circular or elgonated base). Slopes 12° to 25+°. Central crater or small caldera. Eruptives vary from basalt to dacite or rhyolite with tendency to explosive activity: Öræfajökull, Snæfellsjökull Snæfell, Hekla (elongated, mainly andesite and dacite) and Eyjafjallajökull (elongated, varied rocks).

Classification: Basalt volcanoes

1. Effusive eruptions:
- short fissure, short duration: Spatter cone (lava ring), Eldborg in Hnappadalur
- long fissure, short/long duration: Spatter cone row, Þrengslaborgir, Stampar
- short fissure, long duration: Lava shield, Skjaldbreiður, Kollóttadyngja

2. Mixed eruptions (lava and tephra):
- long fissure, short/long duration: Spatter and/or scoria cone row, Snagaborgir at Krafla/Lakagígar
- long fissure, high tephra output: Scoria cone row, Seyðishólar
- short fissure, short/long duration: spatter cone/scoria cone, Eldborg at Drottning/Búðaklettur, Eldfell

3. Explosive, hydromagmatic eruptions (groundwater/lake) or phreato-magmatic activity (magmatic gases):
- long fissure, high tephra output: Ash (tuff) cone row, Vatnaöldur
- short fissure, high tephra output: Ash (tuff) ring (tephra ring), Hverfjall, Lúdent, Hrossaborg
- long fissure, gases/steam predominant: Explosion chasm, Valagjá
- short fissure, gases/steam predominant: Explosion crater/maar, Augu/Grænavatn, Víti

4. Effusive subglacial eruptions:
- long/short fissure: pillow lava ridge/pillow lava hill, Kverkfjallarani/Sandfell

5. Effusive -› explosive, subglacial eruptions:
- long/short fissure: hyaloclastite (móberg, tuff) ridge/cone, Sveifluháls, Skriðutindar/Keilir, Stapafell

6. Effusive -› explosive, submarine eruptions:
- long/short fissure: pillow lava-tuff ridge/seamount, Eldeyjarboði/Jólnir, Syrtlingur

7. Effusive -› explosive -› effusive, subglacial eruptions:
- long fissure: hyaloclastite (móberg, tuff) ridge capped by lava, Jarlhettur
- short fissure: table mountain (stapi or tuya with lava cap), Herðubreið, Gæsafjöll, Hrafnabjörg, Skriðan

8. Effusive -› explosive -› effusive, submarine eruptions:
- short/long fissure: lava capped tephra (tuff) island(s), Surtsey

(Partly based on: R.S. Williams, S. Þórarinsson and E.C. Morris 1983 and Th. Thordarson and A. Höskuldsson 2002, extended by the author.)

eruptive behaviour and volcanic history. With the evolution of geophysics and geochemical measuring methods, however, it became possible to hypothesise about and explain processes and conditions which are inaccessible within the Earth. Specialists can produce models which describe conditions beneath and within the crust that cannot be seen. New techniques in mass spectrometry and chemical analysis of minerals and rocks, as well as seismic measurements, measurements of subglacial topography, gravity, geomagnetism, conductivity, radar topography and others have opened up a new vision of the basics of volcanology. The escape of magmatic gases has also been monitored.

Now research is directed at obtaining even better and more exact answers to questions such as: where and how does magma form, how are different magma types formed, how and why does magma migrate to the surface, by what routes and what can delay it, how is the plate margin related to the hot spot, what are the properties of the crust and mantle, how do volcanism and the volcanic zones evolve, how do the volcanic systems and individual volcanic centres behave, what are the precursors to eruption and what are the controlling factors?

The aim of volcanological research is not only to increase basic knowledge but also to realise the possibility of preventing damage and disruption by volcanic eruption. Advances in the monitoring of volcanoes reached their height in the last decades of the 20th century. A continuous network of seismographs, altimeters and deformation instruments, strain-meters and gravitometers was set up, in addition to which GPS-based measurements and radar measurements from satellites were developed to track crustal change. The instruments are sited on dangerous or especially active volcanoes. The system is still being improved. Already there has been success in forecasting the likelihood of increased volcanic activity or eruption. Examples are the more recent eruptions of the Krafla Fires, Hekla eruptions and the volcanic activity in 1996, 1998 and 2004 in Vatnajökull. Increased seismic activity or a change in the seismic pattern, uplift and increased strain in the rocks are some of the properties on which forecasts of volcanic activity are based. Three institutions have been most involved up to now: the Geophysical Department of the Meteorological Office, the Science Institute of the University of Iceland and the Nordic Volcanological Institute

The Hekla central volcano seen from the east. It has erupted about 20 times since the 12th century. As a young volcano, it still has a prominent elongated shape. (RTH)

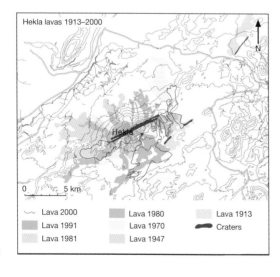

The 20th-century lava flows from Hekla 1913–2000. (Main source: Á. Hjartarson 1995)

(now merged within the Institute of Earth Sciences). The National Emergency Agency has made evacuation and emergency plans in case of earthquakes, eruptions and jökulhlaup floods for all inhabited areas at risk. Wide-ranging volcanic research has also been carried out at these three institutions as well as at the Natural History Museum and within the National Energy Authority (now the Iceland Geosurvey). In addition, many individual scientists, Icelandic and foreign, including those working abroad, have contributed to research. Further advances in monitoring volcanoes and in forecasting can be expected in the coming decades. No less can be expected when dealing with this unavoidable aspect of Iceland's nature.

The Icelanders are often asked how they cope with the threat from volcanoes. A survey close to the Katla volcano shows that many people simply repress the thought of danger ("We don't talk about Katla here"). However, the majority of people, living within or close to volcanic areas simply take their chances and rely on the fact that they will be warned and be able to escape, while accepting material loss. This also applies to the people responsible for power stations built in active highland areas.

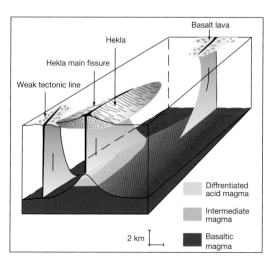

A model of the Hekla volcanic centre. A large magma chamber (or reservoir) is situated at a depth of 7–8 km and consists of layers of different composition. Hekla erupts intermediate or acid magmas while fissures within the volcanic system produce basalt. (Main source: O. Sigmarsson et al 1992)

Eruptions in the Hekla Volcanic System in historical times

Year	Duration yrs or less	Dormant yrs	Lava km³	Tephra km³	Location	Damage
1104	?	at least 300 yrs	?	2.5	Hekla	Very great
1158		53	>0.2	>0. 3	Hekla	Great
1206	?	47	>0.15	0.03?	Hekla	Substantial
1222?	?	15	?	0.01	Hekla	Little
1300	12	77	>0.5	0.5	Hekla	Great
1341	?	40	?	0.08?	Hekla	Great
1389	?	47	>0.2	0.08	Rauðöldur	Substantial
1440	?	?	?	?	N/S of Hekla	?
1510	?	120	>0.75	0.32	Hekla	Great
1554	6 weeks		<0.1	?	Vondubjallar	
1597	>6	86	?	0.24?	Hekla	Small
1636	12	39	?	0.08?	Hekla	Small
1693	7–10	56	?	0.3	Hekla	Great
1725	6-8 weeks		0.1–0.2	?	N/S of Hekla	
1766	24	72	1.3	0.4	Hekla	Substantial
1845	7	77	0.63	0.28	Hekla	Small
1878	1–2 months		0.1-0.2	?	At Krakatindur	
1913	few weeks		0.1	?	NE of Hekla	
1947–8	13 months	102	0.8	0.21	Hekla	Substantial
1970	2 months	16	0.2	0.07	at Hekla's base	Small
1980	3 days	10	0.12	0.06	Hekla	Substantial
1981	7 days	(7 mths.)	0.03	–	Hekla	None
1991	53 days	9.5	0.15	0.02	Hekla	Small
2000	11 days	9	0.11	~0.02	Hekla	Small

The eruptions not in bold occurred outside Hekla but within the volcanic system. The rock is basalt whereas Hekla erupts intermediate or acid rocks, ranging from basaltic andesite (or icelandite) to dacite.

(Main sources: Sigurður Þórarinsson 1967, Árni Hjartarson 1995 and Haukur Jóhannesson, pers. comm.).

GPS-surveys are useful in volcanological research. A mobile unit in Grímsvötn, Vatnajökull (left). Dozens of fixed, automated survey stations in volcanic systems show when terrain rises or subsides, as well as monitoring earthquakes and tectonic movements. The main survey centre is in Reykjavík (right). (RTH)

An overview of the volcanic systems

A description of typical localities and cases serves to promote further studies. The following list directs readers to some of the more typical study sites. For more information refer to scientific papers or the road guide by Th. Tordarson and A. Höskuldsson: *Iceland, Classical Geology in Europe 3.* Terra 2002.

1. *Reykjanes Volcanic System.* The system is 35 km long (40–45 km including submarine section) and 5–15 km wide. There are about 50 eruptive units from several rifting and volcanic episodes as well as 14 shield volcanoes. The shield volcano Háleyjabunga is composed of picrite. The last eruption occurred 1,500–1,800 years ago and the Reykjanes Fires in 1211–1240. There was eruption in the sea at this time and the younger Stampar crater row also dates from this time, as do Eldvörp and Illahraun near the Blue Lagoon. The basalt of the system is from the tholeiitic series. Belongs to the WRZ.

2. *Trölladyngja Volcanic System.* The system is 40–50 km long and 4–7 km broad. There are 40–50 volcanic units from several rifting and volcanic episodes, as well as 3 shield volcanoes. One of them,

Volcanic eruptions of the 20th century

Year	Volcano	Magnitude	Remark
1902–1903	N of Grímsvötn and at Þórðarhyrna	Quite large	Flood in the rivers Skeiðará, Súla, Jökulsá and others
1906–1908	Probably Grímsvön	Quite large(?)	Documented
1910	In western Vatnajökull	Quite large	Documented. Flood in Súla river(?)
1913	Northeast of Hekla (Lambafit-Mundafell)	Fairly small	Fissure eruption with lava flow
1918	Katla	Large flood	Tephra eruption and very powerful
1919	Grímsvötn	?	Tephra layer in Vatnajökull
1921	Askja	Small	Bátshraun lava
1922	Grímsvötn	Quite large	Flood in Skeiðará river
1922	Askja	Small	Mývetningahraun lava
1923	Askja	Small lavas	Kvíslahraun and Suður-botnahraun
1924–1929	Askja	Quite large	Eruptive episode, fissure eruption south of Askja
1926	Askja	Small	Island in Askja lake
1933	At Grímsvötn	Small	No flood
1934	In Grímsvötn	Quite large	Preceded by a large flood
1938	N of Grtímsvötn	Quite large flood	Considerable eruption and large
1947–1948	Hekla	Large	Long, very large eruption following 101-year quiescence
1955	Katla(?)	Small(?)	Small flood, two glacier depressions observed
1959	Kverkfjöll	Small	Mud and steam eruption, large glacial depression
1961	Askja	Fairly small	Short fissure eruption, Vikrahraun lava
1963–1967	Surtsey	Large	Total of 3 islands, two disappeared
1970	Hekla	Quite large	Main eruption close to Hekla

Year	Volcano	Magnitude	Remark
1973	Eldfell	Fairly small	Much damage due to proximity of settlement
1975	Krafla	Very small	1. fissure eruption in an episode
1977	Krafla	Very small	2. eruption in an episode
1977	Krafla	Very small	3. eruption in an episode
1980	Hekla	Quite large	
1980	Krafla	Very small	4. eruption in an episode
1980	Krafla	Small	5. eruption in an episode
1980	Krafla	Small	6. eruption in an episode
1981	Hekla	Small	
1981	Krafla	Small	7. eruption in an episode
1981	Krafla	Small	8. eruption in an episode
1983	Grímsvötn	Small	
1984	Krafla	Fairly small	9. eruption in an episode
1991	Hekla	Quite large	
1996	N of Grímsvötn (Gjálp)	Quite large	Large flood in Skeiðará river
1998	Grímsvötn	Fairly small	No flood
2000	Hekla	Quite large	
2004	Grímsvötn	Small	Preceded by a flood

A total of 37 events in the volcanic history of the past century are accounted for. If the Krafla Fires are treated as one event then the total is 29, i.e. there is an eruption every 3.5 years. It must, however, be borne in mind that there were in fact nine Krafla Fires, the Askja eruption 1924–29 may have been several events and the number of individual eruptions in Vatnajökull is uncertain. If all such eruptions are counted, then the total figure could be closer to 50 than 40, with the resulting frequency increasing to one eruption every 2 to 2.5 years. Eruptions in the sea off the Reykjanes peninsula are not included (compiled from many sources in: A.T. Guðmundsson 2001: Íslenskar eldstöðvar, Reykjavík).

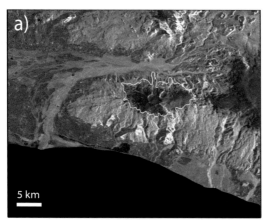

Earthquakes were numerous in Eyjafjallajökull around 1991 and reached two peaks in 1994 and 1999. GPS and InSAR measurements by the Nordic Volcanological Institute showed a swelling of around 35 cm during the period of observation. At the height of the later episode (1999) it appears that a dyke had intruded the base of the volcano in the southeast, at a depth of about 5 km. Calculations show that it could be as much as 0.7 m thick, 5 km long and 4 km deep, and probably originated in the magma chamber of the volcano. A larger intrusion could have led to eruption. (From Rikke Pedersen, Nord. Volc. Inst. 2006).

Þráinsskjöldur, is among the largest shield volcanoes on the peninsula. The last eruptions occurred about 2,000 years ago and in the Krýsuvík Fires of 1150–1180. The lava on which the aluminium smelter at Straumsvík stands belongs to the latter as does the Ögmundarhraun lava at Krísuvík. The basalt of the system belongs to the tholeiite series. Belongs to the WRZ.

3. *Brennisteinsfjöll Volcanic System.* The system is 45 km long and 5–10 km wide. Volcanic units are believed to number 30–40 from several rifting and volcanic episodes as well as 3 shield volcanoes, including Heiðin há. The last confirmed eruptions occurred 2,000

One of many young but prehistoric scoria and
spatter cones on the Reykjanes peninsula:
Eldborg undir Geitafelli. (RTH)

years ago and in the 10th–11th centuries. They produced the lavas
at the Bláfjöll skiing area, at Grindaskörð and also the lava flow
Svínahraunsbruni, crossed by the main (ring) road at Sandskeiði.
The lava in the Elliðaár valley in Reykjavík (Leitahraun lava) dates
from around 4,700 years ago. The cave Raufarhólshellir and the
Rauðhólar rootless craters belong to this lava. Basalts of the system
are from the tholeiite series. Belongs to the WRZ.

4. *Hengill Volcanic System.* The largest system on the Reykjanes
peninsula, 100 km long and 3–16 km wide. There have been at
least 20 eruptions from several rifting and volcanic episodes as well
as 6 shield volcanoes, the last eruptions occurring 5,000 years ago
and 2,000 years ago (Nesjavellir Fires). The eruption fissure from
the latter is just above the geothermal energy plant at Nesjavellir.
Sandey island was formed in this episode. The prominent rift
valley/graben and faults at Þingvellir belong to the system's fissure
swarm. The basalt of the system belongs to the tholeiite series but
in the young central volcano of Hengill there are also intermediate

189

Houses in the town on the island Heimaey (the
island group of Vestmannaeyjar), far too close to
the fiercely active, new volcanic fissure. (ATG)

The eruption on
Heimaey in 1973
went on for
several months.
Lava and tephra
buried about
40% of the town
area. (ÆJ)

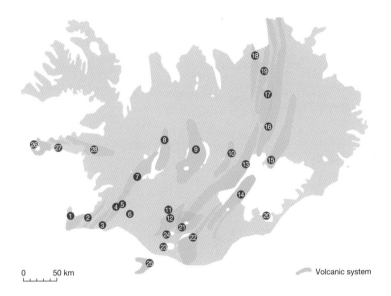

0   50 km

Volcanic system

and acid rocks. Two smaller systems with central volcanoes occur east of the Hengill system, Hrómundartindur (5. Hrómundartindur system) and Grensdalur which is quite old. The highland area at Hrafnbjörg and Skriðutindur could be an independent activity centre or belong to the Langjökull volcanic systems. Magma intrusion was detected in the roots of the Hrómundartindur system in 1993–98. Shield volcanoes are mostly large, the largest being Skjaldbreiður which is about 10,000 years old (more than 20 km³ including lavas). The large faults at Þingvellir occur in lava which flowed from a row of small shield volcanoes and scoria craters east of Hrafnabjörg. Belongs to the WRZ

6. *Grímsnes Volcanic System.* The system is the smallest in the country, 12 km long and 4 km wide. Eruptions last occurred 5,000–6,000 years ago. There are 10–12 eruption fissures, some of them dating from the same period and consisting of about 20 scoria and spatter craters and one crater lake: Kerið. The area is now built up with summer cottages. The volume of eruptive rocks

Many lava-tunnel caves line the Hallmundarhraun pahoehoe lava flow from the 9th century

in western Iceland. Viðgelmir is one of the
largest examples. (RTH)

is >1 km³ and the lava area 54 km². Tholeiite basalt is characteristic of the system. Probably belongs to the WRZ

7. –8. *Langjökull.* The two volcanic systems are partly covered by the Langjökull ice cap which has an area of about 920 km². The centre of the northern system forms highland beneath the northern part of the glacier (including a large shield volcano and table mountain) and there is a caldera of about 25 km². The centre of the southern system forms the highland of the Geitland glacier. The northern system (here referred to as Baldjökull Volcanic System) is 55 km long and 5–18 km wide, while the southern system (here referred to as the Geitland Volcanic System) is 70 km long and 5–17 km wide. Volcanic activity in the Holocene has been confined to 4–5 shield volcanoes and 5 fissures, the last eruptions in the northern system occurring early in the 9th century (the Hall-

mundarhraun lavas). They contain the largest known lava caves in the country (1–3 km long), including the Surtshellir cave. Eruptive rocks are mainly basalt from the tholeiitic series but acid rocks are found in at least two places including Prestahnúkur. Belongs to the WRZ.

9. *Hofsjökull Volcanic System.* A 1,782 m high ice cap, Hofsjökull (890 km^2), covers a central volcano which has a caldera. The caldera is 6–7 km wide and 30–40 km^2 in area. The volcanic system is 90 km long and 30–35 km wide and has 6 Holocene volcanic units (fissure eruption centres) outside the glacier. None of them dates from the historical period. The eruptive rocks are from the tholeiitic series. To the south at the limit of the system rises the Kerlingarfjöll range (1,200–1,488 m) which forms a central volcano with two calderas, the larger of which is 7 km long and 5 km wide, the smaller 4 km wide. No activity has occurred there in the Holocene. All these volcanic systems belong to the WRZ.

10. *Tungnafellsjökull Volcanic System.* A small volcanic system surrounding a central volcano with two calderas. The glacier, 1,523 m high and 40 km^2, covers part of the highland. The larger caldera is 10 km long and 4 km wide and in the middle of the volcano; the other is considerably smaller and lies further east. The volcanic system is 55 km long and 15 km wide and there are two small Holocene volcanic units (fissures). Hágöngur represents acid volcanic activity from a glacial period. Belongs to the NRZ.

11. *Hekla Volcanic System.* The system is centred around the ridge-shaped Hekla stratovolcano (1,480 m) and is 40–50 km long and 7 km wide. Beneath the mountain and volcanic system lies an elongate magma chamber at a depth of about 7–8 km. Hekla has been the most productive volcano in Iceland during the Holocene (33 km^3 which is sufficient to cover Vatnajökull to a depth of 4 m). At least 23 eruptions are known in the historical period: the last in 1913, 1947, 1970, 1980/81, 1991 and 2000. A large number of volcanic units bears witness to the very active nature of the system and central volcano. There are at least 27 basalt volcanic units outside Hekla and a further 70–100 if intermediate and acid tephra layers from Hekla are included. Four of these are very substantial

The eruption of Hekla in 1947–48 released a total
volume of 1 km³ (1 billion m³) of lava and tephra.
The rock is andestic. (SP)

A typical magmatic explosion in one of the main craters during the 1947-eruption of Hekla. Large lava lumps and bombs shoot into the air along with more fine-grained tephra and gasses. (SÞ)

tephra layers. The youngest date from around 900 BC and 1104 AD. The volcanic rocks are from the transitional series and the system belongs to the SIVB.

12. *(Vatnafjöll Volcanic System)*. The system is 40 km long and 9 km wide and is generally considered to be either an independent system or part of the Hekla system. There are about 30 Holocene volcanic units, most basaltic from the transitional series. Volcanic products are not dated but appear to span a period from before 7,000 years ago to about 2,000 years ago. Belongs to the SIVB.

13. *Bárðarbunga Volcanic System*. The longest and widest volcanic system in the country, 180–190 km long and 10–25 km wide, with its volcanic centre at Bárðarbunga which is a large volcano that has a 60–70 km^2 ice-filled caldera under the northwestern part of Vatnajökull (8,000 km^2). Hamarinn is a smaller, ice-covered central volcano southwest of Bárðarbunga (2,005 m). The system is very active as nearly 100 eruptions or volcanic episodes prove. The last eruptions in the glacier were in the 15th and 18th centuries but outside the glacier in Vatnaöldur around 870 AD, in Veiði-

vötn around 1480 and in Tröllagígar 1862–1862. Of these the first eruption produced a large amount of tephra and lava but the last was a typical volcano-tectonic episode with lava flow (volume 0.3 km³). The southwestern part of the fissure swarm runs towards the Torfajökull system and is an indication of propagating rift activity. The last eruption in both systems occurred at the same time. Eruptive products are from the tholeiite series and the system belongs to the NRZ.

14. *Grímsvötn Volcanic System.* The Grímsvötn volcanic system is the most active in the country and the largest high-temperature geothermal area when episodal volcanism is at a maximum. The central volcano extends from north of Grímsvötn to Þórðarhyrna. The Grímsvötn caldera is threefold, 40–45 km² in area and contains a 100–200 m deep lake under a 100–200 m thick ice cover. Beneath the volcano is a small magma chamber. Þórðarhyrna is believed to be older and is part of a group of small peaks of which at least one is made of acid eruptives. The volcanic system is 100–110 km long and 4–20 km wide. About 60 eruptions are known to have taken place in the last 1,100 years in the system, including at least 8–9 in the 20th century. The last eruptions under the glacier in Grímsvötn or vicinity occurred in 1934, 1938, 1983, 1996, 1998 and 2004. The last eruption episode outside the glacier was the Skaftá Fires (Laki eruption) of 1783–85 (15 km³ of eruptives and 600 km² of lava). The majority is evolved tholeiitic basalt in Grímsvötn and in the southwestern part of the fissure system (outside the glacier). Belongs to the NRZ.

15. *Kverkfjöll Volcanic System.* The system is 90–100 km long and 10–15 km wide. The volcano Kverkfjöll (1,920 m) with two calderas, each of which is 8 km long and 5 km wide, is considered to be the centre of the system. The mountain is dissected by a huge valley glacier and there is a large geothermal area which is accessible. Four volcano-tectonic episodes have occurred in the northern part of the fissure swarm during the Holocene, the last 1,000–2,000 years ago (Biskupsfell eruptive fissure). There may have been a minor eruption in the glacier in the 20th century. Basalts of the tholeiitic series are most conspicuous. Belongs to the NRZ.

The centre of the Bárðarbunga Volcanic System is a large volcano (Bárðarbunga) with a 700 m deep caldera covered by the glacial ice of Vatnajökull. (OS)

16. *Askja Volcanic System*. A major volcanic system, 150–160 km long and 5–20 km wide. The central volcano is called Dyngjufjöll with the caldera of Askja (45 km^2) and at least two other caldera depressions. At least 50 volcanic units from the Holocene have been mapped. A vigorous volcano-tectonic episode occurred in 1874–75 with a tephra eruption in Askja (acid products, 2 km^3 as tephra) but 6–7 basalt effusive eruptions in the northern part of the system, at Sveinagjá and elsewhere. Several fairly small eruptions occurred in 1921–29 and a fissure eruption with lava eruption and fountains in 1961. Hrúthálsar is situated north of Askja and volcanic products there suggest an independent active centre with a separate volcanic system which is at present allocated to the Askja system. The rocks in the system belong to the tholeiitic series, mostly basalt. Belongs to the NRZ.

Subglacial Grímsvötn eruptions pierce the glacier ice shelf that floats on the caldera lake.

In 2004 a small, symmetrical island emerged during a short but lively tephra eruption. (RTH)

17. *Fremrinámur Volcanic System.* A typical rift-zone volcanic system without a prominent central volcano but with a developing centre at the Ketildyngja lava shield. The system is 150 km long and 5–15 km wide. Volcanic activity has been confined to effusive eruptions forming lava shields and mixed eruptions on volcanic fissures, the last 2,000–3,000 years ago (Kræðuborgir). The eruptive products are mostly basalt from the tholeiitic series but acid rock is also found at Ketildyngja where there is a high-temperature geothermal area as well. Belongs to the NRZ.

18. *Þeistareykir Volcanic System.* This system is quite noteworthy for the fact that in its centre rises a composite volcano made of overlapping lava shields and thus resembling a shield volcano similar to those in Hawaii (albeit much smaller). It is about 75 km long and 5–12 km wide. The centre is defined by the composite Þeistar-

eykjabunga lava shield and surrounding area which is also a high-temperature geothermal area. There are 10–12 volcanic units, mainly resulting from effusive eruptions, the last of which occurred about 2,500 years ago (Þeistareykjahraun lava). The rocks are mostly olivine basalt from the tholeiitic series. The system belongs to the NRZ.

19. *Krafla Volcanic System.* The volcano-tectonic episode in 1975–84 (the Krafla Fires) shed light on the dynamics of volcanic systems, their existence and types. There were 9 eruptions during 22 magma injections, accompanying a total widening of up to 8 m in the fissure swarm which is 100 km long and 5–10 km wide. A similar episode is known from 1725–29. There is easy access to the main eruption area of the Krafla Fires above the geothermal energy plant. The central volcano has an old caldera (8–10 km wide) and there are many types of crater and volcanic formations in the area, for example a maar (Víti), spatter cones, scoria craters, rootless craters (pseudocraters) at Mývatn, large tephra rings (e.g. Hverfjall) and others. A huge lava flow (the Younger Laxárhraun Lava), produced by a crater row east of Mývatn, Lúdent and Þrengslaborgir, created Mývatn in its present form just over 2,000 years ago (the later Hólseldar Fires). Heiðarsporður and the surroundings of the Lúdent and Þrengslaborgir craters might classify as an independent activity centre. The eruptive rocks belong to the tholeiitic series and the system to the NRZ.

20. *Öræfajökull.* Öræfajökull is not strictly speaking a volcanic system but rather a single ice-covered stratovolcano, 2,114 m high, which extends outwards from the south of Vatnajökull. It is 18–20 km in diameter and about 250–300 km^3 in volume, making the mountain one of the biggest in the country as well as the highest. The glacier is about 80–100 km^2 in area. At least 5–6 prehistoric eruptions are known to have taken place, in addition to the catastrophic eruption of 1362 during which dozens of farms in the area were destroyed. Finally there was a smaller eruption in 1727–28. Both the latter eruptions caused violent floods. The eruptive rocks are acid, intermediate and basic. Öræfajökull belongs to the intraplate lateral volcanic belt (ÖVB), along with Snæfell and Esjufjöll.

Lava shield top crater and a pit crater (collapsed
lava-tube roof) at Þeistareykjabunga, northeast
Iceland. (RTH)

21. *Torfajökull Volcanic System.* This system is situated between the
propagating rift (NRZ) and the lateral volcanic belt known as the
SIVB. It is 50 km long and 30 km wide and forms a very colourful
highland centre where a huge caldera, 18 km long and 12 km wide,
has formed over a long period of time (700,000–800,000 years).
The Holocene volcanic units number about 20. A small glacier
caps the highest elevation: Torfajökull-Kaldaklofsjökull which is
about 15 km^2 in area. The last eruptions were around 100 AD,
870 AD (including Vatnaöldur) and 1480 (including the Laugahraun lava in Landmannalaugar and the Ljótipollur maar), the
result of basalt-magma intrusion from the Bárðarbunga system
(NRZ) into the central volcano. The eruptive rocks are mainly
from the transitional series, mostly acid rocks. Belongs to the
SIVB.

The Torfajökull area is the most extensive expanse of acid (rhyolitic) bedrock in Iceland. At Brennisteinsalda, thick rhyolitic lava was extruded in the 1480s, forming Laugahraun. The well-known hot springs of Landmannalaugar emerge from the front of the lava flow. (RTH)

22. *Katla Volcanic System.* This system is one of the most active and productive in the country. It is about 90 km long and 5–30 km wide. The central volcano of Katla has a 100 km² caldera and possibly a secondary active centre at Goðabunga. The Mýrdalsjökull ice cap largely covers the central volcano and caldera, apart from a few nunataks on the caldera rim. The glacier area is about 580 km² and its height 1,510 m. A catastrophic ultraplinian eruption occurred about 12,000 years ago, when part of the caldera may have formed. At least 100 volcanic units date from the Holocene and 20 eruptions have occurred in Katla in the last 1,100 years, the most recent in 1918 and probably in 1955. A major eruption (Eldgjá eruption) outside the glacier occurred around

Eyjafjallajökull lies close to the Katla volcano in South Iceland. This glaciated central volcano, a somewhat shield-like, composite cone, erupted in 1821–23. (OS)

930 AD, accompanied by enormous lava flow to the south (18.1 km^3 and 780 km^2) as well as copious tephra production (1.4 km^3). The eruptive materials are from the transitional series, mostly basalt, but acid rocks are also found. Belongs to the SIVB.

23. *Eyjafjallajökull.* Eyjafjallajökull is a flat, elongated (W–E) strato-volcano, 1,667 m in height, the glacier covering an area of about 80 km^2. The active fissure swarm on the summit runs towards Fimmvörðuháls and is 30 km long and 1–5 km wide. At least two lava eruptions are known to have taken place just before the Holocene, while tephra eruptions with floods occurred in 1612 and 1821–23, at approximately the same time as activity in Katla. The eruptive rocks belong to the transitional series and are mostly basalt but also intermediate. Belongs to the SIVB.

24. *Tindfjöll Volcanic System.* The system is small, only 10 km long and up to 7 km wide. There is an old central volcano with a caldera

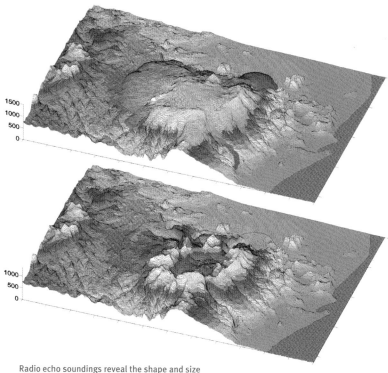

Radio echo soundings reveal the shape and size
of the Katla volcano and caldera.
(H. Björnsson et al 2000)

(35–40 km²) from which a huge glowing ash cloud and pyroclastic
flow exploded to the south some 53,000 years ago. Ignimbrite in
Þorsmörk came from this eruption. The greatest height of individual peaks is 1,464 m and the glacier is about 19 km². There are
10–12 volcanic units dating from the Holocene and the rocks are
from the transitional series. Belongs to the SIVB.

25. *Vestmannaeyjar (Westman Islands) Volcanic System.* The system is
about 35 km long and 25 km wide, most of which is on the sea
floor. The active centre is on Heimaey where there are the foundations of a large central volcano. About 70 volcanic units can be
found in the area, most younger than 10,000–15,000 years old.
Eruptions last occurred in 1963–67 (Surtsey) and 1973 but there
were two episodes 8,000–9,000 years ago (Suðureyjar) and 5,000–

In the famous novel, Jules Verne made his little expedition to the centre of the Earth start in the crater of Snæfellsjökull, seen here from the air.

A middle-aged, composite cone volcano, the mountain has been dormant for 1,800 years. (RTH)

6,000 years ago. Stórhöfði, Helgafell and some of the larger islands formed at this time. Eruptive rocks belong to the alkali series and are mainly basalts. Belongs to the SIVB.

26. *Snæfellsjökull Volcanic System.* Contains a central volcano, Snæfellsjökull (1,446 m), which is a typical stratovolcano. The size of the system is 30 km long and 20 km wide. The glacier is about 10 km². Two eruptions, producing large amounts of acid tephra, have occurred in the central volcano in the late Holocene and a third is likely. The last eruption was about 1,800 years ago. Between 10 and 15 fissure eruptions have occurred outside the volcano itself and are represented mainly by scoria and spatter cones. The eruptive

rocks are acid, intermediate and basic from the alkali series. Belongs to the SNVB.

27. *Lýsuskarð Volcanic System.* This has no central volcanoes but an active centre with a group of peaks and acid rocks in the highland area of Lýsuhyrna and Lýsuskarð. The system is 30 km long and 5 km wide. At least two eruptive spells have occurred in the Holocene (basalt) from fissures which have large scoria craters. The rocks fall between the alkali and transitional series. Belongs to the SNVB.

28. *Ljósufjöll Volcanic System.* No central volcano but an active centre with acid rocks resides in Ljósufjöll. The system is 90 km long and 3–20 km wide. Altogether 23 volcanic units have been mapped; some are obviously contemporary formations. Craters include large scoria craters such as Rauðumelskúlur and symmetrical lava spatter rings, such as Eldborg in Hnappadalur which is at least 5,000 years old. The last eruptions took place around the year 1000 AD (Rauðhálsar) and 2,600 years ago (Grábók in Norðurárdalur). The eruptive rocks lie between the alkali and transitional series. Grábrók is the easternmost of the volcanic structures. Belongs to the SNVB.

Selected bibliography

Surnames are written in italics. The Icelandic letters é, ó, á, ú, í and ý should be written as e, o, a, u, i and y, ö as ö, oe or simply o, æ as æ or ae, ð as d and þ as th when searching for references and papers in most databases.

Krafla Volcanic System

T. *Árnadóttir*, F. *Sigmundsson* and P.T. *Delaney* 1998. Sources of crustal deformation associated with the Krafla, Iceland, eruption of September 1984. *Geophysical Research Letters* 25: 1,043–1,046.

A. *Björnsson* 1985. Dynamics of crustal rifting in NE Iceland. *Journal of Geophysical Research* 90: 10,151–10,162.

B. *Brandsdóttir*, W. H. *Mencke*, P. *Einarsson*, R. *White* and R. *Staples* 1995. Faroe-Iceland ridge experiment 2. Crustal structure of Krafla central volcano. *Journal Geophysical Research* 102: 7,867–7,888.

K. *Jónasson* 1994. Rhyolite volcanism in the Krafla central volcano, north-east Iceland. *Bulletin of Volcanology* 56: 516–528.

F. *Sigmundsson*, H. *Vadon* and D. *Massonnet* 1997. Readjustment of the Krafla spreading segment to crustal rifting, measured by Satellite Radar Interferometry. *Geophysical Research Letters* 24, No. 15: 1,843–1,846.

E. *Tryggvason* 1984. Widening of the Krafla fissure swarm during the 1975–1981 volcano-tectonic episode. *Bulletin of Volcanology* 47: 97–118.

S. *Þórarinsson* 1979. The postglacial history of the Mývatn area. *OIKOS* 32: 17–28. Copenhagen.

Askja Volcanic System

K. *Annertz*, M. *Nilson* and G. E. *Sigvaldason* 1985. The postglacial history of Dyngjufjöll. *Nordic Volcanological Institute, report* 8503. Reykjavík.

B. *Brandsdóttir* 1992. Historical accounts of earthquakes associated with eruptive activity in the Askja Volcanic System. *Jökull* 42.

Á. *Guðmundsson* and K. *Bäckström* 1991. Structure and development of the Sveinagjá graben, Northeast Iceland. *Tectonophysics* 200: 111–125.

H. *Sigurðsson* and R.J. *Sparks* 1978. Rifting episode in North Iceland in 1874–1875 and the eruption of Askja and Sveinagjá. *Bulletin of Volcanology* 41:149–167.

G. E. *Sigvaldason* 1979. Rifting, magmatic activity and interaction between acid and basic liquids. The 1875 Askja eruption in Iceland. *Nordic Volcanological Institute report* 7903. Reykjavík.

G. E. *Sigvaldason*, K. *Annertz* and M. *Nilsson* 1992. Effect of glacier loading/deloading on volcanism: postglacial volcanic producton rate of the Dyngjufjöll area, Central Iceland. *Bulletin of Volcanology* 54: 385–192.

G. E. *Sigvaldason* 2002. Volcanic and tectonic processes coinciding with glaciation and crustal rebound: an early Holocene rhyolitic eruption in the Dyngjufjöll volcanic centre and the formation of the Askja caldera, north Iceland. *Bulletin of Volcanology* 64: 192–205.

E. *Sturkell* and F. *Sigmundsson* 2000. Continous Deflation of the Askja Caldera, Iceland During the 1983–1998 Non-Eruptive period. *Journal of Geophysical Research* 105: 25,671–25,684.

E. *Tryggvason* 1989. Ground deformation in Askja, Iceland: Its source and possible relation to flow of the mantle plume. *Journal of Volcanology and Geothermal Research* 39: 61–71.

S. *Þórarinsson* and G. E. *Sigvaldason* 1962. The eruption of Askja 1961. A preliminary report. *American Journal of Science* 260: 641–651.

Þeistareykir and Fremrinámur Volcanic Systems

H. *Ármannsson*, G. *Gíslason* and H. *Torfason* 1986. Surface exploration of the Theistareykir high-temperature area, Iceland, with special reference to the application of geothermal methods. *Applied Geochemistry*, vol.1: 47–64.

H. *Reginiussen*, K. *Grönvold* and N. *Óskarsson* 1999. Geochemistry and petrogenesis of the Trölladyngja lava-shield, Eastern Rift-Zone. Abstract. *Geoscience Society of Iceland Symposium*. Reykjavík.

M.J. *Rossi* 1996: Morphology and mechanism of eruption of postglacial shield volcanoes in Iceland. *Bulletin of Volcanology* 57: 530–540.

L. *Slater* et al 2001. Melt generation and movement beneath Theistareykir NE Iceland. *Journal of Petrology* 42: 321–354.

Kverkfjöll Volcanic System

H. *Björnsson* and P. *Einarsson* 1990. Volcanoes beneath Vatnajökull, Iceland: Evidence from radio echo-sounding, earthquakes and jökulhlaups. *Jökull* 40.

R. *Karhunen* 1988. Eruption mechanism and rheomorphism during the basaltic fissure eruption in Biskupsfell, Kverkfjöll, North-Central Iceland. *Nordic Volcanological Institute report 8802*. Reykjavík.

S. *Þórarinsson*, K. *Sæmundsson* and R. S. *Williams* 1973: ERTS-1 image of Vatnajökull; Analysis of glaciological structures and volcanic features. *Jökull* 23.

Grímsvötn Volcanic System

H. *Björnsson* 1988. Hydrology of ice caps in volcanic regions. *Vísindafélag Íslendinga (Societas Scientarium Islandica)*, 45. Reykjavík.

H. *Björnsson* and P. *Einarsson* 1990. Volcanoes beneath Vatnajökull, Iceland: evidence from radio-echo sounding, earthquakes and jökulhlaups. *Jökull* 40.

P. *Einarsson*, B. *Brandsdóttir*, M T. *Guðmundsson*, H. *Björnsson*, K. *Grönvold* and F. *Sigmundsson* 1997. Center of the Iceland Hotspot experiences volcanic unrest. *Eos, Transactions, American Geophysical Union*, 78, no. 35: 369–375.

K. *Grönvold* and H. *Jóhannesson* 1984. Eruption in Grímsvötn 1983: course of events and chemical studies of the tephra. *Jökull* 34.

M. T. *Guðmundsson* 1989. The Grímsvötn caldera, Vatnajökull: subglacial topography and structure of caldera infill. *Jökull* 39.

M. T. *Guðmundsson* and H. *Björnsson* 1991. Eruptions in Grímsvötn, Vatnajökull, Iceland 1934–1991, *Jökull* 41.

M. T. *Guðmundsson* and J. *Milsom* 1997. Gravity and magnetic studies of the subglacial Grímsvötn volcano, Iceland: implications for crustal and thermal structure. *Journal of Geophysical Research* 102, no. B4: 7,691–7,704.

M. T. *Guðmundsson*, F. *Sigmundsson* and H. *Björnsson* 1997. Ice-volcano interaction of the 1996 Gjálp eruption, Vatnajökull Iceland. *Nature* 389: 954–957.

M.T. *Gudmundsson*, F. *Pálsson*, H. *Björnsson* and Þ. *Högnadóttir* 2002: The hyaloclastite ridge formed in the subglacial 1996 eruption in Gjálp, Vatnajökull, Iceland: present day shape and preservation. In: J.L. Smellie and M.G. Chapman (eds): *Volcano interaction on Earth and Mars*. Geol. Society London Special Publ. 2002: 319–335.

G. *Larsen*, M. T. *Guðmundsson* and H. *Björnsson* 1998. Eight centuries of periodic volcanism at the center of the Iceland hotspot revealed by glacier tephrastratigraphy. *Geology* 26, no.10: 943–946.

O. *Sigmarsson*, M. *Condomines*, K. *Grönvold* and Th. *Thordarson* 1991. Extreme magma homogeneity in the 1783–1784 Lakagígar eruption: origin of a large volume of evolved basalt in Iceland. *Geophysical Research Letters* 18, no. 12: 2,229–2,232.

O. *Sigmarsson*, H. R. *Karlsson* and G. *Larsen* 2000. The 1996 and 1998 subglacial eruptions beneath the Vantajökull ice sheet in Iceland: contrasting geochemical and geophysical inferences on magma migration. *Bulletin of Volcanology* 61: 468–476.

H. *Sigurðsson* and S.R.J. *Sparks* 1978. Lateral magma flow within rifted Icelandic crust. *Nature* 274:126–130.

S. *Steinþórsson* 1977. Tephra layers in a drill core from the Vatnajökull ice cap. *Jökull* 27.

Th. *Thordarson* and S. *Self* 1993. The Laki (Skaftár) Fires and Grímsvötn eruptions in 1783–1785. *Bulletin of Volcanology* 55: 233–263.

Bárðarbunga Volcanic System

G. *Larsen* 1984. Recent volcanic history of the Veiðivötn Fissure Swarm, South Iceland. An approach to volcanic risk assessment. *Journal of Volcanology and Geothermal Research* 22: 33–58.

Torfajökull Volcanic System

D. *McGarvie* 1984. Torfajökull: A volcano dominated by magma mixing. *Geology* 12: 685–688.

B. *Gunnarsson*, B.D. Marsh and H.P. Taylor 1998. Generation of Icelandic rhyolites: silicic lavas from the Torfajökull central volcano. *Journal of Volcanology and Geothermal Research* 83: 1–45.

Hekla Volcanic System

T. *Einarsson* 1950. Chemical analysis and differentiation of Hekla's magmas. In: *The Hekla Eruption 1947–1948 IV. Vísindafélag Íslendinga (Societas Scientarium Islandica)*. Reykjavík.

K. *Grönvold*, G. *Larsen*, P. *Einarsson*, S. *Þórarinsson* og K. *Sæmundsson* 1983. The Hekla eruption 1980–1981. *Bulletin of Volcanology* 46: 349 –363.

Á. *Guðmundsson* et al 1992. The 1991 eruption of Hekla. Iceland. *Bulletin of Volcanology* 54: 238–246.

E. *Kjartansson* and K. *Grönvold* 1983. Location of a magma reservoir beneath Hekla volcano, Iceland. *Nature* 301: 139–141.

G. *Larsen* and S. *Þórarinsson* 1977. H4 and other acid Hekla tephra layers. *Jökull* 27: 28–46.

O. *Sigmarsson*, M. *Condomines* and S. *Fourcade* 1992. A detailed Th, Sr and O isotope study of Hekla. Differentiation processes in an Icelandic volcano. *Contributions to Mineralogy and Petrology* 112: 20–34.

S. *Þórarinsson* 1967. Eruptions of Hekla in Historical times. In: *The Hekla Eruption 1947– 1948 I. Vísindafélag Íslendinga (Societas Scientarium Islandica)*. Reykjavík

S. *Þórarinsson* and G. E. *Sigvaldason* 1971. The Hekla eruption of 1970. *Bulletin of Volcanology* 36: 1–20.

Tindfjallajökull Volcanic System

K. A. *Jörgensen* 1980. The Þórsmörk ignimbrite: an unusual comenditic pyroclastic flow in Southern Iceland. *Journal of Volcanology and Geothermal Research* 8: 7–27.

Öræfajökull

H. J. *Guðmundsson* 2001. The relationship between volcanic eruptions, crustal movements and the pattern of glacial fluctuations – an example from the Öræfi district, Iceland. Personal communication and manuscript.

H. J. *Guðmundsson* 2001. Holocene tephrochronology of the Öræfi district, Iceland. Personal communication and manuscript.

J. *Helgason* and R.A. *Duncan* 2001. Glacial-interglacial history of the Skaftafell region, southeast Iceland, 0–5 Ma. *Geology* 29, no.2: 179–182.

T. *Prestvik* 1982. Petrography, chemical characteristics and nomenclature of Öræfajökull rocks. *Jökull* 32.

T. *Prestvik*, S. *Goldberg*, H. *Karlsson* and K. *Grönvold*. 2001. Anomalous strontium and lead isotope signatures in the off-rift Öræfajökull central volcano in south-east Iceland. Evidence for enriched endmember(s) of the Iceland mantle plume? *Earth and Planetary Science Letters* 190: 211–220.

S. *Þórarinsson* 1958. The Öræfajökull eruption of 1362. *Acta Naturalia Islandica* Vol. 2. Reykjavík.

Katla Volcanic System

H. *Björnsson*, F. *Pálsson* and M. T. *Guðmundsson* 2000. Surface and bedrock topography of Mýrdalsjökull, Iceland: The Katla caldera, recent eruption sites and routes of jökulhlaups. *Jökull* 49.

E. H. *Einarsson*, G. *Larsen* and S. *Þórarinsson* 1980. The Sólheimar tephra layer and the Katla eruption of 1357. *Acta Naturalia Islandica* 28. Reykjavík.

K. *Grönvold*, N. *Óskarsson*, S. J. *Johnsen*, H. B. *Clausen*, C. U. *Hammer*, G. *Bond* and E. Bard 1995. Ash layers from Iceland in the Greenland GRIP ice core, correlated with oceanic and land sediments. *Earth and Planet. Science Letters* 135: 149–155.

Ó. *Guðmundsson*, B. *Brandsdóttir*, W. *Mencke* and G. E. *Sigvaldason* 1994. The crustal magma chamber of the Katla Volcano, South Iceland, revealed by 2-D seismic undershooting. *Geophysical Journal Int.* 199: 277–296.

G. *Jónsson* and L. *Kristjánsson* 2000. Aeromagnetic measurements over Mýrdalsjökull and vicinity. *Jökull* 49.

G. *Larsen* 2000. Holocene eruptions within the Katla volcanic system, South Iceland: Characteristics and environmental impact. *Jökull* 49.

J. *Miller* 1989. The 10th century eruption of Eldgjá, South Iceland. *Nordic Volcanological Institute report 8903.* Reykjavík.

E. *Sturkell*, F. *Sigmundsson*, P. *Einarsson*, S. *Hreinsdóttir* and M. B. *Stinesen* 2003. Recent unrest and magma movements at Katla and Eyjafjallajökull volcanoes, Iceland. Simultaneous activity of coupled volcanic systems. Abstract. *Journal of Geophysical Research,* 108 (B8): 2369.

Th. *Thordarson*, J. *Miller*, G. *Larsen*, S. *Self* and H. *Sigurdsson* 2001. New estimates of sulfur degassing and atmospheric mass-loading by the AD934 Eldgjá eruption, Iceland. *Journal of Volcanology and Geothermal Research* 108 (1–4):33.

Vestmannaeyjar Volcanic System

Þ. *Einarsson* 1973. *The eruption of Heimaey.* Mál og menning. Reykjavík.

S.P. *Jakobsson* 1968. The geology and petrology of the Vestmann Islands. A preliminary report. *Surtsey Research Progress Report* 4: 113–129.

S. P. *Jakobsson* 1978. Environmental factors controlling the palagonitization of the tephra of the Surtsey volcanic island, Iceland. *Bulletin of the Geological Society of Denmark* 27 (Special issue).

H. *Mattsson*, H. and Á. *Höskuldsson*, 2003. Geology of the Heimaey volcanic centre, south Iceland: early evolution of a central volcano in a propagating rift? *Journal of Volcanology and Geothermal Research* 127:55–71.

O. *Sigmarsson* 1996. Short magma chamber residence time at an Icelandic volcano inferred from U-series disequilibria. *Nature* 382: 440–442.

S. *Þórarinsson* 1969. *Surtsey; the new island in the North Atlantic.* Cassell. London.

S. *Þórarinsson*, S. *Steinþórsson*, Þ. *Einarsson*. H. *Kristmannsdóttir* and N. *Óskarsson* 1973. The eruption of Heimaey, Iceland. *Nature* 241: 372–375.

Reykjanes Peninsula, SW-Iceland

A. E. *Clifton* et al 2002. Surface effects of faulting and deformation, resulting from magma accumulation at the Hengill triple junction, SW Iceland, 1994–1998. *Journal of Volcanology and Geothermal Research* 115: 233–255.

Á. *Guðmundsson* 1986. Mechanical aspects of postglacial volcanism and tectonics of the Reykjanes Peninsula, Southwest Iceland. *Journal of Geophysical Research* 91, no. B12: 12,711–12,721.

S. P. *Jakobsson*, J. *Jónsson* and F. *Shido* 1978. Petrology of the Western Reykjanes Peninsula, Iceland. *Journal of Petrology* 19: 669–705.

M.J. *Rossi* 1996. Morphology and mechanism of eruption of postglacial shield volcanoes in Iceland. *Bulletin of Volcanology* 57:530–540.

K. *Sæmundsson* 1967. Vulkanismus und Tektonik des Hengill-Gebietes in Südwest-Island. *Acta Naturalia Islandica* Vol.II – No. 7.Reykjavík.

K. *Sæmundsson* 1992. Geology of the Thingvallavatn area. *OIKOS* 64: 40–68. Copenhagen.

Grímsnes Volcanic System

S. P. *Jakobsson* 1966. The Grímsnes lavas, SW-Iceland. *Acta Naturalia Islandica*, vol. II. Reykjavík.

Hofsjökull and vicinity

H. *Björnson* 1990. Hofsjökull: landslag, ísforði og vatnasvæði. (Hofsjökull: landscape, ice mass and watersheds – in Icelandic with English abstract) *Náttúrufræðingurinn* 60, 3. volume.

Snæfellsnes

B. S. *Harðarson* and J.G. *Fitton* 1991. Increased mantle melting beneath Snæfellsjökull Volcano during Pleistocene deglaciation. *Nature* 353: 62–64.

T. S. *Johansen* 2000. Petrogenesis of the alkaline off-rift basalts at Snæfellsnes, Iceland. *Eos, Transactions, American Geophysical Union* 81: 48.

H. *Jóhannesson*, R.M. *Flores* and J. *Jónsson* 1981. A short account of the Holocene tephrochronology of the Snæfellsjökull central volcano, W-Iceland 1981. *Jökull* 31.

H. *Sigurðsson* 1966. Geology of the Setberg area, Snæfellsnes, Western Iceland. *Vísindafélag Íslendinga Greinar IV. 2. (Societas Scientiarum Islandica).* Reykjavík.

On volcanism in general in Iceland

R. M. *Allen*, G. *Nolet*, W.J. *Morgan*, K. *Vogfjörð* and B. H. *Bergsson* et al 1999. The thin hot plume beneath Iceland. *International Geophysical Journal* 137: 51–63.

R. M. *Allen* 2001. The mantle plume beneath Iceland and its interaction with the North-Atlantic Ridge: a seismological investigation. *Princeton University.*

K. *Beddam* 2002. Primitive melt from the Iceland mantle plume. *Journal of Petrology* 43: 345–373.

I. Þ. *Bjarnason*, W. H. *Menke*, Ó. *Flóvenz* and D. *Caress* 1993. Tomographic image of the Mid-Atlantic plate boundary in Southwestern Iceland, *Journal of Geophysical Research* 98: 6,607–6,622.

A. *Björnsson*, K. *Sæmundsson*, P. *Einarsson*, E. *Tryggvason* and K. *Grönvold* 1977. Current rifting episode in North Iceland. *Nature* 266: 318–323.

H. *Björnsson* 1992. Jökulhlaups in Iceland: Prediction, characteristics and simulation, *Annals of Glaciology* 16: 95–106.

S. *Björnsson* 1983. Crust and upper mantle beneath Iceland. In: *Structure and development of the Greenland-Scotland Ridge.* Eds: Bott et al. p.31–61. Plenum Press, New York.

K. *Breddam* 2002. Primitive melt from the Icelandic mantle plume, *Journal of Petrology* 43: 345–373.

Ó. G. *Flóvenz* and K. *Gunnarsson* 1991. Seismic crustal structure in Iceland and surrounding area. *Tectonophysics* 189: 1–17.

Ó. G. *Flóvenz* and K. *Sæmundsson* 1993. Heat flow and geothermal processes in Iceland. *Tectonophysics* 225: 123–138.

P. *Frogner*, S. R. *Gíslason* and N. *Óskarsson* 2001. Fertilizing potential of volcanic ash in ocean surface water. *Geology* 29: 487–490.

G. R. *Foulger* 2003: On apparent eastern migration of the spreading ridge in Iceland. The Hot Spot Handbook, proceedings of the Penrose Conference Plume IV: Beyond Plume Hypothesis. Hveragerði, Iceland.

G.R. *Foulger*, Z. *Du* and B.R. *Julian* 2003: Icelandic-type crust. *Geophysical Journal Int.* 155: 567–590.

Á. *Guðmundsson* 1995. Ocean-ridge discontinuities in Iceland. *Journal of the Geological Society* 152: 1,011–1,015.

Á. *Guðmundsson* 1995. Infrastructure and mechanics of volcanic systems in Iceland. *Journal of Volcanology and Geothermal Research* 64: 1–22.

Á. *Guðmundsson* 2000. Dynamics of Volcanic Systems in Iceland: Example of Tectonism and Volcanism in Juxtaposed Hot Spot and Mid-ocean Ridge Systems. *Annual Review of the Earth and Planetary Sciences* 28: 107–140.

A.T. *Gudmundsson* 1996: *Volcanoes in Iceland*. Vaka-Helgafell. Reykjavík.

A. T. *Guðmundsson* 2001. *Íslenskar eldstöðvar* (in Icelandic, *Icelandic volcanoes*). Vaka-Helgafell. Reykjavík.

H. *Hansen* and K. *Grönvold* 2000. Plagioclase, ultraphyric basalts in Iceland: the mush of the rift. *Journal of Volcanology and Geothermal Research* 98: 1–32.

S.P. *Jakobsson* 1979. Outline of the petrology of Iceland. *Jökull* 29: 57–73.

S. P. *Jakobsson* 1979. Petrology of Recent basalts of the Eastern Volcanic Zone, Iceland. *Acta Naturalia Islandica* 26. Reykjavík.

J.G. *Jones* 1969. Intraglacial volcanoes of the Laugarvatn region, Southwest Iceland, 1. *Geological Society of London. Quarterly Journal* 124: 197–211.

J.G. *Jones* 1970. Intraglacial volcanoes of the Laugarvatn region, Southwest Iceland, 2. *Journal of Geology* 78(2): 127–140.

G. *Larsen*, M. T. *Guðmundsson* and H. *Björnsson* 1996. Tephrastratigraphy of ablation areas of Vatnajökull Ice Cap. In: S.C. Colbeck (ed.): Glaciers, ice sheets and volcanoes. *CRREL Special Report* 96: 75–80.

G. *Larsen* and Á. *Guðmundsson* 1998. Geometry, morphology and formation of crater rows in Iceland. *Annals of Geophysics* 16: C189 (abstract).

S. *Larsen*, A. *Dugmore* and A. *Newton* 1999. Geochemistry of historical-age silicic tephras in Iceland. *Holocene* 9: 463–471.

A.L. *Lawver* and R.D. *Müller* 1994. Iceland hotspot track. *Geology* 22: 311–314.

J. C. *MacLennan* 2000. Melt generation and movement under N-Iceland. *University of Cambridge.*

D. *Massonet* and F. *Sigmundsson* 2000. Remote sensing of volcano deformation by radar interferometry from various satellites. In: Remote sensing of volcanoes. *American Geophysical Union Monograph*, vol. 116: 207–221.

P. S. *Meyer* et al. 1985. Petrological and geochemical variations along Iceland's neovolcanic zones. *Journal of Geophysical Research* 90, no. B12: 10,043–10,072.

N. *Óskarsson*, S. *Steinþórsson* and G. E. *Sigvaldason* 1985. Iceland Geochemical Anomaly: Origin, volcanotectonics, chemical fractionation and isotope evolution of the crust. *Journal of Geophysical Research* 90: 10,011–10,025.

G. *Pálmason* and K. *Sæmundsson* 1974. Iceland in relation to the Mid-Atlantic Ridge. *Annual Review of the Earth and Plantetary Sciences* no. 2:25–50.

G. *Pálmason* 1986. Model of crustal formation in Iceland and application to submarine mid-ocean ridges. In (eds.): P.R. Vogt and B.E. Tucholke: The Geology of North America vol. M: the Western North-Atlantic Region. *Geological Society of America:* 87–97.

R. C. *Searle*, J.A. *Keaton* et al. 1998. The Reykjanes Ridge: structure and tectonics of a hot-spot-influenced, slow-spreading ridge, from multibeam bathymetry, gravity and magnetic investigations. *Earth and Planetary Science Letters* 160: 463–478.

F. *Sigmundsson* 1991. Postglacial rebound and asthenosphere viscosity in Iceland. *Geophysical Research Letters* 18: 1,131–1,134.

O. *Sigmarsson*, C. *Hermond*, M. *Condomines*, S, *Fourcade* and N. *Óskarsson* 1991. Origin of silicic magma in Iceland revealed by Th isotopes. *Geology* 19: 631–624.

O. *Sigmarsson*, M. *Condomines* and S. Fourcade 1992. Mantle and crustal contribution in the genesis of recent basalts from off-rift zones in Iceland, constraints from Th, Sr and O isotopes. *Earth and Planetary Science Letters* 110: 149–162.

H. *Sigurðsson* and R.S.J. *Sparks* 1978. Lateral magma flow within rifted Icelandic crust. *Nature* 274: 126–130.

R.K. *Staples*, R.S. *White*, B. *Brandsdóttir*, W. *Menke* et al. 1997. Faroe-Iceland Experiment 1. Crustal structure of northeastern Iceland. *Journal of Geophysical Research* 102: 7,849–7,866.

E. *Sturkell*, P. *Einarsson*, F. *Sigmundsson*, H. *Geirsson*, H. *Olafsson*, R. *Pedersen*, E. de *Zeeuw-van Dalfsen*, A. L. *Linde*, I. S. *Sacks*, and R. *Stefansson*, 2006. Volcano geodesy and magma dynamics in Iceland, *Journal of Volcanology and Geothermal Research*, 150: 14–34.

K. *Sæmundsson* 1979. Outline of the geology of Iceland. *Jökull* 29.

G. E. *Vink* 1984. A hotspot model for Iceland and the Vöring Plateau. *Journal of Geophysical Research* 89: 9,949–9,959.

P. R. *Vogt* 1983. The Iceland Mantle Plume: Status of the hypothesis after a decade of work. In: *Structure and development of the Greenland-Scotland Ridge.* Eds. Bott et al. Plenum Press. New York.

R. *Werner*, H.U. *Schminke* and G. *Sigvaldason* 1996. A new model for the evolution of table mountains: volcanological and petrological evidence from Herdubreid and Herdubreidartögl volcanoes (Iceland), *Geologische Rundschau* 85: 390–397.

R.S. *Williams*, S. *Þórarinsson* and E.C. *Morris* 1983. Geomorphological classification of Icelandic volcanoes. *Jökull* 33.

C. J. *Wolfe* et al. 1997. Seismic structure of the Iceland mantle plume. *Nature* 385: 245–247.

S. *Þórarinsson* 1981. The application of tephrochronology in Iceland. In: S. Self and R.S. Sparks (eds.): *Tephra studies.* D. Reidel Publ. Dordrecht: 109–134.

Steinsholtsjökull, northern Eyjafjallajökull.
(RTH)

6 The cold regime

Water is a remarkable substance. It is one of very few chemical compounds that change from a liquid to a solid or to vapour within the temperature range found in our daily environment. Ice mayform as fresh water or sea water freezes: ice can develop from snow due to overburden pressure and complex metamorphosis and ice is known to form when vapour condenses and immediately solidifies on a very cold surface. The ice that lends Iceland its name is formed by all these processes. In winter, common water ice is found on lakes or rivers and clogging the thousands of large or small waterfalls. The ice made from old snow forms numerous glaciers and ice caps. Hoar ice commonly forms in these high areas or on cold days in lowlands. Water in soil freezes, expands and gives rise to different periglacial phenomena. And, finally, the sea in the High Arctic may freeze over to form enormous fleets of ice floes, interspersed with glacial icebergs, sailing like a quiet unstoppable armada to the coastline of Iceland.

A chilly history

Snow transforms gradually into glacier ice in highlands that rise above a certain elevation, which is termed the glaciation limit or firn line. A common term is snowline. The glaciation limit in Iceland now varies from around 750 m above sea level in the northwest, to 1,100 m in the

---

Key words

Glacier ice • glaciation limit • Little Ice Age • glacial periods • interglacial periods • glacier • ice cap • Alpine glacier • outlet glacier • cirque glacier • piedmont glacier • surge • rock glacier • cirque and valley landscape • glacier budget • glacial history • subglacial volcanic eruption • meltwater flood/flooding/jökulhaup • sands/sandur • glacial sediment • nunatak • moraine • periglacial formations

southeast and 1,600 m in the northeast. The elevation varies according to the annual precipitation and summer/winter temperature. The limit was lower down during the "Little Ice Age" from 1400 to 1900 and it is rising at the present. In our time, therefore, about 11% of Iceland (approx. 11,000 km²) is sufficiently high to sustain glacier cover. Some 6,000–7,000 years ago, a warmer climate kept the glaciers very much smaller. Still further back in time lie peculiar climatic fluctuations, which are collectively termed the (Quaternary) Ice Age. The Ice Age comprised at least 20 cold glacial periods, interspersed by much warmer interglacial periods resembling our present climate. Large temperature oscillations were common during these different climatic periods.

During glacial periods, most of Iceland was covered by ice of varying volume and the snowline was mainly at very low altitude. The fjords, bays and coves of Iceland, as well as the valleys and many steep-sided mountains, were carved out of high lava plateaus by successive glaciers during the local "Icelandic" Ice Age which spanned just over 3 million years, each glacial period lasting about 100,000 years or even longer, while the interglacial periods lasted for about 10,000–20,000 years each. The last glacial period came to a very abrupt end about 9,700 years ago. The extensive ice cover almost vanished but attained its present size over the past 2,000–2,500 years.

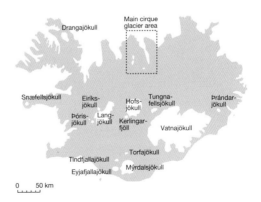

The ice caps and glaciers or glacier areas in Iceland. There is relatively easy access to most of them at least at the margins and in areas of glacier deposits. The most frequented study areas are along the main road on the south coast. The total glaciated area is 11,048 km² (2005) and the number of glaciers and ice caps is close to 270 (Annual report (2006) of the Nat. Energy Authority).

Steep glaciers (Goðalandsjöklar) flow into deep,
narrow flank valleys on the Mýrdalsjökull ice
cap, South Iceland. (RTH)

Not all alike

Glaciers may be classified according to their appearance, size and location. To most people glaciers mean steep Alpine ice curtains and
cracked ice streams that drape high mountains and crawl through
mountain valleys. Such glaciers or ice falls are also found in Iceland, for
example at Hrútfjallstindar and Þverártindsegg. A few high and quite
steep mountains are draped with thin ice aprons that cover the upper
sections, much like a parallel, interconnected row of Alpine glaciers.
These are volcanoes like Eyjafjallajökull and Snæfellsjökull. In a few
cases, like at Svínafellsjökull, steep (Alpine) glaciers from Hrútfjallstindar
and Öræfajökull merge and form one ice stream resembling a valley
glacier. Another morphological type of glacier is more common than
the Alpine. These are dome-shaped and cover varied landscape or even
vast highlands. These more or less circular ice-masses feed steep glaciers
(like ice falls) or gently sloping outlets and are termed ice caps. The
massive ice blanket in the larger ice caps measures up to 900 m thick.

Two rock glaciers. Hólabyrða, Hjaltadalur, North
Iceland. (OS)

In addition, much smaller and thinner ice caps occur on large, individual mountains like Eiríksjökull and Hrútfell. A different glacier type is found in the small cirque glaciers, located in deep glacially eroded bowls and hanging valleys. They are most numerous in the Tröllaskagi highlands between Eyjafjörður and Skagafjörður. Yet another group is found in rock glaciers in steep terrain: the piedmont glacier category can be said to have one representative, Breiðamerkurjökull (at Vatnajökull). As with many a classification of this kind, some glaciers are hard to put in a definitive category.

Icelandic glaciers are temperate, that is the ice temperature below 20–30 m remains at 0°C throughout the year. In most polar regions, glaciers are frozen to the bedrock. A few glaciers partly float on deep water, like the eastern section of Breiðamerkurjökull.

Another way of classifying glaciers is to look at their physical environment and behaviour. According to this, the Icelandic glaciers would classify as non-surging glaciers, surging glaciers (with periodic, very rapid advances), tidewater and floating glaciers, debris-covered glaciers, glaciers on top of volcanoes or volcanic vents, and finally glaciers that cover active geothermal fields. The last two categories are subjected, respectively, to fast and sudden or gradual but long-term melting in addition to the normal weather-induced melting processes.

The ice domes

There are five ice caps in Iceland, ranging in size from the 146 km^2 (Drangajökull) to the approximately 8,000 km^2 Vatnajökull. A large ice cap like Vatnajökull has over 20 outlet glaciers. The steep ones resemble Alpine ice falls or valley glaciers (like Morsárjökull, Skaftafellsjökull, Brókarjökull and Fláajökull) but the flat ones are broad, spoon-shaped lobes with a gentle surface angle (like Síðujökull or Brúarárjökull).

Ice caps have formed in areas of extensive highland where local glaciers have gradually coalesced, especially when the firn line falls to a lower level during long cold periods. The glacier covers the land surface under the ice for the greater part. Large, gently sloping glacial domes form over the highlands and shallow troughs where valleys occur. Only sharp, high peaks and the very highest mountain ranges protrude from the ice as nunataks. Ice flows slowly from the ice divide at the top of each ice cap, downwards and outwards towards the edges. In the largest Icelandic ice caps this can take 500–1,000 years.

Valleys under the ice or the broad slopes of the subglacial highlands channel the ice into glacier streams or glacier outlets. Here the main ablation/melting takes place below the so-called equilibrium line. Warm airstreams usually cause most melting in the mild island climate of Iceland and direct solar radiation is, on the whole, of less importance. Ice and snow melt result in a small amount of water vapour escaping into the atmosphere but most of the water is runoff from the glacier edge in the form of streams and rivers.

From half to two thirds of large ice caps can be above the glaciation limit, now that the climate has again become warmer after the main period of glacier formation. Much of the land underneath the glaciers does not reach the present day glaciation limit. Thus it can be said that in our time, large ice caps are self-sustaining and would not form in the highlands under present-day conditions. Nowadays, new glacier ice

The Hofsjökull ice cap covers 890 km² of land and contains about 220 km³ of ice. A large volcano with a deep caldera (left) lurks under the ice. (RTH and US Army aerial photo)

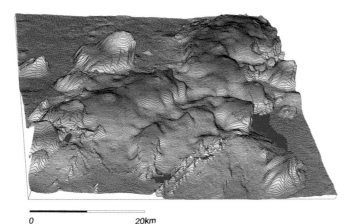

0   20km

The bedrock topography beneath the masses of the Langjökull ice cap, as revealed by radio echo soundings. The row of table mountains (subglacial volcanoes) and subaerial lava shields (ice-free conditions) is impressive, reaching from Þórisjökull in the southwest to the northeastern end of Langjökull. The chain of lower fells and hills in the southeast is also of volcanic origin. A caldera marks the location of a volcanic centre (upper right hand corner). Another volcanic centre occurs in the vicinity of Geitlandsjökull (lower corner, left). Presently, the ice is 700 m thick close by. (Institute of Earth Sciences of the University of Iceland/H. Björnson and Finnur Pálsson)

forms on the highest parts of the existing glaciers as global warming pushes the firn limit ever higher.

All the largest glaciers in Iceland are ice caps of the type mentioned above. They are in fact miniature versions of Ice Age glaciers or the present-day Greenland ice cap. Similar glaciers can be found, for example, on Spitzbergen (Svalbard) or Ellesmere Island, Canada in the northern hemisphere and in Patagonia and South Georgia in the southern hemisphere.

The smaller ice caps and glacier domes on large and high, individual mountains are probably up to 300 m thick. They shed ice, mainly through steep outlet glaciers or at more gentle sloping margins on the plateaus that form the mountaintops.

The present ice caps of Iceland probably attained their current extent in the early part of a Holocene cold period, which began around 500 BC. Before that there were glaciers of various sizes, small in the warm

Small ice caps crown individual flat-topped
mountains like Eiríksjökull in West Iceland.
(RTH)

periods of the Holocene, but much larger in the earliest cold spell,
around 9,700–9,800 years ago. Glacier ice formed before the settlement
of Iceland is probably all accounted for on the edges of the largest ice
caps and has thusflowed to sea as meltwater. The oldest ice in Vatnajökull is thought to be just over 1,000 years old and that on the edge of
Tungnaárjökull is 700–750 years old, based on the age of tephra layers
found there.

Large ice caps

Vatnajökull 8,ooo km²

Langjökull 920 km²

Hofsjökull 890 km²

Mýrdalsjökull 590 km²

Drangajökull 146 km²

Small ice caps

Tungnafellsjökull 48 km² (single mountain)

Þórisjökull 32 km² (single mountain)

Eiríksjökull 22 km² (single mountain)

Þrándarjökull 22 km² (highlands)

Torfajökull 15 km² (highlands)

Hrútfell 10 km² (single mountain)

The smaller ones

The shape of Icelandic glaciers is somewhat localised. Within and close to the active volcanic zones most of the mountains are recent volcanic formations. Many of them are little weathered and eroded compared to the older parts of the country. Their shape has been influenced more than anything else by the accumulation of the mountains in eruptions and by external factors. Some suppport glaciers. Outside the active zones, in western Iceland, the western fjords, the west of northern Iceland and in the eastern fjords the crust is very old by Icelandic standards. Widespread lava piles constitute a layered and eroded bedrock. The mountains are either flat on top with steep sides, i.e. the remains of an ancient plateau or peneplain, or they form sharp peaks which are also erosion features from repeated glaciations. Such mountains also contain glaciers

Ice-Age glaciers have covered the country many times during the past three million years. On each occasion they scoured and eroded the bedrock for at least 50,000–100,000 years. The ice cap was both large and thick during glacial periods and was especially thick along the central axis of the country but much thinner towards the coast, especially

223

Some high, steep mountains in Iceland are covered by a system of flank glaciers, forming a continuous, crevassed ice cover. Snæfellsjökull stratovolcano in West Iceland. (RTH)

where there was highland. There the mountains protruded from the ice and many peaks had small local cirque glaciers. Glaciers of this type were also common for a time during the few thousand years and centuries it took for the huge ice cap to retreat inland and finally disappear as each glacial period drew to a close. At the end of the glacial periods many small glaciers occupied cirques and depressions on the sides of the valleys and fjords. These are now ice-free or occupied by small glaciers, i.e. cirque glaciers. There are about 170 such glaciers in the highland area between Skagafjörður and Eyjafjörður (Tröllaskagi), plus in the area between Fnjóskadalur and Skjálfandi, while additional examples can be seen in the mountain ranges of the east and northwest. Cirque glaciers still exist in the Hornstrandur area and at the edges of the Gláma highlands, while small glaciers have existed on the northern slopes of the Skarðsheiði massif north of Reykjavík.

Glacial ice, more or less entirely covered by rock debris/moraine in the highland areas just mentioned, forms moving rock glaciers. These resemble large moraine piles but always with a definite creep form, such as curved waves or even glacier crevasses. The seat of the cirque glaciers is usually a bowl-like depression or valley bottom in the side of a mountain. The head of each cirque tends to be more or less vertical while the lateral slopes are steep and at the front there is commonly a threshold. The bottom may therefore be somewhat deeper than the threshold elevation. The ice in a cirque glacier moves downwards and forwards, eroding the cirque still deeper through time. Also, while glacial erosion is taking place, repeated freeze-thaw activity results in debris fall from the mountainsides directly onto the glacier or to produce scree, which may cause still further downward erosion. Debris can also be added to the ice during glacier flow. In many places rock glaciers are the remains of old cirque glaciers which have disappeared. Other active rock glaciers are in fact the lower part of active cirque or valley glaciers.

A typical steep flank glacier of Alpine character on the southern slopes of Hrútfjallstindar, northwest of Öræfajökull. (RTH)

Small bowl-shaped corrie or cirque glaciers dot a number of highland areas. Many classify partly as rock glaciers. About 160 cirque glaciers are found in the Tröllaskagi highlands between Eyjafjörður and Skagafjörður. The three glaciers shown here are Teigardalsjökull (left), Búrfellsjökull (surging) and Grýtujökull (right) in the Tröllaskagi highlands. (OS)

Moves and budgets

Glacier ice moves down and outwards from the high point of an ice field or dome. Many metres of winter snow, added onto the glacier above the equilibrium line, ensure that more ice forms, but below the line all the winter snow melts each summer. Even some of the older underlying firn and ice melts too, especially close to the glacier margin. At the same time, ice is constantly fed to the outlet glaciers and ice margins. The ice flow is a combined internal deformation of ice plus a slip-like movement of ice across the surface of the earth. A thin layer of water at the glacier base and water-saturated sediments facilitate the latter type of movement. The normal ice velocity in most Icelandic glaciers is probably between 10 cm and 1–2 m per day, equivalent to a few dozen or a few hundred metres per year (e.g. Breiðamerkurjökull about 400 m/yr). Higher velocities have been recorded. The steeper and thikker a glacier is, the faster it flows on land.

Öræfajökull, with the highest peak, Hvanna-
dalshnúkur (2,114 m), feeds a number of steep

glaciers, including Svínafellsjökull which
resembles an Alpine valley glacier. (RTH)

If, on the whole, more snow and ice melts than is compensated for by new ice formation and the ice flow, glaciers retreat and vice versa. Increased accumulation of snow and less extensive melting induce glaciers to advance. The glacier budget is said to be positive (negative in the former case). At present, Icelandic glaciers and ice caps are subjected to a negative annual balance. This is indicated by measurements of dozens of retreating outlet glaciers and annual thinning of the ice in all regions of the monitored glaciers or ice caps. Balance measurements are also made directly at the glacier surface. Model calculations show for example that the volume of an ice cap like Hofsjökull may diminish by half in a century.

New SAR-technology (time-lapse comparison of airborne radar images) enables scientists to map glacier elevations and ice margins with accuracy, as well as to assess volume changes and analyse morphological and subglacial features.

Winter accumulation is measured on the Vatnajökull ice cap. Ice cores are drilled in the snow and firn, down to the last autumn ice layer. The density of the snow is checked at varying intervals and the water equivalent calculated. The snow on the ice caps may range from 3–5 to 12–15 m in depth. A programme of drilling through the main ice caps is under way. Ice cores contain information on climate and volcanic activity for 500–1,000 years back in time. (RTH)

Shortly after the settlement of Iceland, the climate seems to have favoured retreating or stagnant glaciers. But in late medieval times the glaciers began to advance and did so for more than five centuries (during the "Little Ice Age"). Grazing areas and farmland were overrun by glaciers or buried in fluvial sediments. This continued until 1910–20. From then on, a very warm period (1920–69) resulted in a different scenario. Many kilometres of land were laid bare in front of almost every glacier snout in Iceland. The Breiðamerkurjökull tidewater glacier is almost at sea level in southeast Iceland. It overrode, for example, the Breiðamörk farm in the late 17th century but started to retreat in the early 20th century. It has retreated continuously, revealing a deep proglacial lake and a flat debris fan. From 1975 and into the early 1990s, however, many other glaciers showed signs of advance, had in other words positive budgets, especially narrow and steep outlets from ice

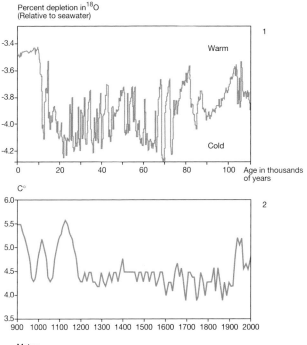

Percent depletion in ^{18}O
(Relative to seawater)

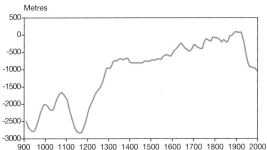

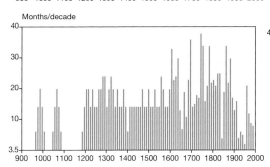

3 These graphs and diagrams indicate climate changes and their effects in Iceland and Greenland. The first graph shows indicates of air temperature obtained from the Summit Ice Core in Greenland (Stuvier and Grootes, 2000, see W.S. Broecker, Jökull 2005). The second graph depicts temperature (for decades in each century) in South Iceland, based on different sources. The third graph indicates the extent of five glaciers in the region and the fourth diagram shows the number of months with pack ice on the coast each decade (P. Bergþórsson, 2006).

The Jökulsárlón proglacial lake in the early 1980s (southern edge of the Vatnajökull ice cap). The glacier advanced to the south coast in around 1900 but has since retreated. The Breiðamerkurjökull glacier outlet has dug a 200 m deep trench that stretches some 20 km inland beneath the ice. Note the medial moraine extending from the Esjufjöll nunataks. (OS)

caps and steep glaciers on high mountains, while a few others were more or less in balance. This points towards a drop in the annual mean temperature, verified by meteorological data from this somewhat chilly period. However, for about the past two decades the trend has become reversed again, as already mentioned. Almost all the close to 50 position-monitored glaciers and glacier outlets show veritable signs of retreat or stagnation

A surging glacier from the air. A crevasse net
forms a labyrinth of séracs. (RTH)

Surging glaciers are a well-observed feature of Icelandic glaciers. Large, flat outlet glaciers from Vatnajökull surge at regular intervals, like Síðujökull in 1994 (margin and upper surface). Small cirque (corrie) glaciers are also known to behave in this way. (RTH)

Galloping/surging glaciers

Glacier ice is brittle in the uppermost 20–40 m slice of each ice cap or glacier. Here, the ugly crevasses appear. Deeper down, pressure (or weight) makes the "frozen water" more plastic and it behaves somewhat like ductile, half-molten metal. The normal flow velocity is barely noticeable unless observed for quite some time. This is the normal state of many Icelandic glaciers.

However, many individual outlet glaciers, especially those flat lobes radiating from the big ice caps, behave from time to time in a completely different manner. After years or decades of retreat by these "abnormal" glaciers, a bulge is observed, growing above or at the equilibrium line. For some reason the glacier is unable to transport ice fast enough to the snout. At a given time, the bulge cannot be held up or halted anymore and it moves down-glacier like a slow wave. The whole upper part of the glacier sinks in and the glacier multiplies its ice-flow velocity by many times. The snout surges forward, and broken-up domes, crevasses and ice towers appear suddenly all over the lower region of the glacier, instead of a fairly smooth surface. This phenomenon is termed glacier surge. The glacier belches brown water, indicating that the water channels in the ice may have been closed off and lots of water forced to flow under the ice, enabling the ice to slide faster. Whatever the exact mechanism, incredible ice-flow velocities have been observed. At 20–100 m per day, one can actually see and feel how giant ice masses move, groaning, squeaking and thundering from time to time. During the surge of the Síðujökull outlet glacier (Vatnajökull ice cap) in 1994, over 200 billion tonnes of ice surged forward. The glacier advanced 1–2 km and looked like a monstrous labyrinth. The same glacier surged in 1964 and 1934. The surface had become smooth again within a few years. The broad lobes of Vatnajökull are all surging glaciers but the steep ones are non-surging. Surging glaciers are known at the southern margins of Langjökull and Hofsjökull but there are probably not any glaciers of this kind at Mýrdalsjökull. Some of Drangajökull's outlet glaciers also surge. Most of the smaller glaciers and ice caps do not show this behaviour but a few small cirque glaciers on Tröllaskagi are known to surge. Surges are known at present in some glaciated areas of the world, for example in Alaska and Yukon, but surges do not occur in Scandinavia, New Zealand or in the European Alps.

Two photos showing a western outlier of
Vatnajökull (Tungnaárjökull) prior to and during
a surge. (OS)

The Kverkfjöll geothermal area and volcanic centre on the north side of the Vatnajökull ice cap. (RTH)

Fire and ice

In addition to the relatively rare surges that can be observed in Iceland, the quite uncommon coexistence of volcanoes and thick glaciers makes the Icelandic world of perennial ice rather special. Four large, high volcanic cones (stratovolcanoes) are active in Iceland: Hekla, Eyjafjallajökull, Snæfellsjökull and Öræfajökull, the latter being Iceland's largest single volcano. They are all capped by glaciers, like similar volcanoes in many parts of the world. The other central volcanoes in Iceland are mountain massifs set with calderas. Most of them are glaciated and the majority have calderas concealed under very thick blankets of ice. Mýrdalsjökull, Langjökull and Hofsjökull contain one caldera each but Vatnajökull has at least five. The Mýrdalsjökull ice cap conceals the very active Katla volcano. The huge volcanic centre (Ketill) beneath the ice of Hofsjökull was mapped in the 1980s. Among the volcanic centres that lurk under the cover of the Vatnajökull ice cap are Kverkfjöll,

Tephra layers in glacier ice can either be traced to known eruptions or else represent eruptions that have not been recorded with any certainty or are unknown (Mýrdalsjökull ice cap). (RTH)

Bárðarbunga and Iceland's most active central volcano, Grímsvötn, which erupts every 10 years on average.

As in 1996 (Gjálp, Vatnajökull), 1998 and 2004 (Grímsvötn), all eruptions that occur beneath ice produce unconsolidated eruptives (explosive tephra eruptions) and lead to sudden or prolonged floods (glacier bursts, jökulhlaups). The floods have created black deserts like Mýrdalssandur and Skeiðarársandur on the southern coast of Iceland. There are geothermal areas in the highlands rising from the ice fields or hidden beneath the ice, e.g. in Kverkfjöll, Lokahryggur and Grímsvötn, which affect the glaciers locally. If ice-free, they create stark contrasts such as boiling mud pots surrounded by snow or ice. If under the ice, they may facilitate ice flow through melting the glacier sole. They also make their presence known through fuming crevasses and steaming ice caves or circular ice cauldrons. Meltwater can be temporarily stored in

Geoscientists have made meticulous surveys of tephra layers in the Vatnajökull ice cap, revealing dozens of known and unknown eruptions that have occurred periodically over the past seven to eight centuries. (RTH)

ice cavities that appear at the glacier surface as cauldrons of this type. Periodic flooding is an evident result *(jökulhlaups)*.

Studies of volcanism in glaciated areas in Iceland may help us to understand more about volcanism during the Ice Age and volcanic activity on other planets such as the cold planet of Mars and still colder moons of Jupiter, Saturn, Uranus and Neptune.

Sources of water

Icelandic ice caps and glaciers store at least 3,700–3,800 km³ of ice. One cubic kilometre of ice weighs almost one billion tonnes (one thousand million) or 900 million tonnes, to be more specific. If all the glacier ice in Iceland were to melt, the island would be covered in 33–34 m of water.

The daily meltwater from Icelandic glaciers is still the main source of energy in the country. Hydropower is utilised to produce electricity.

Many glacial rivers discharge 50–700 tonnes per second in the spring and summer, and have been considered good power sources for middle-sized hydropower stations. Because of the low winter discharge, the power plants require dammed water reservoirs.

In some cases, melting is not governed by the weather. Sudden melting or the storing of water can induce sudden flood events. These glacier bursts or jökulhlaups may be confined to tunnels or they may disperse water over large areas beneath the ice (or do both) before they emerge at the glacier margin. Glacier thickness, the angle of the flow bed and the water temperature are among the general factors governing the course of events. In Iceland, the causes of jökulhlaups are more varied than in many other countries. Geothermal fields are concealed beneath glacier ice and subglacial volcanic eruptions produce vast volumes of meltwater. In other instances subglacial lakes or lakes at glacier margins manage to lift overlying ice and release water into otherwise manageable rivers which then overflow and may even threaten life or property. The floods from glacial lakes seldom discharge more than a few hundred or up to 2,000 m^3 per second. Floods caused by geothermal activity tend to be somewhat larger; around 600–5,000 m^3 per second. Such events have occurred for decades, for example in the Skaftá river on the western side of Vatnajökull every second year and in Skeiðará every fourth to fifth year due to flooding in the Grímsvötn volcano after intense melting by geothermal activity.

Volcanic eruptions produce the largest floods in which several cubic kilometres are discharged over one or two days. This means a discharge of 10,000–300,000 m^3 per second of turbulent water, heavily laden with sediments or fresh tephra. The discharge is governed by several factors. Very high discharge results from a high output of magma at the base of a thick glacier, where most of the magma is effectively fragmented (strong hydro-magmatic, phreatic activity). At Gjálp in Vatnajökull (1996) the initial ice-melting rate was probably about 5,000 m^3 per second. Recent studies of the course of events during the initial stage of the more powerful Katla eruption in 1918 indicate that higher magma output and more effective granulation of magma caused ice to melt about ten times more rapidly. This helps to explain why meltwater floods (jökulhlaups) from Katla occur a few hours after an eruption

An iceberg flushed onto the outwash plain of
Skeiðarársandur during a volcanic meltwater
flood *(jökulhlaup)* in 1996. (RTH)

starts and why the discharge is 5–10 times larger than most floods from
the Grímsvötn area in Vatnajökull.

On land, the sediments and glassy tephra from glacier bursts form
black deserts. In the ocean they add to other marine sediments on the
shelf around Iceland and to the chemical content of sea water. The suspended sediment load in glacial rivers is important when it comes to
fixing carbon dioxide in sea water.

In historical times, glacier bursts have often caused damage to fertile
land, to farms and rural areas as well as to modern constructions like
roads, bridges and power lines. Potential sources of large glacier bursts
are monitored.

Erosive features emerge from beneath a glacier: an erratic boulder, denuded whaleback cliff (roche moutonnée) and glacier grooves or "claw" marks (glacial striae or striations) on the bedrock. In front of Steinsholtsjökull. RTH)

Out of the icy womb

The bottom (or sole) of a glacier contains rock debris. The ice constantly plucks and grinds the bedrock, thereby not only creating landforms but also producing gigantic volumes of loose material; glacial sediment. This ranges from minute-particle clay and silt to gravel and heavy boulders. Most particles become somewhat rounded and scratched. Sediments of this type can be found in front of any active glacier. Some of the material commonly forms moraine ridges and hills. Another part is unveiled along the fringes of ice fields and glaciers, lying here and there on top of the ice. But much of the bottom sediment is revealed as the glaciers retreat. This was the case when the extensive cover during the last glacial period of the Quarternary Ice Age suddenly disappeared. It is still possible to study these glacial remains almost everywhere in Iceland. The loose material that covers much of the highlands is the product of Ice-Age glaciers.

The nunatak Pálsfjall in the Vatnajökull ice cap
is seen here during the surge of Tungnaárjökull
in 1995. (RTH)

The bedrock itself bears the claw-marks of the ice. Valleys, fjords, steep-sided mountains and whaleback forms occur in many parts of the country. The pressure at the bottom of a 500 m thick glacier is the equivalent of 45 kg on every square centimetre. Rock debris gets stuck to the bottom of the glacier as it creeps forward. The debris erodes the underlying surface at the same time as it breaks down itself. Thus glacial ice on the move is like a huge file which moulds the landscape through time.

Landscape sculpted by glaciers. Reykjafjörður
and Veiðileysufjörður, Strandir. (RTH)

Loose rubble and rock surfaces that have suffered the onslaught of
glaciers bear various signs when they are uncovered after glacier retreat.
Boulders and rock outcrops are covered in scratches or striations. On
solid outcrops the striations are parallel and, in addition to other environmental features, indicate the direction of the glacier flow. Large
boulders and rocks can leave even larger glacier grooves behind on outcrops. The rock outcrops generally resembe waves. The surface itself
and the upper parts of the cliffs are domed; smooth on the side facing
the direction of glacier flow, and steep and uneven on the down-flow
side. The term whaleback has been used to describe this landform.
Whaleback forms are often surrounded by moraine deposits, gravel
and rocks, while on top of them single rocks (erratics) sometimes
occur.

Ice caps which cover large land areas do not cover them completely
since the highest peaks protrude from the ice. Nunatak has become the
most favoured technical term for these "islands in the ice sheets". Features of this type vary in Iceland. Some are small peaks, 0.5–2 km in
diameter, rising 50–250 m above the ice. Examples are Eyjólfsfell in

southern Vatnajökull and Pálsfjall, southwest of Grímsvötn. The Há-steinar peaks in Hofsjökull are of the same type and also Þursaborg in Langjökull and Goðasteinn in Eyjafjallajökull. Other nunataks are much larger highland areas with a number of peaks such as Esjufjöll in Vatnajökull and the area including Fjallkirkja and Péturshorn in Lang-jökull.

During the Pleistocene glacial periods many peaks rose above the ice surface, in particular close to the high upland coasts. Ice movement sculpted the peaks into sharp serrated ridges and pointed horns and these are a common feature of the Icelandic landscape in the older regions.

If glacial sediment forms mounds or thick layers containing conside-rable amounts of coarse material it is known as moraine or glacial till. Such moraine deposits either occur as a rubble cover on flat or sloping land, or form high, steep linear features of various types. Moraine de-posits remain after the glaciers retreat as ground moraine. Moraine which is deposited at the margins of outlet glaciers, either from material which falls onto them or which remains after retreat, is called lateral, ridge-shaped moraine. Moraine can also be deposited at the end of active glaciers as material is transported there by glacier movement

End-moraines in front of the Múlajökull glacier outlet on the southern edge of the Hofsjökull ice cap. (RTH)

243

(terminal moraine). Long, narrow moraine tongues or stripes extend the length of outlet glaciers on the down-glacier side of nunataks where two glaciers combine to form medial moraines. Finally, moraine can be pushed up by a sudden surge of the glacier (push moraine). Rounded, moulded ridges oriented in the direction of glacier flow and alternating with ground moraine are known as drumlins, while eskers are meandering ridges that are chiefly made up of sediments from fluvial channels in glaciers. All these features occur widely in Iceland, especially along the margins of Vatnajökull.

Various periglacial phenomena

Cryoturbation features are prominent in polar areas. Where there is constant frost in the soil (permafrost areas), except in the top-layer in the sumer, frost activity forms the most typical features of the landscape. These are less conspicuous in marginal areas like Iceland, but are nevertheless quite widespread.

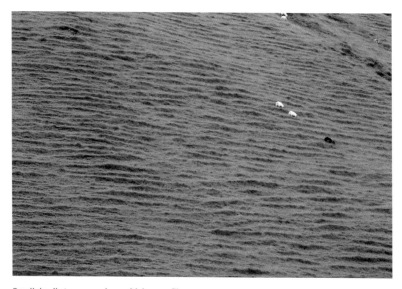

Parallel soil steps on a slope with low-profile vegetation, caused by slow creeping of the soil and frost lifting. (RTH)

Patterned, bare soils with stone polygons are
one of the widespread periglacial phenomena
found in Iceland. (SÞ)

Icelandic soil is an unusually active material. This is the result of considerable precipitation in the country, the high water content of the
soil, little cohesion and frequent frost activity. This involves freezing of
water in the soil and sediments with an associated volume increase.
The uppermost part of the soil or sediment swells. Sudden melting
results in movement within the unconsolidated material which subsides as the ice melts. Many features relating to such processes can be
seen in unvegetated or vegetated areas in Iceland, both on sloping and
level land.

Unconsolidated sediment on sloping land automatically moves
downhill. It makes no difference whether there is vegetation or not.
Nevertheless, vegetation succeeds to some extent in binding fragmental
sediment or soil on slopes. Mostly the movement is gradual, the vegetation moving slowly along with it. Sometimes another more rapid
kind of event occurs, mainly in sudden thaw, torrential rain or as a
result of repeated thaws between periods of frost, especially if only the

uppermost part of the soil melts on top of a frozen under layer. Rock- or mudslides (debris flows) can occur under all these conditions.

On vegetated grassy slopes long parallel steps or small terraces can be seen in many areas. They resemble folds when viewed from the side. These are solifluction terraces and are very widespread. They are formed by a combination of frost heaving and downhill movement of the soil. This solifluction is of the order of a few centimetres per year. On slopes with little or no vegetation, the movement is greater, ranging from several centimetres to tens of centimetres per year. On unvegetated and gently sloping gravel slopes, stripes are formed by solifluction in which lines of pebbles and finer-grained soil alternate.

In flat or gently sloping soil the soil grains, both coarse grained and fine, move due to continual frost and thaw. Frost activity results in patterned ground forming on the surface with varying height and characteristics. This occurs in both vegetated and unvegetated ground.

Unvegetated gravel originates mainly as ground moraine in which clay, gravel and boulders are mixed together. Repeated freeze-thaw cycles result in pores forming under the stones during frost. They are then filled by finer-grained material which sinks into them during thaw. Gradually the soil is lifted upwards from the surface. Thus the stony sediment is uppermost in most Icelandic gravel areas, with finer-grained material underneath. In addition, the uneven grain-size distribution means that the gravel is covered in small hummocks and hollows during frost. The volume increase of water forces the soil grains laterally and vertically by different amounts. Pebbles are pushed to the side and also sink downhill into the hollows during thaw. Over a long period of time a polygon pattern develops and the finer-grained materials remain in the polygons. This is one phenomenon of patterned ground.

On vegetated, fairly flat land a similar process leads to small hummocks or earth mounds alternating with elongated depressions. When the temperature falls below freezing point the soil and vegetation are pushed up, higher in some places than in others. In thaws between frost periods the soil sinks and the grains become displaced to new positions. Vegetated hummocks formed in this manner become more pronounced with time and the intervening depressions deepen. Sometimes

Earth mounds or hummocks (þúfur) of different types exist in Iceland due to repeated freezing and thawing. Large mounds (with an ice core) and small ponds characterise the local tundra terrain found in some highland areas (Möðrudalsöræfi). (RTH)

the tops of the hummocks are breached and they become eroded. Hummocks are common in all peaty areas and bogs as well as in drier pastures. In tundra areas the hummocks contain an ice core all year round and can become larger than usual (e.g. Þjórsárver). The formation of such hummocks follows a well-defined evolutionary path in which small tarns or pools which form over time in the permafrost bogs play a part.

The hummocky soil in Iceland has often evoked questions among people unfamiliar to such phenomena. A common humorous answer is that the hummocks in fact are man-made; i.e. made by farmers in order to enlarge fields or grazing areas. In reality, levelling hummocks with machinery was one of the first taske in modern agriculture.

Large rock and debris slides frequently occurred towards the end of the last glacial period and early in the Holocene. Drápuhlíðarfjall, Snæfellsnes. (RTH)

Scree slopes (talus) occur on the slopes of most Icelandic mountains. Repeated frost weathering supplies most of the broken rock. Debris-flows may deposit diamictites. Slumping of large flank areas or rockslides produce an appearance similar to this mountainside close to Álfta-fjörður. (RTH)

Selected bibliography

Surnames are written in italics. The Icelandic letters é, ó, á, ú, í and ý should be written as e, o, a, u, i and y, ö as ö, oe or simply o, æ as æ or ae, ð as d and þ as th when searching for references and papers in most databases.

H. *Björnsson* 1979. Glaciers in Iceland. Jökull 29, p. 74–80.

H. *Björnsson* 1988. Hydrology of ice caps in volcanic regions. Societas Scientiarum. *Islandica* 45. Reykjavík.

H. *Björnsson* H. and P. *Einarsson* 1990. Volcanoes beneath Vatnajökull, Iceland: Evidence from radio echo sounding, earthquakes and jökulhlaups. *Jökull* 40, p. 147–169.

Frost weathering. Even the largest boulders may
split and here movements of the soil have
widened the crack. (RTH)

H. *Björnsson* H. 1990. Hofsjökull; landslag, ísforði og vatnasvæði. *Náttúrufræðingurinn* 60. 3. hefti (vol. 3).

H. *Björnsson,* F. *Pálsson,* M.T. *Guðmundsson* and H. *Haraldsson* 1998. Mass balance of western and northern Vatnajökull, Iceland 1991–1995. *Jökull* 45, p. 35–38.

H. *Björnsson,* F. *Pálsson* and M.T. *Guðmundsson* 2000. Surface and bedrock topography of Mýrdalsjökull, Iceland: The Katla caldera, recent eruption sites and routes of jökulhlaups. *Jökull* 49.

Þ. *Einarsson* and K.J. *Albertsson* 1988. The glacial history of Iceland during the past three million years. Philosophical Transactions of the Royal Society of London 318, p. 673–644.

Þ. *Einarsson* 1994. *Geology of Iceland – rocks and landscape.* Mál og menning, Reykjavík.

M.T. *Guðmundsson,* F. *Sigmundsson,* H. *Björnsson* and Þ. *Högnadóttir* 2004. The 1996 eruption at Gjálp, Vatnajökull ice cap, Iceland: efficiency of heat transfer, ice deformation and subglacial water pressure. *Bulletin Vocanol.* 66, p. 46-65.

G. *Larsen,* M.T. *Guðmundsson* and H. *Björnsson* 1998. Eight centuries of periodic volcanism at the center of the Iceland hotspot revealed by glacier tephrastratigraphy. *Geology,* vol. 26, no. 10, p. 943–946.

H. *Norðdahl* and H.G. *Pétursson* 2005. Relative sea-level changes in Iceland: new aspects of the Weichselian deglaciation of Iceland. In (eds): Caseldine C., Russell, A., Hardardottir, J. and Knudsen O., *Iceland-Modern processes and past environment,* p. 25–78. Elsevier, Amsterdam.

F. *Sigmundsson* 1991. Postglacial rebound and asthenosphere viscosity in Iceland. *Geophysical Research Letters* 18, p. 1,131–1,134.

O. *Sigurðsson* 1998. Glacier variations in Iceland 1930–1995. *Jökull* 45., p.3–27.

O. *Sigurðsson* 2005. *Íslenskur atlas:* Gerðir jökla á Íslandi og saga jöklabreytinga. Mál og menning. Reykjavík. p. 14–17.

T.E. *Thorhallsdottir* 1996. Seasonal and annual dynamics of frozen ground in the central highland of Iceland. *Arctic and Alpine Research* 28(2), p. 237–243.

Marine erosion in a high profile coastal
landscape. (RTH)

7 The changing coastline

The coastline of Iceland is close to 6,000 km long. It features varied landforms, ranging from steep cliffs alive with birds in the spring and summer, to flat, black, desert-like sands with dunes. The steeper coasts characterise the northwestern, northern and eastern parts of Iceland while the typical landforms of the southern coastline are flat beaches and estuaries. The North-Atlantic Ocean batters the edges of Iceland with a heavy hand, while the changing sea level during the past 10,000 years has played a significant role in forming the landforms in coastal as well as adjacent areas.

Varied submarine landscape

Contrary to popular belief, Iceland does not rise steeply from the surrounding sea floor. The island sits on a platform, made of the same basaltic magma as the island proper. This platform or island shelf extends some 90 km on average out from the coastline and has an area of over 100,000 km². The ocean depth is 300–400 m at its edge. A generally gentle slope leads down into the 2,000–3,000 m deep basins of the North-Atlantic Ocean. The shelf is cut by deep canyons that are extensions of the fjords, carved by Ice-Age glaciers, and some steeper slope angles are found there.

Key words

Ocean conditions • fjords • wave-cut cliff • raised beaches • berm • spits • river banks • isostasy • delta • sandur • outwash plain • shoreface terrace • tombolo • connecting bar • semi-saline lagoons

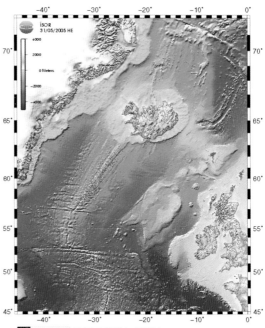

Sea-floor topography of the North Atlantic Ocean. The Mid-Atlantic Ridge (MAR) with fracture zones turns into the Reykjanes Ridge southwest of Iceland and continues as the Kolbeinsey Ridge in the north. The relief shows the Iceland hot-spot swell, the trace of the hot spot as the Greenland-Scotland Ridge and detectable V-shaped ridges pointing northward at the MAR, southwest of Iceland. (Source: H. Eysteinsson and K. Gunnarsson 1995)

Four ridges radiate from Iceland. The inactive Greenland/Scotland Ridge connects Iceland to Greenland in the northwest and to the Faroe Islands in the southeast. It is thought to be a fossil trace of the active hot spot. On the sea floor to the southwest of Iceland lies the active part of the Mid-Atlantic Rifting Ridge that cuts across Iceland. This is the Reykjanes Ridge. It connects to the active rift zone on land and the submarine continuation can then be traced north of Iceland far into the cold Iceland Sea (the Kolbeinsey Ridge). Submarine eruptions and earthquakes occur on these two rift segments. The sea is roughly 300–600 m deep above the ridges. A submarine transverse fault and fracture zone (the Tjörnes Fracture Zone, TFZ) connects the Northeast Iceland Rift Zone and the Kolbeinsey Ridge (a submarine rift zone). The TFZ is a location of frequent earthquakes and less frequent volcanic eruptions.

The seabed off the active ridges is characterised by a relatively flat landscape. It has been covered to a large extent by soft sediments from

While the late glacial (interstadial and preboreal) sea level rose 40–130 m higher than today, cliffs like the majestic Lóma-gnúpur (600 m) were authentic sea cliffs, pounded by the North Atlantic Ocean. (RTH)

rivers and glaciers, such as coarse moraine material, sand, silt and clay. There are also deposits from tephra-producing eruptions on land as well as wind-blown soils. The sediments are mixed with sediments of organic origin such as molluscs and remains of silica- or calcium algae (foraminiferous ooze). On the active ridges, however, the landscape is more rugged. Pillow lava and breccia ridges, open faults and fissures, tephra banks and submarine volcanic structures line the sea floor. Boiling or hot geothermal fields are known to exist at numerous locations (off Reykjanes, in Eyjafjörður and around the island of Kolbeinsey), some with strange-looking chimneys and mineral deposits. Corals thrive in some of the warmer and more secluded locations.

Surprisingly warm

Ice-cold polar sea water flows south between Greenland and Spitzbergen (Svalbard). It meets warm currents from southerly latitudes. Iceland lies on the battlefront between these very different water masses. The warm sea water is salty, as opposed to the less saline polar sea water which, however, is richer in oxygen than its sun-warmed counterpart. The crux of the encounter is that a branch of the warm Gulf Stream almost surrounds Iceland (the Irminger Current). It prevents the polar water from approaching the coast and results in the coastal waters' having a higher temperature than might be expected at these latitudes.

Off the eastern coast the warm sea water has cooled and mixed with the cold currents, so there one finds the coldest coastal waters, as can be seen from the mean annual sea temperature. Off the west and south coasts, the surface temperature varies from 3–7°C in March to 10–12°C in July/August. In the north the variation is from 1–2°C to 6–8°C, while off East Iceland measurements range from 1–7°C according to season. These figures have been rising in recent years.

Sub-zero sea temperatures are rare, except in calm inland coves or fjords, but 30–100 nautical miles off the coast the sub-zero Arctic waters are a chilling winter reminder of how conditions could well be if the Gulf Stream flowed along a different path. Then, the average winter sea temperature would be approx. -1 to -2°C.

All these figures are valid for the topmost 20–40 m. The seasonal temperature range becomes smaller with increasing depth. There is a deep-seated and very important flow of cold sea water from the Arctic region to the south. As saline sea water cools in the polar ocean, it sinks and then travels south at very deep levels, partly maintaining the surface ocean currents in the North-Atlantic Ocean, including the important Gulf Stream that reaches to high northerly latitudes.

The only place where warm sea water can be expected around Iceland is immediately above geothermal vents on the sea floor.

The common tidal current approaches Iceland from the southeast, before travelling clockwise around the island in a matter of 12 hours and 25 minutes. High water varies between 1.5 and 4 m in the south and west, and 0.5 to 1.5 m in the north and east.

The Lóndrangar sea stacks are remains of a
volcanic formation. The Snæfellssjökull volcano
in the background. (RTH)

At least 30 significant islands line the coast, apart from the bays of
Faxaflói and Breiðafjörður where they number well over 1,000 if small
islets are included.

Creeping peril from the North

Although salt lowers the freezing point of water, sea water does freeze
over, given enough time and enough frost. Such conditions are very
rare in Iceland but common along the East-Greenland coast and in the

Pack ice drifts from time to time onto the coast
of Iceland along with glacial icebergs from
Greenland. (RTH)

Arctic waters. There, a thin top layer of sea water mixed with fresh water floats on heavier, salty sea water. In winter, enormous areas of sea freeze over. The ice grows at least 2–3 m thick and in most years, the edge of the pack ice stretches from the Greenland coast, west of Iceland, along a line about half the distance between Iceland and Greenland, turning eastward to an area north of Jan Mayen. Normally, the pack ice should lie at a distance of 80–200 nautical miles off the north coast of Iceland, the shortest distance being in the northwest.

The pack ice is interspersed with gleaming icebergs; chunks broken off the numerous glaciers that calve into the East Greenland fjords. Some icebergs are 50–100 m high and they may reach hundreds of metres into the abyss of the sea.

Long-term northerlies and westerlies can push the pack ice to Iceland. If ice enters the ocean currents which encircle Iceland, it is transported along the northern coastline, perhaps aided by the prevailing winds. There, the ice may close off all shipping and then move into the eastern fjords and even further westward along the coast of South Iceland. Existing records show that on a few occasions each century, the sea ice has actually reached eastern or southern Iceland and on rare occasions even into the bay of Faxaflói where Reykjavík is located. Icelanders speak of "ice years" with awe. Bad ice years, sometimes several in a row, are recorded from the 17th and 18th centuries and more recently, in 1965–1971, the pack ice seriously affected transport and farming as well as the fisheries sector. One reason for this was the cold weather caused by the ice. Another reason was that all the harbours were closed off and neither cargo ships nor fishing vessels were able to navigate through the ice. The presence of ice for a prolonged period also affects the distribution of fish stocks and the marine coastal environment in general. It may take the ice many months to melt. Furthermore, the ice affects marine erosion, reducing much of the wave action and icebergs may bring in sediments of another composition than that found in the Icelandic bedrock, like pink-granite boulders or dark pieces of gneiss.

The appearance of most of the islands in the bay of Breiðafjörður suggests that they are glacially eroded, low ridges. (RTH)

The land of fjords

The Icelandic coast was probably less dissected by inlets before the start of the Quaternary Ice Age (i.e. the late Tertiary) than it is now. Bays and inlets were most common but small fjords probably also existed, formed by fluvial erosion, marine erosion and rifting with associated subsidence. Lava cliffs and wave-cut cliffs were more widespread than sandy beaches. It is difficult to envisage large deep fjords such as cut the coast today. Modern Icelandic fjords are mostly 5–50 km in length (Eyjafjörður is one of the longest at 70 km) and, at an estimate, 2–20 km wide. Very broad fjords with a curved bottom profile, equal in length and breadth, are usually called bays (*flóar* in Icelandic), such as for example Faxaflói where Reykjavík is situated.

Icelandic fjords, in their present form, have been formed by outlet glaciers from the Ice-Age glacier domes during at least 20 glaciations.

The shapes of mountain and hills in the Tertiary regions are dictated by Ice-Age glacial erosion, isostatic uplift and the release of strain within the rock by movement on old tectonic lineations and frost weathering. From Northwest Iceland. (RTH)

The glaciers must have exploited trenches, valleys and inlets or the small Tertiary fjords, eroding the bedrock. They have deepened these features and through time have eaten deep into the old lava pile, especially in the east, west and north. It can be assumed that many glaciers of different ages have eroded a particular fjord because it is likely that each new glacial period has spawned a new glacial tongue or tongues which chose the same channels as their forerunners. During glacial periods the environment resembled that of the central east coast of Greenland today. Bays are the final stage for large outlet glaciers that calved into the sea in their time. It is known that outlet glaciers from Vatnajökull have planed off up to several hundred metres of the crust over particular areas in a matter of a few centuries or one to two millennia.

The formation of each major fjord usually involved one main outlet glacier, which crept forward on the sea shelf. Smaller tributary glaciers joined it. Their tracks are represented by the innermost fjords or inlets, such as can be seen in, for instance, Ísafjarðardjúp, Arnarfjörður, Hvalfjörður and elsewhere, as well as hanging valleys. Glacial erosion also carved the sheer mountains of the highland promontories between fjords where small local glaciers were active. Above the fjords are valleys with typical U-shaped profiles, a shape similar to that seen on sea-floor maps of the fjords themselves and also the hanging valleys already

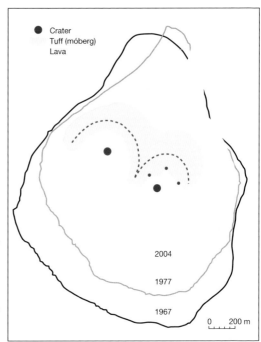

The coastline and shape of Surtsey have changed dramatically since its creation. The central part, set with the main craters, is made of palagonite tuff (compacted, altered tephra).

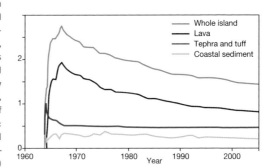

Marine erosion of Surtsey, formed in 1963–1967. The rate of erosion diminishes with time as the submarine island platform increases in size relative to the island itself and, mainly, as the tephra gets more and more compacted (palagonitization). Surtsey will remain as a high-rising, small island for thousands of years to come. (Modified from: S.P. Jakobsson and G. Guðmundsson, *Náttúrufræð-ingurinn* 71 (3–4. vol.) 2003)

mentioned. The position of the strandline in each instance therefore determines which part of the main outlet glacier is dry land (valley) and which is sea floor (fjord). Isostatic uplift, as a result both of decreasing glacial overburden and also of the amount of crust removed by erosion and weathering, maintains the majestic landscape. On the whole it has risen at least 1,000–2,000 metres in this manner.

When each glacial period was at its maximum the shoreline was up to 100–150 m lower than at present and the glaciers extended far beyond the present situation of the fjord mouths without floating. Bathometric maps of the shelf area clearly show indentations extending off most large fjords where the ice movement and debris has cut broad, deep channels at the maximum extent of the glaciers.

The main fjord areas are in the northwest of the country, in the central northern area and in along the central eastern coastline. In the former area, comprising Barðaströnd, Vestfirðir and Strandir, there are over 50 fjords, bays not included. Fjords are much rarer in the northern area but on the other hand some of them are broader and longer. In the east there are at least 20 fjords and bays between Vopnafjörður in the north and Lónsfjörður in the south.

The restless waves

The restless ocean is a powerful landscape sculptor. Pure sea water which crashes onto rocks has considerable erosive power. It forces its way into fractures and is sucked out again, breaking the rock down. Salt crystallises in fractures, exerting pressure on the walls. At intervals air pockets are trapped in the waves and explode, accompanied by great energy release, when the waves thunder onto the rocks. However, the erosive power of the waves is mainly due to the fact that they carry with them sand, gravel and boulders which hammer the rocks and churn together when the waves break on shore. The backwash from each wave also drags the debris along the bottom, so that the surf erodes it further, as well as the bedrock.

The rate of erosion can be clearly seen for example on Surtsey which has decreased in size by about half (from 3.0 to about 1.5 km²) in just

Sand or gravel beaches characterise some bays and coves as well as almost the entire south coast of Iceland. Dyrhólaey, an eroded volcanic structure, is seen in the background. (RTH)

A typical coarse-grained berm (behind the person) marks the high-level wave action on a flat sandy beach. (RTH)

under 40 years. When the question is raised as to whether the area of Iceland increases every century due to plate movement, volcanism and sediment from glacial rivers, the answer is probably that it only increases slightly, on the whole, because of vigorous coastal erosion which tends to balance it.

But the sea also transports large amounts of sediment from one place to another. The waves play a part in this because of the difference between the angle of attack and backwash, and so do the tidal currents. The sediment follows a zigzag path in either direction along the coast (as will be discussed later).

The flat beaches

Low-lying beaches are widespread in Iceland but mostly in the south. Such sedimentary beaches occur right along the southern coastline, at the bottom of fjords and bays (e.g. Húnaflói, Öxarfjörður and Héraðs-flói) and along the shores of lowland headlands in bays and fjords. Sedimentary shorelines are characterised by gently sloping beaches.

Marine erosion is greatest on exposed coasts and least at the heads of fjords and inlets. Wave erosion produces well-rounded debris and grain size decreases through time. Erosion is very rapid. Fine-grained material such as sand and clay is transported far from the coast by backwash and currents.

The bulk of the sediment on sedimentary coasts usually originates fairly locally, e.g. from nearby wave-eroded cliffs. Along the southeast coast and in the estuaries of large glacial rivers this does not apply. There, a large amount of sediment is transported by rivers to the sea (or by *jökulhlaup* floods). Most of the material is sand, silt and clay. It becomes mixed with marine-eroded sediment on beaches and in shallow waters.

In most places there is active transport of material along the coast. On sedimentary coasts the sediment is transported quite rapidly laterally due to obliquely approaching waves as a result of prevalent wind direction followed by backwash, which moves in the opposite direction outwards from the coast. Following waves carry the sediment still further laterally and then the backwash transports the material directly outwards again. This is known as longshore drift or shoreline transport of material. Foreign rocks found on the beaches have either been carried here by the sea ice from Greenland or originated as ballast in sailing ships in former times

The grain-size distribution on sedimentary coasts depends on the access of the sea to new material, as well as on wave action. A lack of new coarse-grained material means that large lowland wave-washed coasts are mainly composed of fine-grained sandy beaches. A similar situation is produced where a large amount of fine debris is transported but there is little wave action. Large amounts of coarse-grained material and frequent and heavy wave action result in boulder-strewn

Surtsey is developing a spit on the leeside while
the south side faces harsh wave-action. (RTH)

beaches, because all the finer-grained material is immediately washed
outwards and settles in shallow water.

Above the high-tide mark there is usually an even distribution of
quite coarse-grained material on sedimentary beaches (sand, gravel
and boulders) but still further up is a ridge of sediment which has been
built up during the greatest storms. It contains most of the coarsest
material. This is known as the storm berm. Just below the spring-tide
mark there is a broad terrace of sediment known as the shoreface terrace. Ancient storm berms and shoreface terraces which have formed at
formerly active beaches can be seen in many places in lowland Iceland.
These formations date from early in the Holocene or late Pleistocene
periods after the glaciers had rapidly melted and isostatic rebounce was
still not fully effective. As a result sea level quickly reached up to 50–
130 m higher than now but only for a while.

A spit in a fjord: Skutulseyri in the northwest, on
which stands the oldest part of the town of
Ísafjörður. (RTH)

Heaps of sediments

Marine sediment consists for the most part of stratified debris which is
carried to the sea by rivers or results from wave action breaking down
the land, but also contains marine fauna. Drilling and core sampling in
the sediment in different locations around the country provide new
information about the Ice Age and in particular about the last glacial
period (see for example IMAGES, http://images.pclab.ifg.uni-kiel.det/
start.html).

Along the coasts of many Icelandic fjords marine sediments display
numerous different formations. For example, in many places pointed
mounds of sediment have formed from marine-transported sediments,
i.e. spits. Most of the sediment is brought by wave action and currents
from nearby wave-eroded cliffs, such as those on headlands outermost
in the fjord. Some of the sediment can also originate locally as sediment
load from rivers. In some cases landslides carry sediment to the sea.

River deltas may form in fjords where there is
low-grade marine erosion. This one is in
Gilsfjörður, West Iceland. (HK)

The material in the sand spits is mainly sand, gravel and boulders. They can form as a result of obstructions, where currents meet, for example, and are sometimes extensive. Many settlements and farms are situated on such spit deposits, such as Flateyri, Ísafjarðarbær and to some extent Siglufjörður, good anchorage often being available in their shelter. The Icelandic terms are *eyri, oddi* and *tangi*, and these can be seen on maps combined with other place-name elements, e.g. Hjalteyri, Suðuroddi, Skildingatangi.

The sand spits foremost in estuaries or in the mouths of inlets, fjords and bays can reach such lengths that they almost completely close them off. The lagoons thus formed are semi-saline, and the surface run-off and tides pass by way of channels through the spit which separates them from the sea. Examples are Miklavatn, Lónsfjörður and, until recently, Tjörnin in Reykjavík.

Spits can also be formed in the shelter of islands that are being eroded by wave action. Spits or points on the northern shore of Surtsey have formed very rapidly in this way.

A tombolo (a sand and gravel bar, a spit)
connects a former island to the mainland.
Geldinganes in Reykjavík. (RTH)

The Icelandic term *eyri*, or more precisely *áreyri*, is also used for much
smaller sediment accumulations in rivers. These are lens-like in cross-
section, stratified and are formed from deposition of sediments from
running water. In glacial rivers and direct run-off rivers sand banks of
this type divide the river into many bifurcating channels. The channels
in glacial rivers shift to the left or right of the current direction when
the sand banks increase in size and new banks produce new channels.
A large part of the Icelandic outwash plains which have been deposited
in the broad channels of the main glacial rivers and jökulhlaup floods
(e.g. Skeiðarársandur and Mýrdalssandur) is composed of thick piles of
alluvial deposits, in which lens-shaped sediment units intersect.

Other formations of marine sediments, other than the common
spits, are connecting bars (*eiði* in Icelandic) and higher bars, called
tombolos (*grandi* in Icelandic). These features share the fact that they
form on islands and skerries a short distance from shore. The prevailing wind from the sea drives the waves onto the island in certain directions. Most erosion takes place on the windward side, while the waves
carry the sediment behind the island. There, in the shelter, part of it
settles. Gradually the waves deposit a narrow bank of sand, gravel and
boulders in the shelter of the island or skerry until a long thin spit
forms and joins to the land. This can be up to several kilometres in

Dramatic sea-level changes were repeated many times from approx. 15,000–16,000 years ago until recently. Today the sea level is rising slowly (2–4 mm per year). This is mainly a eusta- tic trend (glaciers are melting worldwide) but downward isostatic movement of the Iceland landmass is also recorded, e.g. in the southwest. (RTH)

length if there is shallow water on the landward side of the island. Usually, however, they are shorter or approx. 0.5–2 km.

The difference between a tombolo and a connecting bar depends on whether the feature dries out at high tide or not. Connecting bars only emerge at low water, when it is possible to reach the island or skerry, which it joins to the land. A connecting bar is referred to as a tombolo or even just a spit when there is sufficient material to prevent the sea from covering it (except perhaps in storms). In the Reykjavík area the Grótta connecting bar is well known. Before the days of roads another connecting bar lay between the island of Örfirisey and land but it has now been built up (Grandinn). The bar joining Geldinganes to Reykjavík is a good example of a fine tombolo or spit and the same applies to Eiðið in Vestmannaeyjar (the Westman Islands).

In many cases rivers have carried sediment into sheltered inlets and fjords and this is visible above sea level. Where there is little movement

High sea cliffs line many parts of the coastline.
This is Látrabjarg, 12–14 km long and well over
400 m high. (RTH)

in the sea, stratified alluvial deposits settle on the bottom of fjords or outside them and many form beautiful, albeit small, deltas.

Rocky bird paradise

In Iceland there is rapid and vigorous marine erosion on steep rocky coasts, which results in precipitous cliffs or stacks. This applies to head-lands and isolated mountains or hills which jut into the sea. The cliff is called a wave-cut cliff.

Where the coast is steep the waves cut a horizontal notch into the base at approximately sea level. The overhanging rock mass above will collapse sooner or later. Surface run-off from the land and frost weath-ering also contribute to the erosion process. This vertical coastal for-mation retreats, i.e. the sea forces its way still further inland, especially if the sea level rises, due for instance to climatic and ocean warming. The smooth sea floor immediately below the wave-cut cliff is known as the wave-cut platform. Here cliffs or stacks rise from the sea while the bottom is covered with debris of various grain sizes. The combination of cliff and platform is sometimes referred to as a shore step. In front of the wave-cut platform there are dipping foreset beds which extend some distance from its edge and out onto the shelf surrounding Ice-land.

Wave-cut cliffs in the process of formation are found all round the coast and some are well known for their bird-life, abseiling egg-collec-tors or shipwrecks. Examples include Krísuvíkurbjarg, Látrabjarg, Hornbjarg (which is highest at around 550 m), Hvanndalabjörg and Dyrhólaey which has a famous and very large but short tunnel in the outermost rock face. Such openings are the result of wave erosion on rocks of different strengths. Isolated remains sometimes stand up from the beach or sea and are known as stacks. This kind of erosive form can easily be seen, for example in the National Park on Snæfellsnes (Arnar-stapi and Lóndrangur) and east of Dyrhólaey, at Reynisdrangar.

Where wave erosion cannot eat into the roots of mountains or upland because of uplift or because the sea level has fallen for other reasons, scree (Icel. *skriða*) reaches down to sea level. In these areas roads are

Hornafjörður is a cove, closed off by a bar of sand and gravel. The sediments partly originate from nearby cliffs and are distributed by waves. Another part is made of fluvial load from glacial rivers. (RTH)

often dangerous, e.g. at Njarðvíkurskriður, Rauðuskriður, Óshlíð or Ennisvegur, as a result of rockfall and landslides.

When the sea level was higher than at present, for example just after the last glacial period, active wave-eroded cliffs were situated much further inland. The strandline was 20–130 m higher then than it is now. Evidence for this can be traced in ancient beaches, shoreface terraces and shell remains which underlie younger materials. In extensive lowland areas, such as in the south, the ancient wave-cut cliff from the late Pleistocene can be found inland as a former coastal cliff with vegetated scree beneath, as well as foreset beds which are now tens of kilometres from the present coast. Closer to the coast, old wave-cut cliffs are also common such as Lómagnúpur (600 m) which once rose sheer from the sea.

Part of the debris which falls from active wave-cut cliffs is carried laterally to nearby lowland coasts where it settles as beach sediment, sand and gravel banks, reefs or other formations.

Rising seas

The huge mass of the oceans appears to be stable, except for occasional unrest during storms and the rhythm of the tides. This is deceptive because the average sea level has not been stable over the millennia. The very high sea level following the end of the last glacial period (of the Ice Age) fell fast. It even fell below the present sea level some 7,000–8,000 years ago and has seemingly risen 4–5 m in the last 3,000 years in the southwest.

Rising sea level has been a global trend during the 20th century, and the phenomenon is evident in Iceland. Why? Some of the rise has been attributed to the rising mean annual temperature worldwide. Glaciers melt and the warm oceans expand. This rise is again partly blamed on the release of different gases, such as carbon dioxide and methane, which increase the so-called greenhouse effect of atmospheric gases. In southwest Iceland, an additional factor is that the aggregation of volcanic rock provides extra mass on the crustal plates. They respond by sinking into the more ductile mantle rocks. In Iceland, accurate measurements indicate a rising sea level in some areas but not all. The data shows that the ocean is creeping at a rate of at least 3 mm per year (almost 10 cm in 30 years) onto land around Reykjavík. Different crustal processes and changes in the global environment affect the sea level but the above-mentioned figure is a rather conservative interpretation of the data. In some other parts of the country, the land is rising out of the sea. This is especially true for the areas south and southeast of the thick Vatnajökull ice cap. Glacial erosion and a decreasing ice mass (due to global warming) allow a rebounce of the crustal plates which more than counteracts the rising sea level due to glaciel meltwater or sea water expanding as it warms up.

In Iceland, as elsewhere in the world, rising air temperatures and a higher sea level will lead to more frequent and intense storm and flood hazards. New boulder walls and berms have already formed on low-profile coasts, for example in the Reykjavík area, and new building regulations take a continuing rise in sea level into account. Automated monitoring stations have been set up all round Iceland.

The landscape in eastern and western parts of Iceland is characterized by stratified mountains, deep fjords and valleys, chiefly eroded by Ice Age glaciers into the Tertiary bedrock. View across Reykjafjörður and Veiðileysufjörður to the highest part of the Strandir mountains, NW-Iceland. (RTH)

Where to go?

The following list directs readers to some of the more typical study sites.

For more information refer to scientific papers or the road guide by T. Thordarson and A. Höskuldsson: *Iceland, Classical Geology in Europe* 3, Terra 2002.

This is a list of some interesting locations where different forms of marine erosion and coastal sediment can be studied.

1. *Reykjanes.* High cliffs and a boulder berm. Sandy beaches and dunes are found nearby (at Sandvík, 2–3 km northeast of Reykjanes).
2. *Festarfjall, Grindavík.* Cliffs and black sand beaches.
3. *Krísuvíkurbjarg.* A well known bird-cliff.
4. *Selvogur.* A coastal lagoon.
5. *Ölfusá.* Flat, black beaches and dunes open to the North Atlantic Ocean.
6. *Eyrarbakki.* An 8,000-year-old lava flow that entered the sea.
7. *Dyrhólaey.* A volcanic island attached to land. Black sand beaches.
8. *Reynisfjall, Reynisdrangar and Vík.* Columnar lava and caves. High sea stacks and black sand/gravel beaches. Former sea cliffs.
9. *Mýrdalssandur.* Flat, black beaches. Jökulhlaup deposits.
10. *Hornafjörður.* Berms and coastal lagoons.
11. *Lónsfjörður.* A coastal lagoon.
12. *Rauðuskriður* close to Álftafjörður. Different formations in front of a scree-covered former sea cliff.
13. *The eastern fjords* from Álftafjörður to Héraðsflói are good sites for various examples of sedimentary formations and erosion features, associated with fjord landscapes.
14. *Langanes.* High cliffs.
15. *Melrakkaslétta.* Sand, gravel and boulder beaches as well as cliffs and sea stack formations.
16. *Öxarfjörður.* Coastal lagoons, fluvial sediments.
17. *Skjálfandi.* Cliffs as well as shoreface sands.

18. *Akureyri/Eyjafjarðará*. Delta formations.

19. *Siglufjörður* and *Miklavatn*. A spit and coastal lagoon.

20. *Hvítserkur*. A sea stack.

21. *The West Fjords* are dotted with marine erosion features associated with fjord landscapes, including the huge Látrabjarg sea cliff with about 1 million marine birds.

22. *Rauðisandur*. An example of a light-coloured mollusc sand beach.

23. *Breiðafjörður* has about 1,000 islands.

24. *The Snæfellsnes National Park*. Gravel and boulder beaches, sea caves, sea stacks and bird cliffs, notably at Arnarstapi, Lóndrangar, Hellnar and Djúpalónssandur.

25. *Borgarfjörður* and *Akrafjall*. Raised beaches.

26. *Hvaleyri* at Hvalfjörður. A spit.

27. *Reykjavík*. Tombolos and connecting bars along the coastline.

Selected bibliography

Surnames are written in italics. The Icelandic letters é, ó, á, ú, í and ý should be written as e, o, a, u, i and y, ö as ö, oe or simply o, æ as æ or ae, ð as d and þ as th when searching for references and papers in most databases.

Þ. *Einarsson* and K.J. *Albertsson* 1988. The glacial history of Iceland during the past three million years. *Philosophical Transactions of the Royal Society of London* 318, p. 673–644.

Þ. *Einarsson* 1994. *Geology of Iceland – Rocks and Landscape*. Mál og menning, Reykjavík.

H. *Norðdahl* and H. G. *Pétursson* 2005. Relative sea-level changes in Iceland: new aspects of the Weichselian deglaciation of Iceland. In (eds): Caseldine, C., Russel, A., Hardardottir, J. and Knudsen, O., *Iceland – Modern processes and past Environment*, p. 25–78. Elsevier, Amsterdam.

U. *Stefánsson* 1994. *Haffræði* I og II (Oceanography I and II). Háskólaútgáfan, Reykjavík.

8 Earth, wind and water

The Icelandic climate is classified as oceanic boreal to subarctic and arctic (in the highest areas) but generally milder than might be expected from its latitude. Climate changes characterise the Holocene, with an ongoing warm period, since the late 1990's. The average annual precipitation amounts to 2,000 mm or 2 metres per square metre of the Icelandic land area. This equals 2 million tonnes of water per square kilometre or a little over 200 billion tonnes on Iceland as a whole. The water creates lakes, rivers, waterfalls, canyons and springs and enters the groundwater reservoirs. The glass-rich andosol-soils of Iceland sustain various types of vegetation and animal life but extensive soil erosion and weathering in the windy climate have taken their toll.

Key words

groundwater • springs • classification of lakes by origin • waterfall • spring-fed rivers • direct run-off rivers • glacial rivers • gorge • canyon • hydropower • hydroelectric station • Andosol soil • peat soil • bogs • soil erosion • desertification • climate • climatic changes

Hraunfossar, Borgarfjörður
(RTH)

The climate in Iceland is characterised by relatively mild winters, cool summers and frequent changes in the weather. Annual precipitation below 500 m altitude in Iceland ranges from 350 mm to over 3,000 mm a year. Abundant groundwater appears in lakes that pierce the groundwater table or in springs (Lake Kleifarvatn). (RTH)

Travelling weather systems

The present climate in Iceland is affected by at least three important factors: the location of the island in the middle of the North Atlantic, a high-profile landscape and the travel routes of moisture-laden, low-pressure systems (cyclones) from the southwest to the northeast across the ocean. The weather systems pass or slide across Iceland. A prevailing high-pressure system (anticyclone) over Greenland, in confluence with the travelling "lows", often leads to strong northerly winds, while the low-pressure systems themselves fling strong southerly winds towards Iceland as they approach from the area around Newfoundland, Nova Scotia and the South Greenland Sea.

Any winds to speak of that blow in from the ocean usually carry fog or clouds and precipitation to a particular coast of Iceland, while on the leeside the resulting dried air simultaneously leads to much sunnier weather (a föhn effect). In addition, an approaching "low" is made up of a front, cloudbanks and precipitation belts which take control of the weather for some time, depending on the speed of the travelling weather system. Calm, generally stable weather prevails if there are no prominent "lows" close to Iceland, if a "high" has built up over the island or if "lows" pass far to the south. Such conditions may occasionally last for one to two weeks.

Relatively mild

In the mean annual temperatures of countries lying at a latitude of 65° and higher, like Iceland, figures of for example -6°C are common. In Iceland, however, the mean annual lowland temperature ranges from about 2–3°C in the northeast to 4–5°C in the south. Iceland is relatively warm with regard to its location. Besides the three factors mentioned above, the warm Gulf Stream ocean current has a strong impact on the temperature. The average lowland temperature in January may hover just below zero, depending on where you are, but in July it is around 10–12°C. Very cold weather is rare, -5°C to -15°C being considered quite a hard frost, although the thermometer plunged to -35°C at Lake Mývatn in 1998. In winter, temperatures above freezing and rain are common in the south but rarer in the north. High temperatures may range from 15°C to 25°C with a good 30°C as a recent maximum. High temperatures, as well as low ones, are most frequently experienced in inland areas of northeast Iceland.

In the highlands, however, winter temperatures hardly rise above zero and -5°C to -20°C are common, while the summer figures rarely top 15°C to 20°C. In general, the Icelandic lowlands have a mild oceanic climate (boreal in nature) while the extreme highlands are characterised by a harsher Arctic climate.

Winter conditions, however, can often turn into dangerous extremes when very high winds or raging blizzards cause air temperatures to drop to -5°C to -15°C bite all warm-blooded living creatures like an Arctic wolf.

The average annual hours of sunshine in Iceland range from around 1,250 hours in Reykjavík to 1,050 hours in Akreyri.

All figures in this chapter are rounded figures from the 1961–1990 period.

Rain in January, snow in June

While it has often rained in late December in Reykjavík, this is rarely the case in the north. About 7% of the annual precipitation falls as snow in Reykjavík, 23% as sleet and 60% as rain. At Lake Mývatn the figures are: rain 40%, snow 48% and sleet 12%. Even if the snow in the southern lowlands can sometimes form a 0.5–1 m thick blanket (and much thicker snow banks due to wind-drift), the snow cover there is quickly reduced by the next thaw. In North Iceland, the snow melts much less readily, leaving the northwest, north and northeast with a winter blanket of sometimes up to several metres of snow, especially inland and on the higher heaths and mountain passes.

The lowest annual precipitation is inland in the north at around 300–400 mm. Precipitation is close to 1,000 mm in the southwest lowlands, 2,000–3,000 mm at some locations on the extreme south coast but in the central highlands of southern Iceland some 3,000–5,000 mm fall annually. Between 4 and 15 m of snow make up the annual snow cover of the Vatnajökull ice cap, the highest figures being in its southern, high-altitude part.

Days with precipitation number 221 per year in Reykjavík and 171 in Akureyri.

Gales and floods

In Reykjavík the mean annual wind speed is close to force 4 on the Beaufort scale, which is almost double the figure for London and one third higher than the average figure for New York. Akureyri is more sheltered (force 3) but in the Westman Islands (Vestmannaeyjar) the wind speed averages around force 5 on the outer rim of the main island. Calm days are not uncommon in Iceland but local, coastal wind, due to faster warming of land than sea, often makes the middle of an otherwise calm day blustery.

Gales (force 8 or about 19 m/sec, around 70 km/hr) and storms (force 10 and over, up to 30–40 m/sec or over 140 km/hr) are quite common, especially in December, January and February. Winds from the northeast, southeast and southwest are most frequent. If a 10-minute-average wind speed is used as marker, high values for Reykjavík are about 70–77 nautical miles per hour (about 135 km/hr). Wind speeds of 100–107 nautical miles per hour (over 180 km/hr) have been registered in the Westman Islands and in the highlands. Single gusts may exceed 116–120 nautical miles/hr or over 200 km/hr. A few times each year, gale-force winds lead to serious property damage, especially at harbours and coastal roads. Combined with snow, such winds also lead to damage of electric power- or telephone lines. In some cases low atmospheric pressure and high tide double the effects of approaching storm waves on low-lying coastlines.

Wind erosion is substantial in Iceland. Wind-scoured lava flows, strangely eroded tuff cliffs, small pot-holes on cliff tops, polished stones (ventifacts) in sandy areas and huge dust clouds are some of the tell-tale signs. Wind also causes much of the soil erosion in Iceland by removing and redistributing soil particles.

Changing climate

Climatic changes during the past 1,100–1,200 years have been quite dramatic, albeit small compared to what happened in the Pleistocene. The first Nordic settlers arrived in the late 9th century, during a cool 2,500-year cycle which started about 500 BC. Soon a warmer spell improved living conditions for a few centuries, but in late medieval times a chillier climate set in once again. Two somewhat warmer centuries ensued but around 1400 AD the mean annual temperature began to drop again to reach a low in the 18th and 19th centuries. The cool period from about 1400 to about 1900 is termed the "Little Ice Age".

Hraunfossar are supplied by clear groundwater that flows a long way under a lava flow (Hallmundarhraun) and emerges in a canyon cut by the Hvítá glacial river (Borgarfjörður region). (RTH)

Glacier advances characterised the period. The years 1920–65 were among the warmest in Icelandic history. Glaciers retreated fast. But once again, a new, somewhat cooler and wetter period ensued in 1965–85. Since then, and especially now at the beginning of the 21st century, Iceland has been affected by global warming. The mean annual temperature has risen rapidly, or around 0.7°C for the past decade or so, heading for an unknown value in the 21st century. Precipitation also seems to be on the increase.

Prehistoric climate changes are dealt with in chapter 10.

What becomes of the water?

The precipitation in Iceland meets a variety of fates. Some of the water evaporates. Some of it falls as snow onto the ice caps and glaciers and remains there for up to centuries until the ice melts and water is released into glacial rivers, finally to enter the sea. Both components, of course, unite with the general circulation of water. Another fraction flows across the soil and bedrock, on the surface, directly into the

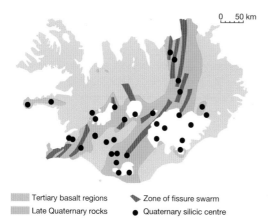

The hydrogeology of Iceland. Permeable volcanic rocks and sediments as well as swarms of open cracks and fissures stimulate strong groundwater currents in the Holocene and Pleistocene bedrock. At volcanic (silicic) centres, geothermal activity influences the water. The less permeable Tertiary bedrock contains less abundant and more widely distributed groundwater. (Source: F. Sigurðsson and K. Einarsson 1988)

ocean. Still another part seeps into the permeable bedrock to become groundwater. Cracks, fissures and different rock porosity govern the permeability of the bedrock.

Groundwater flows from a higher to a lower elevation in bedrock layers to join the sea as spring water from the surface or as groundwater, entering the ocean below sea level. In addition, a percentage of the glacial run-off, surface run-off and groundwater is retained in lakes for a while. A droplet of rain which falls on Iceland may therefore have quite a complex journey ahead of it.

Abundant run-off

The estimated annual surface or direct run-off in Iceland is about 1,580 mm per square metre or almost 160 billion (thousand millions) tonnes, including water that has been retained as glacier ice for a while. Evaporation occurs when surface water or shallow groundwater is transformed into vapour that disappears into thin air. This could amount to around 350 mm or close to 35 billion tonnes. The direct run-off obviously accounts for most of the precipitation and is the basis of Icelandic hydroelectricity used for the production of electric energy. The glacial component of the run-off is substantial and understandably so as some 11% of Iceland consists of glaciated highlands.

Perennial ice in soils (tundra or taiga) is of no significance in Iceland, except as a habitat for plants and birds. The most significant of these permafrost areas is Þjórsárver, south of the Hofsjökull ice cap (a pro tected RAMSAR area).

The precious groundwater

Of the over 200 billion tonnes of water which falls on Iceland only a small fraction joins the groundwater. The average figure is probably about 6–7 billion tonnes per year. The groundwater reservoir as a whole nevertheless ranks as large.

The water that sinks through pores, fissures and cavities into the abysses below Iceland acquires its own character. It interacts chemically with the volcanic soil and the volcanic bedrock, dissolving minerals and enriching the clay fraction of the soil. The water becomes low in calcium compounds (alias chalk) but relatively high in chlorine (a result of its marine origins) and has an underground pH-value of 9–10. It retains a small fraction of minerals and gases, making it pleasant-tasting and healthy drinking water. It is filtered through cold, sterile volcanic rock to become absolutely pure. In addition, there is very little environmental pollution in Iceland outside the largest towns.

If groundwater circulates very deep into the crust or comes close to shallow magma sources it turns into a still different liquid, a mixture of hot geothermal water and steam, which then rises and flows subterraneously or on the surface towards the sea (see chapter 9).

A strong groundwater flow characterises the active volcanic zone with its young lavas and porous tuffs, breccia and pillow lavas, whereas older regions have a lower and more dispersed groundwater flow. There, compaction, secondary minerals in pores and cavities and altered rocks counteract the flow of water into the bedrock.

Where geological features such as fissures, permeable interbeds (sediments) and dykes allow, groundwater appears on the surface in sparkling springs. These are common in the volcanic zone but rarer elsewhere.

Three main types of cold springs exist in Iceland:

Fissure springs are associated with tectonic fissures and faults or cracks associated with dykes. These may be found in the Tertiary bedrock but many more are located in the active volcanic zones. A good example is the water-filled fissures at Þingvellir, such as Flosagjá and Peningagjá.

Inter-lava springs are located at interfaces between sediments or soils and lava flows or between hyaloclastites, such as tuffs or breccias, and lava flows. Erosion and weathering may expose such interfaces and produce clear-water springs. These are easily studied at locations such as Hraunfossar in the Hvítá river, in Eyjafjöll and along the canyon of Jökulsárgljúfur.

Talus or scree springs are found where thick sediments, mainly produced by frost weathering, fluvial processes or rock slides, have accumulated above an impermeable bedrock. Water collects within the sediments and flows out into the open from the base of the sediment pile at an open section. Glacial deposits are seldom good groundwater reservoirs because of their high fraction of impermeable clay.

Cold springs are sometimes used as a source of drinking water and in fact one can safely consume water from almost any brook or river in Iceland. However, the most common method of obtaining water for domestic or industrial use is to sink shallow wells into aquifers in the bedrock or in surface sediments. The food industry, especially fish-processing plants and the agricultural sector, rely heavily on good water. In homes, pure, cold tap water is used everywhere. The production of bottled drinking water is for export only. The Municipal Water Works (now an integral part of the Reykjavík Energy company) of Reykjavík supply the Greater Reykjavík Area with up to 100,000 tonnes a day of excellent water from wells in recent lava flows and could increase that amount five- to tenfold. The Reykjavík Water Works became one of the first of its kind in the world to operate according to an international quality system of standards.

Öxnadalsá is a typical direct run-off river.
(RTH)

The many rivers

It is customary to classify Icelandic rivers into three groups: direct run-off rivers with typical surface water from ice-free areas, glacial rivers flowing from glaciers and finally spring-fed rivers carrying groundwater. Each type has its own character.

The **direct run-off rivers** are chiefly characterised by surface water that stems from coalescing streams and lakes. The water is precipitation which does not percolate to any extent through the strata in the catchment area.

The main characteristics of direct run-off rivers are:

• Considerable fluctuations in the discharge amount. Spring thaw and heavy precipitation swell the river. Drought and frost result in less discharge. Small direct run-off rivers can become major rivers during storms or thaw.

• The temperature of the water is to some degree dependent on the ambient air temperature after the snow has melted. Long periods of mild weather can make direct run-off rivers quite warm. The rivers are cold in spring due to the melting of snow and also during the winter due to frost. Ice formation can be considerable in winter and the rivers often freeze. The ice is often thick. In spring the direct run-off rivers break free and a great deal of ice floats along with the flow.

• The channels of direct run-off rivers are generally stony due to frequent floods, and under normal conditions the rivers only make use of part of each channel. Alluvial deposits are thus partly dry and the banks can be high.

Direct run-off rivers are found mainly in areas where the bedrock is old and impermeable. These are areas outside Iceland's active volcanic belt or close to it where there are volcanic formations from the Ice Age. Direct run-off rivers are thus found on the rocks of the Tertiary Formation (Blágrýtismyndun), e.g. in the west of the country, the West Fjords, the northwestern area and the East Fjords. They also occur in the Hreppur area between the southwestern volcanic belt and the eastern volcanic belt in the south. Direct run-off rivers and related rivers number in their hundreds, most of them quite small judged from their mean discharge, except during flood periods. An example with one of the highest discharge values is Fnjóská. The mean annual discharge is 39.5 m³ per second and the catchment area is several hundred square kilometres. Grímsá in the east of the country has a mean discharge of 30 m³ per second, but can reach more than 300 m³ per second in the spring, i.e. a tenfold increase. Other direct run-off rivers are for example: Laxá í Hreppum, Laxá í Kjós, Norðurá, Mjólká, Laxá í Ásum and Hoffellsá.

Skjálfandafljót is a glacial river north of Vatnajökull and boasts a picturesque waterfall (Aldeyjarfoss). Glacial rivers have braided channels with many sand and gravel banks (Tungnaá river). (RTH)

The **glacial rivers** drain melting glaciers. The water gathers from small rivulets or larger streams at the glacier edge to form a continuous river. Rivers emerge at many places from tunnels or ice caves at the glacier extremity. In many cases the glacial rivers are the discharge from glacial lakes, mainly proglacial lakes at the snouts of outlet glaciers.

Many Icelandic glacial rivers have mixed sources. If at least 75% of the water in a particular river is glacial in origin, the river is classified as glacial. The main features of glacial rivers are as follows:

The catchment areas are the largest in the country. The water often collects in rivulets from the glacier and also runs in braided channels over the main part of its course, except where rivers have eroded gorges. On flat lowland areas the glacial rivers spread out into many rivulets with alluvial deposits and there are large areas of sediment. Enormous sands gradually build up. The bifurcating streams of glacial rivers are changeable and little vegetation manages to take root along their stony courses.

Glacial rivers are often turbulent with rapid flow. The water is grey or peaty in colour as a result of the suspended load (clay and silt). The temperature is low, even as low as 1–4° C near the source.

Two kinds of regular fluctuation occur in the discharge pattern of glacial rivers. Daily fluctuations occur because the temperature falls at night but increases during the day. As a result the least discharge is in the morning and the most late in the day. Annual fluctuations occur when the ice melts rapidly in summer, but less during the winter. As a result there is little flow in winter and the greatest discharge is in summer. Daily fluctuations can reduce the discharge of a glacial river by up to half but the annual fluctuations are much greater. A glacial river with a discharge of 100–200 m³ per second in July can fall to 5–10 m³ per second during a cold spell in January.

As well as regular fluctuations, there have been *jökulhlaup* floods in glacial rivers in historical times. Jökulhlaups are sudden, voluminous floods (compared to the mean discharge in a particular river). They are

A common glacier burst of meltwater (*jökul-hlaup*) in Skeiðará in the Skaftafell National Park (top). The water flows some 50 km beneath the Skeiðarárjökull glacier from the Grímsvötn caldera lake that overflows regularly due to ice melting by geothermal activity, and finally across Skeiðarársandur outwash plain. From time to time volcanic eruptions in Grímsvötn or vicinity cause larger floods. This is a view of the flood at Skeiðarársandur in 1996 (above), shortly after an eruption north of Grímsvötn (Gjálp). (RTH)

often one of two kinds which have different causes. In some cases a reservoir can form at the glacier margin. Usually this happens because the glacier itself has dammed the surface run-off in the surrounding area, e.g. a river in a valley or gorge (e.g. the jökulhlaup in the Súla river draining the western part of Skeiðarárjökull, originating in Grænalón in Vatnajökull). Such floods can occur fairly regularly in glacial rivers where suitable conditions prevail. They are seldom very large (less than 0.5 km^3 of water) and discharge in the order of 200–2,000 m^3 per second. Geothermal heat or volcanic eruptions melt the ice in some glaciers and a considerable amount of water can thus collect underneath the ice before the water bursts out. Jökulhlaup due to geothermal activity can reach 600–5,000 m^3 discharge and the flood volume can amount up to around 0.2–1.5 km^3 (e.g. Skaftá jökulhlaup and normal Skeiðará jökulhlaup). Jökulhlaup associated with eruptions are much larger with a discharge of at least 5,000–300,000 m^3 per second and a volume up to several km^3 of water (e.g. Skeiðará jökulhlaup and Katla jökulhlaup).

Glacial rivers occur in all parts of the country and do not follow any particular distribution pattern associated with bedrock permeability, as is the case for the other river types.

Large glacial rivers include Hvítá in Borgarfjörður (mean annual discharge: 190 m^3 per second), Jökulsá á Fjöllum (190 m^3 per second, catchment area 7,850 km^2), Jökulsá á Dal (220 m^3 per second), Kúðafljót (250 m^3 per second) and Þjórsá (380 m^3 per second).

The **spring-fed rivers** are groundwater that rises to the surface and collects in small or large rivers. In some cases the rivers are discharge from lakes, which are mainly groundwater. Since many Icelandic rivers are mixed in origin, spring-fed rivers are defined as having at least 75% spring water. The main features of spring-fed rivers include:

Catchment areas (the area from which they collect water) are in most cases smaller than the catchment areas of direct run-off rivers or glacial rivers. The water of spring-fed rivers has its source in springs, tarns or lakes. The rivulets coalesce in one main channel, the river itself. If the river is discharge from a lake there is usually a well-defined estuary in the lake.

The eerie desert-like appearance of Skeiðarársandur. The dark basalt sand has been carried
southward by wind, rivers and glacier bursts
(jökulhlaups). The Öræfajökull volcano rises in
the background. The people are climbing the
Ingólfshöfði promontory. (RTH)

Spring-fed rivers are often slow flowing in sections, deep and rather
cold. This is because the groundwater in them approaches the mean
annual temperature in the catchment area, usually 4–7°C.

Spring-fed rivers carry less sediment than direct run-off rivers or glacial rivers and the surface level fluctuates little over the year. Spring
thaw, however, causes a rise in the level and long-lasting droughts can
lower it somewhat. Vegetation then grows as far down to the river bank
as it can.

In Iceland spring-fed rivers are mainly found in areas where there is
plentiful groundwater and the water table is quite high, or in other
words lava and móberg areas. They occur within the active volcanic
and rifting zones or close to them. This applies to the northeast, part of
the central highlands, central southern Iceland and the southwest,
especially the Reykjanes peninsula and the area between Hengill and
Langjökull. Spring-fed rivers are in places the only visible surface run-
off. In other places they share the terrain with glacier-fed run-off, such
as in the northeast. There are nevertheless large areas with practically

no surface run-off, for example on the Reykjanes peninsula. Two of the largest lakes in the country supply rivers that are classified as pure spring-fed rivers. Sogið is the largest Icelandic spring-fed river (110 m^3 per second mean annual discharge) and flows from Þingvallavatn. From Lake Mývatn, which collects groundwater from adjoining volcanic formations, the Laxá flows through Þingeyjarsýsla (or Aðaldalur). Its mean discharge is 44 m^3 per second. The catchment area is 2,150 km^2. Among other spring-fed rivers are the Elliðaár, Kaldá (above Hafnarfjörður), Eystri-Rangá, Fossálar, Lindá at Herðubreiðarlindir, Grafarlandaá and Kráká.

Canyons, valleys and waterfalls

Rivers abrade the bedrock in accordance with the discharge volume, sediment load and flow velocity. In Iceland, they have cut a vast number of creeks, gullies and canyons. Landscape features of this type are almost without exception younger than approx. 10,000 years old. This reveals how effective and fast fluvial erosion tends to be in Iceland. One reason is the relatively friable bedrock. Among the more spectacular canyons are the Gullfossgljúfur canyon, Fjaðrárgljúfur canyon (not far from Kirkjubæjarklaustur) and Hafrahvammagljúfur canyon at Kárahnjúkar in the northeastern highlands, which is affected by the large Kárahnjúkar Power Plant scheme. The largest canyon by length and volume is Jökulsárgljúfur in northeastern Iceland, containing the waterfall Dettifoss. The lower part is included in a national park. Large floods of glacial or volcanic origin have helped in moulding the largest canyons. At least four catastrophic floods followed the path of the present Jökulsá river through the Jökulsárgljúfur National Park in Holocene times (the past 10,000 years). The Gullfoss canyon also shows signs of catastrophic, prehistoric floods.

Although most Icelandic rivers are short (20–240 km), many have a high head due to Iceland's high relief. Canyons are common and hundreds of waterfalls line cliffs throughout the country. They may be broad and multi-stepped like Fjallfoss (Dynjandi), high and narrow like Seljalandsfoss, veil-shaped like Skógafoss or big, thundering, broad chutes like the mighty Dettifoss (45 m) or the two-stepped, elegant

Fossálar classify as a spring-fed river.
(RTH)

A fan-shaped debris cone on a slope
below a typical river-cut gorge.
(RTH)

Gullfoss (close to 35 m). Their height ranges from 20 m to almost
200 m, the highest being Glymur (198 m) at Hvalfell in Hvalfjörður.
Large waterfalls, like Dettifoss and Gullfoss, alter their shape visibly in
decades as they erode the waterfall step and "move upstream" at a rate
of a few centimetres per year.

Floods caused by geothermal or volcanic activity in ice caps and
glaciers have been mentioned. The rivers of Iceland flood for other
reasons too. Sudden spring thaws, often combined with heavy rain, can
flood rivers and may cause them to rise by many metres. Large low-
lying areas become flooded and in some cases farms and towns, roads
and bridges have been affected. Landslides sometimes accompany the
flood events, along with soil erosion.

Three different types of impressive waterfall:
Fjallfoss (100 m) in northwest Iceland (left, top),
Seljalandsfoss (65 m) in the south (above) and
Gullfoss (35 m, left lower). (RTH)

Glacial rivers carry the largest sediment load. The annual quantity of suspended sediments may reach a value of 2–10 million tonnes in the larger rivers, of which basaltic glass and fine-grained basaltic rocks constitute the bulk. Extensive outwash plains have formed in front of existing ice caps and glaciers, and thick sedimentary deposits are conspicuous in glacially cut valleys. Most flat-bottomed valleys in Iceland retain their shape due to such infill and are not a sign of progressive fluvial erosion, as is the case in countries with a much longer geological history. Over a long period, the coastline in front of the largest outwash plains advances into the sea.

Research shows that Icelandic rivers carry about 0.7% of all the material which moves from dry land to the sea. It is important to the marine life.

Numerous postglacial canyons have been cut into the highlands. This is the longest and largest, Jökulsárgljúfur, containing Europe's most powerful waterfall, Dettifoss. The lower part of the canyon falls within a national park. (RTH)

Árskarðsárgljúfur is at the foot of the
Kerlingarfjöll massif. (RTH)

The blue pearls

Abundant precipitation and a rugged or undulating surface relief usually mean that freshwater lakes are common. This is precisely the case
in Iceland although most lakes are small. Some 200 lakes exceed an area
of 1 km^2, of which only 27 have an area larger than 5 km^2. The largest
lakes are Þingvallavatn, Þórisvatn, Lögurinn and Mývatn (84, 70 (mean
value), 53 and 36 km^2 respectively). The lake depth varies from a few
metres as in Lake Mývatn to 114 m in Lake Þingvallavatn and 220 m in
the Askja caldera lake (Öskjuvatn).

303

Lake Lögurinn resembles a Scottish loch and its
origins are identical: glacial erosion. (RTH)

Icelandic lakes have surprisingly varied origins. Lakes in depressions
formed by glacier erosion are very common and moraine-dammed
lakes and proglacial lakes (glacier lagoons) like Jökulsárlón are well
known too. Another large group of lakes is volcanogenic lakes, lava
dammed and located in craters and calderas. The beautiful Veiðivötn
lakes are a prolific example. They were formed during a volcano-
tectonic episode around 1480. In addition, lakes formed as coastal
lagoons, dammed by rock-slides or subglacial volcanic formations, are
also found in Iceland.

An overview is as follows, excluding man-made lakes:

Glacial origin:

Glacial depressions from the Ice Age. These are troughs or depressions carved into the bedrock by moving ice. Most of the lakes have an oval or elongated shape and occur in groups. An example is provided by the numerous lakes west of the Langjökull ice cap (on Arnarvatnsheiði). This is the most common type of lake in Iceland.

Lochs or glacially moulded, long, narrow lakes in valleys also date from the Ice Age. The deepest parts of glacially cut valleys may collect water. Lögurinn is an example, about 35 km long, up to 2.5 km wide and 111 m deep. Another example is Skorradalsvatn. Active glaciers at the southern margin of Vatnajökull are known to extend below sea level, thus providing future basins for lakes of this type.

Proglacial lakes are lagoons in front of active (receding or advancing) outlet glaciers from ice caps or in front of alpine glaciers. The glacier may or may not calve into the lake and an end-moraine may act as a dam in front of the lake. The best-known example is Jökulsárlón in front of Breiðamerkurjökull. It has been growing in size (since the late 1930s) as the outlet glacier retreats, and the basin extends at least 20 km underneath the present glacier. The lake is about 200 m deep and contains many icebergs. Among other proglacial lakes are Hvítávatn, Gígjökulslón and Fjallsárlón.

Ice-dammed lakes are located at glacier margins where the moving ice dams an ice-free valley by closing it off. Water may then become stored in the valley and sooner or later it will overflow or lift the ice. Floods (glacier bursts or jökulhlaups) occur from such lakes at regular intervals. A well-known example is Grænalón at the western margin of Skeiðarárjökull. Floods in the rivers Súla and Núpsvötn originate at Grænalón every one to two years and commonly discharge 1,000–2,000 m^3 of water per second.

Lake Þórisvatn is one of the largest lakes in
Iceland, of mixed origin, but also dammed and
thus man-made to some extent. (RTH)

The Grænalón glacier lagoon is located at the
western margin of the Skeiðarárjökull outlet
glacier (Vatnajökull ice cap). (RTH)

A dead ice pit on Skeiðarársandur outwash plain. The iceberg, flushed by the 1996 jökulhlaup (glacier burst), is melting. (RTH)

Kettle holes or dead-ice pits are found in ground-moraine sediments in front of retreating glaciers or where glaciers were once active but have since vanished. They are small and usually of a circular shape.

Cirque or bowl lakes are located in the former seats of small cirque glaciers on mountain slopes. They are fairly common in the high-profile-relief, Tertiary landscape.

Lava-dammed lake in Hnappadalur.
(RTH)

Rockslide lakes:

Quite a few Icelandic lakes were formed when large rockslides were released from steep mountains, commonly by the end of the last (Weichselian) glaciation. The slides dammed valleys and allowed water to accumulate on the upward side. Examples of rockslide lakes are Flóðið in Vatnsdalur and Hraunsvatn in Öxnadalur.

Volcanic origin:

Lava-dammed lakes occur where lava flows have closed off valleys or depressions in the bedrock. A small lake of this type is Ástjörn within the town of Hafnarfjörður and a large one is Lake Mývatn (approx. 36 km^2 and only 4 m deep)

Crater lakes may form where craters are deep enough to penetrate the groundwater table. The craters may be of phreato-magmatic origin (formed in violent gas-pressure explosions) or hydro-magmatic origin

Ljótipollur and Tjörvapollur (Bláhylur) not far from Landmannalaugar. Both are craters formed in two recent explosive volcanic events which have pierced the groundwater table. (RTH)

(water interaction with magma). Explosion pits containing lakes are sometimes termed maars. Examples of crater lakes are Víti in Krafla, Víti in Askja, Ljótipollur, Grænavatn, Kerið and various lakes in the Veiðivötn group.

Caldera lakes are found within volcanic calderas or cauldrons. They are not common in Iceland but as some calderas are covered by glaciers, the exact number is not yet known. Two noteworthy examples will be mentioned here. In ice-free Askja, a caldera subsidence occurred in 1875 and a lake formed over the next two decades, 220 m deep, covering 11 km^2. The subglacial Grímsvötn caldera lake is hidden beneath an ice shelf of up to 200 m thick in Vatnajökull. Geothermal activity and the local glacier budget stipulate its size. The heat flux melts ice and the meltwater mixes with a small fraction of juvenile geothermal liquids. After growing in size for a few years, from approx. 10 km^2 to around 20 km^2, it overflows. The resulting jökulhlaup (flood) emerges at the

Calderas commonly form in large volcanic centres in Iceland. Interlocked, ice-free calderas occur in Dyngjufjöll (Askja, top). Glaciated calderas are filled to the brim by ice or contain a lake with a floating ice shelf, like Grímsvötn in Vatnajökull (above). (RTH and OS)

margin of the Skeiðarárjökull outlet glacier and sweeps over the Skeiðarársandur outwash plain (700 km²).

Lakes dammed by tuff-mountains (móberg or hyaloclastite-ridges and table mountains or stapis) are found close to or within the active volcanic zone. Most of the mountains were formed during the last two to three glacial periods, notably the last one (Weichselian). Parallel ridges formed on volcanic subglacial fissures provide a lake basin at a number of locations, forming long, narrow lakes like Kleifarvatn and Langisjór. Table mountains (on a short fissure or circular vent) may also form a dam, resulting in features like Hvalvatn behind Hvalfell, a small (4.2 km²) but deep (160 m) lake.

Lárós is a semi-saline lake, cut off from the sea
by a berm (Snæfellsnes). (RTH)

Coastal lakes:
These lakes are mainly of two types: **large estuaries**, dammed by a bar
made of gravel and sand, like the mouth of the Ölfusá river, or **beach
lagoons** where a similar bar has cut a cove or small bay off from the sea.
The latter receive plenty of fresh water from inland but sea water also
enters via a channel through the bar, especially at high tide. Many such
lakes are semi-saline. Examples include Hlíðarvatn, Hóp, Hraunsvatn,
Lónsfjörður and Hornafjörður.

Life in the water
Wetlands, estuaries, lakes and rivers cover thousands of square kilometres in Iceland. Obviously, these are habitats for varied flora, insects,
birds and freshwater fish. Salmon is plentiful in Iceland but angling is
rather expensive. However, this does not apply to fishing for Arctic
char, sea or salmon trout and brown (mountain) trout. Angling is
therefore very popular in Iceland.

Two Icelandic lakes are world renowned: Lake Þingvallavatn and Lake
Mývatn. A large area at Þingvallavatn has been included in UNESCO's
list of World Heritage Sites. The lake itself is of mixed tectonic, glacial
and volcanic origin with crystal-clear waters and a unique ecosystem.
Lake Mývatn is famous for its volcanic formations and very special
harmonic ecosystem formed of insects, plankton, fish and a multitude
of birds.

The utilisation of hydropower
Iceland's many, powerful rivers are an excellent source of hydropower.
Some 30 TWh are said to be economically harnessable, but environmental concerns reduce that figure. Almost 25% of the hydro-energy
has been put to use (2005). Power plants have been built on rivers where they cross the edge of the highlands, providing a high water head.
Commonly, dams and reservoirs are used to regulate the flow. Other
hydropower plants use natural lakes as reservoirs. In total, here are
about 30 hydropower plants operating in Iceland. Of these, under 10

Three small hydroelectric plants line the Sog river from Lake Þingvallavatn. The oldest was built in 1937.(RTH)

are rated at between 120 and 260 MW in size and the newest, the 690 MW Kárahnjukar Power Plant, will soon supply power to an aluminium smelter in Reyðarfjörður. About one third of the electric energy is for domestic and low-energy industrial consumption (35%) and two thirds go to energy intensive industry (aluminium and ferro-silicate plants, owned by foreign companies, or 65% in 2003) which is a growing branch of industry, demanding still more electric energy.

The production of electric energy by hydropower is an almost pollu-tion-free method and therefore an important environmental move. However, dams, reservoirs, flow channels, buildings and power lines require a great deal of space. The dams may retain a lot of the sedi-ments which, in turn, help to bind carbon dioxide in the sea, sustain the coastline and affect the marine biosphere. Hydropower plants also have quite an impact on the environment, especially since they often require the submerging of highland areas valuable for their vegetation, wildlife or as tourist attractions. The utilisation of the excess electric energy currently requires either some kind of metal or chemical indus-

313

try or else direct export of energy. In view of this, the environmental and economic impact of energy production in Iceland, notably the hydropower exploitation, has become a widely debated issue.

The energy sector in Iceland is expanding. New hydropower plants are under construction, new geothermal plants have been built or are envisaged and new energy-intensive industrial plants are in the making or planned. Existing geothermal-power and hydropower production plans could triple the current energy production. More than half the increase would require more energy-intensive industrial plants or an underwater cable to export electric energy to Europe. If fully implemented, the plans should involve the utilisation of one third of the energy resources for the production of electricity.

For further information on the energy sector see the following websites: www.os.is, www.or.is, www.hs.is, www.isor.is, www.idn.stjr.is, www.nordurorka.is, www.samorka.is and www.lv.is.

For further information on environmental issues see the following websites: www.landvernd.is, www.inca.is, www.natturuverndarsamtok.is, www.natturuvaktin.is, www.ust.is, www.umhverfisraduneyti.is.

Geothermal power plants and hydrogen

The planned increase in geothermal exploitation within a decade is still small in relation to the enormous potential. Attention could be shifted from hydropower for production of electric energy to production of steam power. In 2004 about 17% of the electric power came from geothermal sources and the remaining 83% from hydropower. The two new plants (Hellisheiði and Reykjanes) will add considerably to the share of geothermal power.

There is a 20,000 GWh short-term potential (close to 2,500 MW) for economically harnessable geothermal energy for electric power plants. However, environmental concerns could somewhat reduce the usable potential. The long-term potential is almost three times this figure, using conventional extraction from geothermal reservoirs. The Iceland Deep Drilling Project, where 4–5 km deep wells are envisaged would greatly enhance the potential, if successful.

The Kerlingarfjöll high-temperature geothermal area could sustain electrical power production but will certainly never do so due to nature conservation interests. (RTH)

Currently, about 72% of the energy consumed in Iceland is produced in an environmentally sustainable way (2003) with regard to pollution. The remaining 28% stems from imported oil. With the non-polluting electric-energy production and the fresh water at hand, the Icelanders have already started research and experiments in the field of large-scale hydrogen production (see **www.newenergy.is**). Hydrogen is made by "splitting" water into oxygen and hydrogen by electrical means (electrolysis). Hydrogen may well be an important fuel in the future as its use is almost non-polluting. Another possibility is to use organic matter to produce alcohol for fuel or use CO_2 from the metal industry to produce oil. Iceland has the resources to become an important supplier of liquid hydrogen or alcohol in the future.

A state-supported target plan stipulates that Iceland should aim to become totally independent of imported carbon-based fuels by about 2030–40.

Soils in Iceland classify as an andosol type. Tephra layers are common in soil profiles and have proved useful dating tools in geology and archaeology (the science of tephrochronology). (RTH)

Volcanic soils

Soil is defined as a mixture of debris or fragments and rotting or rotted organic remains. The proportion of organic material can be very low, e.g. old glacial moraine with a little humus. But even in brown soil with a high proportion of organic material (humus 50% or more) there is always a certain proportion of mineral material. Soil can be classified by various properties, for example grain size, chemical composition, etc. Icelandic soil is a mixture of fragments, tephra, clay minerals, air, water and humus. It is of the soil class known as andosols or volcanic soils. The rock fragments in it originate as wind-blown material from glacial sediments, from alluvial deposits or as wind-borne sediment from other desert areas of the country. The tephra is wind borne directly from volcanoes or tephra layers which are being eroded. The soil has a high content of such material, which is the main reason for the soil being classified as volcanic. Glassy tephra and rapid chemical weathering (formation of clay minerals) produce a light soil which has little cohesion.

The smallest grains are known as clay. There can be some content of mechanically derived clay in the soil, which is considered to be wind borne. Clay minerals, on the other hand, are the result of chemical weathering and form when rock-forming minerals in the rock fragments, tephra and underlying bedrock become altered by chemical reactions. Water in the soil contains dissolved materials which react with the materials in the rock fragments, tephra or bedrock surface. Common clay minerals formed in this way in Icelandic soils by the weathering of tephra are called allophane, imogolite, halloysite and ferrihydrate, the latter giving the soil a red-brown colour. The amount of such clay minerals in Icelandic soils can reach 5–50% in the upper 10–40 cm, the majority being allophane. In areas in and close to the volcanic belt, cations released from the tephra have a tendency to maintain quite a high acidity level and allophane is the commonest clay mineral. Further from the volcanic belt where there is less tephra the proportion of metallic-humus compounds is much higher and the acidity level lower.

With rapid chemical weathering due to the effect of groundwater, the basalt rock-forming minerals (90% of the bedrock) alter to clay minerals, e.g. plagioclase to kaolinite. When chemical weathering of the surface sediments and the uppermost layer of the bedrock is considered as a whole it appears that it is 40% more rapid than the average for dry land in general.

Dry-land soils	Peaty soil (vegetated)
	Gravel (little or partial vegetation)
	Wasteland (mostly denuded gravels, moraine, sand, lava)
Wetland soils	Topogenic bogs (in hollows, by lakes or rivers)
	Slanting bogs (on valley sides and mountain slopes)
	Palsa bogs (in permafrost areas)

Soil banks show the former appearance of
areas with dwindling vegetation and soil cover.
(RTH)

Soil in Iceland thickens rapidly (accumulates from wind erosion, ash fall) or up to 1–3 mm per year. As a result separate clay layers do not form as they do in soils abroad. Normal mechanically derived clay and clay minerals increase the cohesion of the soil and balance out the effects of the tephra content.

Clay minerals and organic material are the basis of soil as an ecosystem. Rotting or rotted plant remains accumulate wherever there is vegetation. Mixed with these are the remains of small animals, mainly of organisms that live in the soil. This organic material is known as humus. It mixes with the sediment to form soil, either locally or where it is borne by wind or water. Organic material in humus forms compounds with, for example, aluminium.

Clay minerals have a very high surface area relative to their weight. In one gram of common pure clay there is a surface area of 800 m². It is obvious, therefore, that Icelandic soil can contain large amounts of water. This in turn encourages frost activity, such as formation of vegetated hummocks, solifluction terraces or stone polygons, and facilitates debris slide when clayey soils become water saturated. If clay and tephra-rich soil dries up, its cohesion is greatly reduced and erosive agents become more effective than would otherwise be the case.

The conventional classification of Icelandic soil has taken into consideration its location and appearance as well as the groundwater conditions. Bogs occur where the soil is wet due to a high water table or proximity to rivers.

Only about one third of the country is covered by vegetated soil, of which bogs can be estimated at 40% and vegetated dry-land soils as 60%. Another third of the country is covered by very thinly or unvegetated soil, which is of very varied fertility. Peaty soils and bog soils reach up to 5–10 cm thick in places but elsewhere there is only a thin soil cover of as little as a few centimetres. Erosion and weathering have removed all the humus-rich soil from a very large area.

Dry or wet soil forms a large part of the peaty soil but if it is very wet as a result of a high water table it becomes bog soil. Bogs form where the water table is high in vegetated land, mainly where the bedrock permeability is low and the groundwater flow does not have easy downward access. Bogs are quite common on mountainsides, while others cover flat land. Some bogs are tarns which have become vegetated.

Bogs are characterised by oxygen-poor conditions where altered and half-rotted plant remains accumulate. In such areas an almost black peat forms rather than normal humus. The peat compresses as the bog thickens and it has quite a high carbon content (50–60%). It is easy to recognise plant remains in the bog, e.g. twigs, grass, small leaves and

Wetlands constitute an important and large
percentage of areas with a healthy vegetation
cover. (RTH)

branches. Icelandic peat layers usually contain two horizons with birch-tree remains. They provide evidence for two mild spells during the Holocene, which reached a climax around 3,500 and 7,000 years ago. Also widespread in the bogs are wind-borne tephra layers, clay layers, sand or reddish limonite. The latter is oxidised, hydrated iron, as in rust. The acid bog waters and streams dissolve iron in the bedrock which is generally iron-rich basalt. Through certain reactions in the bog water, iron is precipitated as limonite and accumulates in thin layers. In earlier centuries Icelanders made use of charcoal and limonite to make soft iron for various tools.

If peat is buried under thick formations such as lavas, it is further altered and the carbon content per volume increases. This leads to the formation of hard, dry lignite (*surtarbrandur* in Icelandic) which is quite common in the Tertiary formation, or even layers of true brown coal, still richer in carbon, which is not found in Iceland. Peat and lignite were used as fuel up until the 20th century.

Soil erosion

Wind and water, freeze-thaw processes and gravitational slumping all play a role in the weathering and erosion of the soil. The main areas of erosion lie within or close to the active volcanic zone. As soon as the vegetation cover is seriously breached, for example by running water, wind becomes the most efficient eroding agent. Soils thicken locally as wind-blown (aeolian) soils and sediments become deposited there. A great deal of soil and sediment ends up in the sea surrounding Iceland.

The settlement of Iceland altered the balance of ecosystems in the country to a large extent. Tens of thousands of people had to build houses and find peat and firewood. The settlers brought with them large flocks of domestic animals, most of which required large grazing

The ground moraine that was left by the glaciers of the last glacial period of the Ice Age underlies fertile soils in wide areas. Soil erosion has revealed the poorly sorted sediments covering large areas (Kjölur). (RTH)

Peat layers in wetlands can be many metres thick. Pollen and other plant remains preserved in the peat provide information on climatic history. (RTH)

areas. So extensive areas were gradually cleared of shrubs and birch trees, the woods shrank or lost their ecobalance and grazing was un-regulated. In medieval times, the climate deteriorated. There was a cold spell that climaxed ("The Little Ice Age") in the 18th century. In some cases large tephra-producing volcanic eruptions and floods from sub-glacial eruptions affected inhabited regions and grazing or forested ar-eas, already weakened by overuse. Glaciers advanced and new fluvial sediment beds formed. It seems that by 1500 increased soil erosion, dwindling shrub-lands or birch woods and encroaching sand already

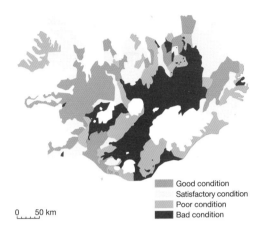

The extent of soil erosion is detectable from the present condition of areas with vegetation and soil cover. In general, the conditions in the central highlands do not favour much vegetation due to high altitude, loose sediments or tephra, young lava and a relatively severe climate. Large outwash plains at low altitude, where floods occur (jökulhlaups), also tend to be desolate. (Simplified after: Ó. Arnalds et al. 2001. Soil erosion in Iceland.)

Good condition
Satisfactory condition
Poor condition
Bad condition

0   50 km

posed problems. These subsequently became increasingly serious until the late 19th century. By the early 20th century at least a third of fertile soils with vegetation had vanished, i.e. from about 20,000 km², and less than a tenth of the original woodlands remained. These are conservative estimates.

Satellite vegetation images of the country show that at present just over 36% of the total area is desert and wilderness. Another 10–15% consists of areas where the soil cover is already considerably diminished. The wilderness or very sparsely vegetated area is now 4–7 times bigger than 1,100 years ago.

Soil erosion produces soil-erosion features in the landscape. The desert areas display features such as gravel plains, sands, sandy gravels, moraine, lava, sandy lava and soil. These features are for the most part self-explanatory. In vegetated areas the following erosion forms occur:

Sand patches. Here the wind-borne sand falls on vegetated land, burying the vegetation and eroding the soil.

Erosion patches. In such cases an entire vegetated area has been eroded in patches, unveiling the unprotected soil below. Enlarged soil patches finally lead to the formation of soil banks or soil stacks (the

323

A dust bowl in the Southern highlands. (RTH)

Icelandic term is *rofbarð*). Off-road driving can play a part in their formation.

Soil banks (stacks). These are isolated soil remains, small islands of soil with a sample of the previous vegetation cover. They are mostly 1–4 m high but do not represent the original soil thickness because they collect wind-blown soil and become somewhat higher than the original surface. If the soil banks decrease in number and size, the area gradually becomes a desert. Most deserts uncovered in this way consist of glacial or alluvial sediments.

Earthquakes are known to have initiated soil eriosion by causing earth slides (South Iceland earthqukes in 2000). (RTH)

Water channels. In such cases water has damaged the vegetation cover and begun eroding the underlying soil. Meltwater is responsible for most water channels in the soil.

Solifluction scars. Slow downhill movement of soil can erode the soil cover and lay it bare to erosive agents.

Debris-slide scars. Debris- and rock-slides result in large scars in the vegetation and soil cover. Other erosive agents can then become more effective.

Erosive forms provide an idea of the extent of desertification (erosive index), as well as indicating the agents at work.

The erosive index is used to estimate the vegetation and soil conditions as a whole. The index is a value from 0 (no erosion) to 5 (extensive erosion). According to expert opinion (1997), based on studies of 18,000 units over the entire country, there is now extensive desertification (erosion index 4–5) in 22% of the land area (about 23,000 km^2). This does not include the area of high mountains, glaciers and lakes.

Considerable, great or very serious desertification (erosion index 3–5) occurs on just over half the land area apart from naturally unvegetated areas. In 48% of the country there is little or limited desertification (erosion index 0–2).

The classification of soil-erosion formations, as well as an inventory of affected or unaffected areas, can be found in the book *Soil erosion in Iceland* (Ólafur Arnalds et al., Reykjavik 2001, see also **www.hvanneyri.is, www.land.is and www.skogur.is**).

Valiant and productive efforts to halt the erosion on all fronts started as early as 1900 but they have not yet counterbalanced the desertification, although they have retarded it to a great extent. Iceland still suffers today from the most rapid desertification in Europe and in other subarctic and Arctic regions. The State Soil Conservation Service, the State Forestry Commission, other institutions, associations, farming communities or individual farmers, firms and non-profiting individuals have joined forces. The land-care movement does not have the funds or manpower to completely turn the tide in a relatively short period. Grazing has been reduced in some regions due to smaller stocks of domestic animals, and in other regions grazing is now more controlled than before. Reforestation is gaining ground. On many fronts, the progress is evident but it will probably take many decades or even centuries to regain the former or natural state of vegetation in most of the larger areas.

Selected bibliography

Surnames are written in italics. The Icelandic letters é, ó, á, ú, í and ý should be written as e, o, a, u, i and y, ö as ö, oe or simply o, æ as æ or ae, ð as d and þ as th when searching for references and papers in most databases.

Ó. Arnalds 2004. *Volcanic soils of Iceland.* Caetena 56, p. 3–20.

Ó. Arnalds, E.F. *Þórarinsdóttir*, S. *Metúsalemsson*, Á. *Jónsson*, E. *Grétarsson* and Á. *Árnason* 2001. *Soil erosion in Iceland.* Soil Conservation Service and Agricultural Research Inst. Reykjavík. 155 p.

S.R. *Gíslason*, S. *Arnórsson* and H. *Ármannsson* 1994. Present chemical weathering of basalt in Iceland. *Mineralogical Magazine* 58A, p. 333–334.

B. *Jóhannsson* 1960. *Íslenskur jarðvegur* (The soils of Iceland). Rannsóknarstofnun land-búnaðarins (Agricultural Research Inst.), reprint 1988. Reykjavík.

A. *Stefánsson* and S.R. *Gíslason* 2001. Chemical weathering of basalts, SW Iceland: effect of rock crystallinity and secondary minerals on chemical fluxes to the ocean. *American Journal of Science* 301, p. 513–556.

Sulphur deposits from geothermal steam.
Sulphur was mined and exported for centuries.
(RTH)

9 The subterranean powerhouse

Geothermal energy is one of Iceland's most important natural resources. The country ranks in fourth place in the world in terms of direct utilisation of geothermal energy. In Iceland, magma and hot host rocks lie close to the surface. Many features of geothermal activity, such as warm springs, steam vents and chemical deposits, are found in most parts of the country, including ice-free areas within glaciers and ice caps. The Great Geysir is world renowned. The Icelanders have learnt to harness and utilise geothermal energy in many ways, from the baking of rye bread and drying fish to sophisticated technical production of hot water for domestic use, steam for industrial use and electricity. The know-how is exported.

Key words

Heat flow • heat gradient • low-temperature geothermal systems (and areas or fields) • high-temperature geothermal systems (and areas or fields) • chemical alteration • geothermal resources • geothermal utilisation • drilling • IDDP-project

Conditions for geothermal activity in Iceland

Hot crust at relatively shallow depth is one of the prerequisites for geo-thermal heat on the Earth's surface and thus for geothermal utilisation. In Iceland there are many magma chambers, old and young, at depths of a few kilometres. Along with smaller cooling intrusions, they heat the surrounding bedrock. Other intrusions, mainly dykes, push partly or completely towards the surface in volcanically active areas and also provide a heat source. Upward and lateral flow of hot mantle material under the whole country also further heats the overlying crust (i.e. the plates). In Iceland the heat flow close to the neovolcanic zone is about four times greater than the heat flow furthest away from it.

For all these reasons the temperature at depths of 500–2,000 m is generally between 30 and 300°C in Iceland. The temperature gradient is high compared to that of the continents, which is around 15–30°C/km. In the Icelandic crust it is generally 50–100°C/km but in places reaches 150°C/km and more. In the Tertiary areas it is 47–86° C/km but in a 15–50 km belt bordering the neovolcanic zone it reaches 120–165°C/km. An area with an anomalous high gradient is found within the Tertiary bedrock in Breiðafjörður. Within the neovolcanic zone the temperature gradient is generally lower in the uppermost rock layers due to groundwater movement, but is high still lower down, reaching 300–400°C/km. The highest recorded temperature from drillholes at just over 2,000 m deep is 380°C, in the Hengill area. At 5 km deep the temperature is believed to be at least 500–600°C.

It takes more to utilise geothermal areas on the Earth's surface than high rock temperature. Copious precipitation in the form of ground-water must penetrate to sufficient depth and become heated there to above the mean annual temperature on the surface. Also, the geother-mal water must have easy access to the surface. Porous, fractured and faulted bedrock with dyke intrusions ensures high permeability. Good permeability is another prerequisite for geothermal utilisation. The third is sufficient groundwater. The water reacts with the rocks and removes chemicals from them. These are dissolved minerals and gases. The water expands on heating, moves towards the surface and out-wards to the limits of each geothermal area where it cools, partly as a result of mixing with cold groundwater. With falling pressure the gas

Winter conditions in the hybrid geothermal area
of Hveravellir, central Iceland. (RTH)

also expands, which contributes to the upward flow. Inflow of colder
surrounding water cools the bedrock and promotes fracturing which
again allows water to enter still deeper into the hotter regions. Most
geothermal areas comprise a system of time-dependent geothermal
fluid convection cells which interact with the general groundwater
flow. Time-dependency is partly a result of the plate spreading as geothermal areas slide away from the rift zones. Furthermore, tectonic
episodes change geothermal fields if new fractures channel steam or
water to the surface. Chemical deposits may also clog fluid channels
and force the fluid to the surface along new channels. Part of the geothermal fluid escapes all the way to the surface, in accordance with the
bedrock permeability, fractures and the landscape, forming the visual
aspect of each geothermal area. The reservoirs, however, hold much
much more energy than is displayed at the surface.

Geothermal areas can be found in most regions (or counties) in the country, but to a lesser extent in the east, although there are a few areas even there. The bedrock is generally hot enough there but there is a shortage of groundwater. Natural hot-water springs outside the neovolcanic zone are not very conspicuous. They yield about 1,800 l/s with individual springs issuing up to 100 l/s. Because of extensive drilling in the regions outside the neovolcanic zone, a total of at least 6,000-7,000 l/s is taken from each of some subterranean hot-water reservoirs while others are left untouched. In the active volcanic regions, however, far more spectacular natural thermal areas boast steam vents (fumaroles), boiling or gas-emission mud pools (solfataras) and colourful patches of altered rocks and chemical deposits. These areas yield a far greater amount of energy in the form of high-pressure steam, blasting through many drilled wells, than do the geothermal fields outside the neovolcanic zone.

Types of geothermal area and their characteristics

Geothermal areas in Iceland are traditionally classified into two groups: high-temperature areas and low-temperature areas. In high-temperature areas the rock temperature is 200°C or more at 1,000 m deep in drillholes but does not exceed 150°C at 1,000 m deep in low-tempera-

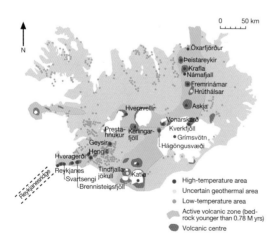

Geothermal areas in Iceland. The number of high-temperature areas may vary according to what is specified as an individual geothermal area. Knowledge of the subglacial thermal fields is limited with the exception of Grímsvötn. (Main source: National Energy Authority and Iceland GeoSurvey)

ture areas. In the latter the temperature is in many areas 100°C or below, although in some cases it is 120–140°C, such as for example in the Reykjavík area, due to the proximity of a 2–3-million-year-old central volcano.

Another classification scheme with four types of geothermal area takes account of the temperature, pressure and proportion of steam in each geothermal reservoir, or in part of it, and is at the same time indicating the the type of the geothermal fluid:

1. A **water system** (liquid-saturated system) where no boiling occurs. This would be typical for low-temperature areas.

2. A **steam system** (steam-saturated system) where all the liquid is present as steam. This type is chiefly found as the uppermost part of a few reservoirs.

3. A **boiling system** (two-phase system) where both water and steam are present. Type 2 and 3 comprise most high-temperature areas down to 3–4 km deep, with type 3 predominant.

4. An **overheated system** (supercritical) with a special type of stem/fluid (plasma) under very high pressure and at temperatures above 375°C at 222 bar pressure. This type would be found as deep-level reservoirs beneath many geothermal fields commonly classified as ordinary high-temperature areas.

Hybrid geothermal areas may incorporate both type 1 and type 3. They are commonly classified as high-temperature areas and include both steam vents and boiling or very hot water springs, even geysers. Examples are Hveravellir in central Iceland, the Hveragerði geothermal fields and the Geysir geothermal area.

The main characteristics of a high-temperature geothermal area are: extensive alteration of the rocks (clay formation), a high proportion of dissolved solids in the geothermal fluid, acid solutions, steam and clay hot springs on the surface, sulphur precipitation and a pervading smell of hydrogen sulphide. The temperature of the springs is 90–100°C

Colourful high-temperature geothermal features
in the Torfajökull Volcanic System. (RTH)

while in drillholes it is 200–350°C. The liquid is acid (pH=2–4) and the
amount of dissolved solids very variable. In many high-temperature
areas it is 1,000–2,000 ppm (or mg/l), silica (as opal), sodium, chlorine
and sulphur compounds being most common. On the Reykjanes
peninsula there are several high-temperature geothermal areas which
have geothermal fluid considerably mixed with sea water and the

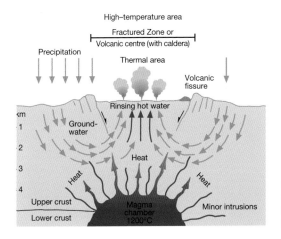

High–temperature area

Fractured Zone or
Volcanic centre (with caldera)

Precipitation

Thermal area

Volcanic
fissure

Rinsing hot water

km
.1   Ground-
      water
.2

.3

.4

Heat

Heat   Heat

Upper crust   Minor intrusions
                    Magma
                    chamber
Lower crust   1200°C

A simplified explanation of
a typical high-temperature
area. (From: A.T. Guðmundsson (ed.) 1989)

amount of dissolved solids reaches over 30,000 ppm because of a very high content of sodium, potassium, calcium and chlorine. Of the gases, the greatest quantities are of carbon dioxide, sulphur dioxide and hydrogen sulphide but hydrogen, nitrogen and others also occur. The clay in high-temperature geothermal areas is mostly altered basalt. A few clay minerals occur, mainly light in colour, with montmorillonite and kaolin being commonest. The clay is usually coloured grey by iron sulphide or red by iron oxides. The clay is also mixed with chemical deposits. The largest quantities occurring are light-coloured silica (silica oxide), yellow sulphur, grey-black iron sulphide or white gypsum (calcium sulphate).

The main characteristics of low-temperature areas are: relatively little alteration of the rocks, much lower amounts of dissolved solids than in high-temperature areas, water springs and pools on the surface and precipitation in the surrounding area. The temperature of the water in the springs and pools is 20–100°C but 50–150°C in drillholes. The water is commonly alkaline (pH 8–10) with a dissolved solid content in the range 150–450 ppm (or mg/l). Silica, sodium, chloride and sulphate are the most common chemical components. The gas content is low. Nitrogen and carbon dioxide are the most common gases and in some cases, such as in Reykjavík, a small amount of hydrogen sulphide

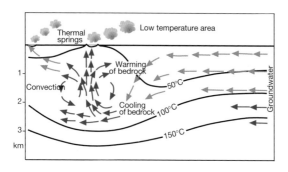

A simplified explanation of a typical low-temperature area. (Modified after: A. Björnsson et al. 1990)

(harmless) gives the hot water a distinct odour. Silica deposits and some calcium carbonate commonly form deposits around thermal vents, the latter compound more around lukewarm springs with a fairly high carbon dioxide content. In water springs and at submarine hydrothermal vents a varied array of organisms exists, comprising bacteria and algae as well as small animals.

Cold or warm geothermal springs containing a large amount of carbon dioxide are found, for example, on the Snæfellsnes peninsula (including Rauðamelsölkelda in Hnappadalur), in Hveragil at Kverkfjöll and in the southeast (including at the lake Þveit at Höfn in the southeast). Precipitation in these cases is mostly silica oxide and a little calcium carbonate (travertine). Icelanders call such common soda water springs ölkeldur which translates literally as ale pits.

Dissolved solids in geothermal fluids provide an indication of their temperature at depth (chemical thermometers). The use of chemical thermometers is based on a determination of the amount of particular chemicals in the fluid at the surface and calculating the fluid temperature when the chemical fluids were last in equilibrium with the reservoir rock. Most frequently used are the quartz/chalcedony thermometer or the cation thermometer (Na^+/K^+, $Na^+/K^+/Ca^{++}$ and $Na^+/K^+/Ca^{++}/Mg^{++}$).

The origins and location of geothermal fields

There are 20 main high-temperature geothermal areas in the country associated with volcanic systems in the rifting and volcanic zones or close to them. An additional 6–8 areas are evident at the surface but less is known about them because they are under glacier ice or have not yet been investigated. Some high-temperature geothermal areas are below sea level on the Reykjanes Ridge and others are in the Tjörnes fracture zone and on the Kolbeinsey Ridge. Vigorous hot springs and precipitation have been found there which suggest the presence of active black smokers.

High-temperature geothermal areas derive their heat from intrusions and magma chambers, while the water sources are fractures and dykes which allow deep flow of groundwater. Strong convection occurs in the reservoirs, especially where the cold groundwater flow is rich. It is estimated that the deep temperature in systems close to shallow magma chambers reaches at least 400–500°C and therefore supercritical level, the water probably penetrating down to a depth of 4–5 km. The energy in geothermal areas is usually variable with time, being most during eruption and in the following years, with considerable cooling taking place between volcanic episodes. When at a maximum the energy of the more powerful areas is in the order of 2,000–5,000 MW, as for example in the case of the Torfajökull area and in Grímsvötn, although energy of between 500–2,000 MW is most common. An efficiency of 10–20% can be assumed in energy production schemes up to the present day. Among the better known high-temperature areas are Krafla, Þeistareykir, Kverkfjöll, Grímsvötn, Torfajökull, Hengill, Svartsengi and Reykjanes. Lesser known areas include Katla and Prestahnúkur in Langjökull.

There are almost 260 low-temperature areas in Iceland with at least 700 hot springs. They are found in all parts of the country although least common in the central highlands and the eastern fjords. Most of the low-temperature areas are related to old tectonic fractures, that are

The main high-temperature areas

Name	Elevation m. a.s.l.	Size km2	Remark
Reykjanes	20	2	Production
Eldvörp	40	1	Wells
Svartsengi	40	10	Production
Krýsuvík/ Trölladyngja	70–250	60+	Wells
Brennisteinsfjöll	300	2	
Hengill (I/II/II)	150–600	100+	Production
Geysir	120	3	Protected
Kerlingarfjöll	900–1000	11	Remote
Hveravellir	600	1	Protected
Torfajökull	600–1,100	140	Partly prot.
Grímsvötn	1,300–1,500	65	Inaccessible (subglacial)
Vonarskarð	1,000	11	Remote
Köldukvíslar- botnar	800	9	Submerged
Kverkfjöll	1,300–1,800	25	Mostly glaciated
Askja	1,100–1,300	25	Remote
Fremrinámar	800–900	4	Remote
Námafjall/ Bjarnarflag	300–400	8	Production
Krafla	400–500	30+	Production
Þeistareykir	400	20	Accessible
Öxarfjörður	0–25	30	Accessible

(Main source: National Energy Authority)

Foul-smelling, sulphur-rich boiling mud pots (solfataras) at Námafjall (Hverarönd), northeast Iceland. (RTH)

variously active, and to dykes or dyke swarms. The heat energy warming up groundwater in low-temperature areas has different origins. The heat may be conducted from old intrusions into the bedrock or from recent intrusions in the case of lateral zones close to the neovolcanic zone. The heat source can also be the result of general heat flux from below or from neighbouring rift zones and volcanic zones. The water in low-temperature areas comes from distant areas as deep flow or from neighbouring areas, in particular geothermal areas. Local movement of the water (upward and downward flow) facilitates heat extraction from the bedrock. It is thought that cold water receives heat mainly by four processes:

— Water flows at deep and hot levels into the hot crust from highland regions to fractured lowlands at a steady state.
— Water undergoes convective flow in young permeable, tectonic fractures in a more or less impermeable hot bedrock. This flow and the local discharge of hot water draw local cold water into the convective flow.
— Water undergoes convective flow in a dying high-temperature reservoir.
— Water receives heat from recent intrusions into permeable bedrock.

The second and third processes seem the most likely, especially in the case of the larger and hotter geothermal fields.

Among the better known low-temperature geothermal areas are Laugardalur in Reykjavík, Reykir in Mosfellsbær, Reykholtsdalur in Borgarfjörður, Reykjanes in Ísafjarðardjúp, Laugaland near Akureyri and Flúðir in southern Iceland. New low-temperature areas are constantly being discovered through exploration and drilling. The efficiency of energy exploitation in low-temperature areas is high.

The above-mentioned mixed or hybrid areas, with hot water and steam springs, are mainly old groundwater-rich high-temperature areas which are gradually changing into low-temperature areas (for example, the Geysir area in Haukadalur). Normal erupting springs such as Geysir and Strokkur are formed where water can suddenly boil in water-filled pipes or fractures. In order to attain flash boiling, the tem-

Strokkur (Geysir geothermal field) –
the start of an eruption. RTH

perature at depth must exceed 100°C, or in other words boiling point at a certain pressure and corresponding depth. A pressure release occurs if the water starts to flow from the over-filled vent. At a given critical pressure the high temperature brings the deep-seated water to a very sudden boil and flash steam production occurs. The phase change causes a manifold volume increase in the pipe and the geyser erupts. In some cases geysers spout constantly but only produce low columns of steamy water. The large geysers are all concentrated in Haukadalur but smaller ones occur in Hveragerði (Grýta), Reykholtsdalur (Árhver),

341

Svartsengi Power Plant (Sudurnes Regional Heating Company), close to the Blue Lagoon, produces electricity and hot water. The new

Reykjanes Power Plant, southwest of Svartsengi, supplies 100 MW to the national transmission grid. (RTH)

Reykjahverfi (Uxahver) and at Hveravellir (Öskurhóll). In all cases, the geysers undergo changes in activity and may lie dormant for long periods. Soap has sometimes been used to bring about the needed pressure release.

Power is so plentiful ...

Iceland's geothermal areas represent an enormous amount of energy. The accessible heat content in the shallow crust (dry or wet, less than 3 km deep) is estimated at an equivalent of 2.8×10^{10} GWh. Technically exploitable energy is thought to be about 900,000 GWh. After taking economic and environmental factors and accessibility into consideration, it is thought to be closer to 40,000–50,000 GWh. Up till now only less than 1% of the technically accessible heat energy has been utilised and somewhat over 10% of the more environmentally exploitable part.

Icelanders use more primary energy than other nations or about 500 GJ per capita per year (2004). For electricity alone the annual energy generation amounts to over 28,000 kWh per person and is explained by the extensive energy-intensive metal industry relative to the population. About 70% of the primary energy is obtained from domestic energy sources, hydro- and geothermal energy, which are for the most part pollution free, geothermal energy accounting for just over half the total amount. Most of it is used for domestic heating rather than for electricity production, although this is increasing rapidly in proportion.

In low-temperature areas which are already largely utilised, the water can be used directly from springs or, as is more often the case, directly from drillholes, for domestic or space heating. The wells are 200–2,000 m deep. In high-temperature areas, on the other hand, steam (seldom water) from drillholes (1,000–2,500 m deep) is utilised. The steam is used in industry or for electricity production. Much of the hot-water supply for space heating is also produced by making use of this steam and/or overflow water in heat exchangers where cold groundwater is heated to the temperature required by the clients. Experiments have been conducted to reinject geothermal fluids into high-temperature reservoirs.

Most of the geothermal energy is used for space heating (about 5,700 GWh or 63%). In 2005 the geothermal energy used to produce electricity was about 18% of the total utilised geothermal energy (about 1,500 GWh) and the power output was 200 MW (20% of the total electrical output) but within a decade or so these figures will have increased dramatically to over 540 MW. In comparison electricity production as a whole was about 7,800 GWh in 2003 and 82% was produced by hydroelectric schemes (or about 1,150 MW). This figure increases considerably as the new Kárahnjúkur power plant comes into operation and changes the relative proportions (see chapter 8). On the other hand, increased energy production using geothermal steam will come about with the new geothermal power plant at Reykjanes (100 MW) and on Hellisheiði at Hengill (up to 210 MW, and later on still more). Further plans have been made for new geothermal power plants.

The many uses of "Earth heat"

In the past, utilisation of geothermal energy was limited to direct use of water from warm or boiling springs. Bathing and washing in "the Earth's warm water" was widespread in the districts where there are surface manifestations of geothermal energy. The medieval "Snorri's Pool" at Reykholt is a prime example of this.

Attempts were made in the 18th and 19th centuries to use geothermal energy in gardening and in the 1920s the first attempts were made to heat greenhouses with hot water or steam. District heating began in 1930 in Reykjavík and by 1944 almost 3,000 buildings in the capital were heated by geothermal means. Soon other applications were found for the hot water from drillholes, such as in an increasing number of swimming pools and in steam turbines for generating electricity. The first small-scale plant was developed in the late 1960s (at Mývatn) and the first large-scale plant in 1974–77 (Krafla Power Plant).

Geothermal energy production is not pollution free, as it speeds up the release of volcanic gases from the interior of the earth. The pollution, however, is quite small relative to the amount of energy and compared to most other means of energy production. Carbon dioxide from high-temperature power plants amounts, for example, to 5% of the total manmade CO_2-emission in Iceland. The energy source is renewable, which should also be taken into consideration.

These are the main forms of geothermal utilisation in Iceland:

1. District space heating (domestic)

Today about 87% of all buildings in Iceland are connected to district heating services (*hitaveita* in Icelandic) or private wells. Now, over 20 municipally owned district heating services operate many dozens of wells (out of more than 200 sunk into the crust), pumping plants and storage tanks to supply water to consumers. In Reykjavík, four main fields, in town and outside, supply about 2,500 l/s of 82–132°C water to all the municipalities in the Greater Reykjavík area. But this amount would not be enough and the low-temperature reservoirs would not cope with a much larger outflow. Therefore, the Hengill high-tempera-

Nesjavellir Power Plant (Reykjavík Energy)
pipes hot water to Reykjavík, 27 km distant,
and produces electricity. (RTH)

ture area (including Nesjavellir Geothermal Power Plant) has been developed to add to the distribution system by producing hot water from
condensate and steam-run heat exchangers (see **www.or.is**, the website
of Orkuveita Reykjavíkur/Reykjavík Energy, for details and new devel-
opments). A similar high-tech power plant operates at Svartsengi on
the Reykjanes peninsula and provides the nearby towns, e.g. Keflavík,
with hot water (see **www.hs.is**, the website of Hitaveita Suðurnesja/
Suðurnes Regional Heating Corporation, for details). The country-
wide geothermal heating system saves an amount of money equal to
the cost of the total oil import to Iceland (2001). The cost of heating an
average family house in Iceland is, for example, about one third of the
cost in Sweden.

2. Hot tap water

Most of the hot tap water is geothermal. The water is either acquired
directly from wells through pumping stations and storage tanks, along
with the water used for space heating, or produced in the above-mentioned power plants and piped to buildings along with the space-heating water. In either case, although harmless, it is not suitable for consumption.

A geothermal drill rig in operation at the Krafla
Power Plant (National Power Company). (RTH)

3. Space heating (cultivation)

Cultivation (mainly flowers and vegetables) in geothermally heated
greenhouses started in 1924. Currently, the area under glass is 190,000 m^2.
The use of artificial lighting and enrichment of carbon dioxide in greenhouses has proven beneficial for the trade. The greenhouses are run by
farmers or small firms and commonly located in small communities or
villages.

4. Soil heating

Outdoor soil heating has been increasingly employed in the past decades. The technique is used to speed up the growth of traditional vegetables such as potatoes, turnips, carrots, and trees for replanting.

5. Electricity

Another widespread use of geothermal power is generation of electricity. This is chiefly done by making high-pressure steam drive special
turbines. The first 3MW geothermal power plant rose at Lake Mývatn

(1969) and subsequently the Krafla Power Plant added 30 MW to the transmission network. It largely escaped damage during the Krafla Fires in 1975–84 and was enlarged to 60 MW in 1997 (possibly to be increased to 100 MW). Two other geothermal power plants produce hot water as well as electricity. At Svartsengi (since 1977) there are now four plants operating: plant 2 produces hot water (75 l/ s from 3 steam/ groundwater heat exchangers), plant 3 puts out 6 MW (back pressure turbine unit), plant 4 has 7 binary units each generating 1.2 MW of electrical power and plant 5 turns out 30 MW electric power by a condenser turbine and 240 l/s of hot water. The company will operate a 100 MW power plant at Reykjanes in 2007. At Nesjavellir, the plant started operation in 1990. The hot-water production was stable at 560 l/s during the plant's first phase but is gradually being tripled. The electricity generation has risen from a few megawatts in the beginning to 90 MW (by 2001), with a 30 MW addition in 2005. At Hellisheiði the company will operate a 120 MW plant in 2007 with a possible 90 MW increase later on and other plants in the vicinity might add still more power. There is a binary plant in Húsavík, northeast Iceland, producing 2 MW for electric consumption and all the necessary hot water for space heating in the town. There are plans for more exploratory drilling and possibly new power plants.

6. Industrial steam

Industrial use of steam or very hot water has included, for example, the production of salt from geothermal brine, the drying of silica (diatomite) filter-aid mud (at Lake Mývatn), the drying of seaweed and kelp processing, the drying of fish and, on a small scale, the production of carbon dioxide, recycling of car tyres, production of concrete blocks and even traditional baking (slow-cooking) of rye bread.

7. Aquaculture

Hot water is used to speed up fish growth in fish farms, mainly at the hatching stage. This is done by using heat exchangers to raise the water temperature from 5°C to 10–12°C. The production from over 50 fish farms increases annually.

8. Health facilities

Popular use of the subterranean hot water in Iceland is manifested in many sorts of health institutions. They range from over 130 geothermally heated swimming pools to specialised hot mud baths for curing, for example, rheumatism. Effluent water from the Svartsengi Power Plant is used to create a warm lagoon of a heavenly blue colour, set in a rough black lava field, the Blue Lagoon Heath Spa. It resembles a tropical paradise and has proved popular and also beneficial in treating skin diseases like psoriasis. A similar but smaller operation is found at Lake Mývatn and more are planned.

9. Snow-melting systems

Geothermal energy is useful in the changeable Icelandic winter weather when it comes to snow-melting and de-icing parking spaces, sidewalks, streets and shopping areas. Waste water from space-heating facilities or directly from buildings is used at 30–35°C but it is common to boost the temperature with hotter water when the load is high. An area of some 350,000–400,000 m^2 is currently underlain by snow-melting pipes, of which 280,000 m^2 are in Reykjavík.

Future prospects

Evidently, Iceland's future prospects are bright in the field of geothermal utilisation. There is still a great deal of energy to harness and the scientific and technical know-how is already at the forefront on a world scale. Expertise is exported to a number of countries and the United Nations Geothermal Training Program operates in context with the National Energy Authority and Icelandic GeoSurvey (**www.os.is and www.isor.is**) in Reykjavík.

Space heating by geothermal means is still growing. Major progress is being made in the search for and utilisation of geothermal reservoirs in areas previously designated as "cold".

When it comes to generation of electricity, the scope is vast. The most economical power plants are those producing electricity as well as hot water or steam for large-scale use. The environmental impact of large geothermal power plants is different and much smaller than that of equally powerful reservoir-based hydropower plants.

Currently, exploratory drilling, power-plant preparations or additions to existing power plants are being carried out at several locations. A new power plant is taking shape at Hellisheiði (Reykjavík Energy), a 100 MW plant is rising at Reykjanes and similar facilities might be constructed at Trölladyngja (both for Suðurnes Regional Heating Corp.). The National Energy Authority plans to extend the Krafla Power Plant and has considered building a new power plant at Bjarnar-flag/Námafjall (**www.landsvirkjun.is**).

The company also conducts studies, in cooperation with the National Energy Authority, of geothermal high-temperature areas in Central Iceland that have not yet been developed. A company based in northeast Iceland is aiming for energy production at geothermal fields such as Þeistareykir. Industrial uses of steam are under consideration, ranging from the extraction of magnesium from geothermal brine to specified production of food or chemical goods. The first steps in replacing fossil fuels in transport and in the fishing fleet with hydrogen produced by electrolysis have already been taken (**www.newenergy.is**). The demand for an environmentally sound generation of electricity for this purpose looks promising for the geothermal power and hydro-power industries.

Perhaps the most interesting project in the future scope of the geothermal industry is the Iceland Deep-Drilling Project. The IDDP is an international project with the involvement of the National Energy Authority, National Power Company, Reykjavík Energy and Suðurnes Regional Heating Corporation. It aims to drill 2–3 exploratory wells 4–5 km into the crust in the Reykjanes, Hengill or Krafla high-temperature areas and to reach reservoir depths at a supercritical level. Drilling of the first well is already underway (2005). If successful, and if the plasma-fluid can be harnessed, it is hoped that each well will produce 20–40 MW instead of the current 4–8 MW (see **www.os.is**). This would vastly increase the potential output of geothermal wells, not only in Iceland but in other countries where high-temperature areas are found.

Beautiful hot-water springs and silica deposits
at Hveravellir, central Iceland. (RTH)

Where to go?

A description of typical localities and cases serves to promote further studies.

The following list directs readers to some of the more typical study sites.

For more information refer to scientific papers or the road guide by T. Thordarson and A. Höskuldsson: *Iceland, Classical Geology in Europe 3*, Terra 2002. The National Energy Authority has published a wealth of reports on the exploration of many geothermal fields and areas (commonly in Icelandic only).

Note: It is vital to take great care when walking through geothermal fields where there are no marked or prepared trails.

1. *Reykjanes.* In the main graben at Reykjanes there is a large high-temperature geothermal area with many easily accessible hot

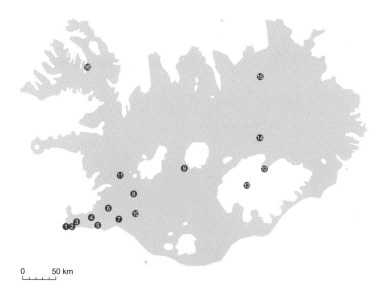

0   50 km

springs. These are mostly steam and mud springs but boiling-water springs also occur. There are around 20 drillholes and part of the steam was used for a period in salt production by distilling and also to dry fish. Information on geothermal energy and its exploitation is provided at the new Reykjanes plant. The reservoir fluids are saline. From 1930 to 1960 geothermal clay from Reykjanes was used, mixed with Pleistocene clay from Búðardalur, in ceramic production with reasonable success.

2. *Eldvörp* is the name of a geothermal area associated with a recent eruptive fissure between Reykjanes and Grindavík. The Suðurnes municipality has its drillholes here. The area is special in that steam emerges from the sides of scoria and spatter craters. A road runs to Eldvörp from Svartsengi.

3. *Blue Lagoon – Svartsengi*. The geothermal area at Svartsengi near the town of Grindavík employs many drillholes to produce hot water for domestic use by heating cold groundwater in heat exchangers and also to produce electricity using steam turbines

The young volcanic centre of Hengill, northeast of Reykjavik. Soon, three geothermal power plants will operate within the volcanic system (last eruption 2,000 years ago). Lake Þingvalla-vatn spreads out behind the mountain. (RTH)

and binary units. There is little evidence of hot-spring activity on the surface although steam from drillholes is clearly visible as well as from effluent water. Part of the latter is used directly in the Blue Lagoon health resort, one of the most popular tourist attractions in the country. In addition the Suðurnes Regional Heating Corporation operates a visitor centre (Eldgjá) beside the power plant.

4. *Trölladyngja* is a móberg mountain about 6 km from the main road between Keflavík and Reykjavík. The mountain provides opportunities to examine eruption fissures, lavas and a high-

temperature geothermal area. Part of the area is still untouched to a large extent (e.g. at Sogin) but in the lowland north of Trölla-dyngja the first research holes have been drilled and may later be connected to the proposed power plant of the Suðurnes Regional Heating Corporation, along with further wells.

5. *Krýsuvík*. An interesting route running alongside Lake Kleifarvatn on the Reykjanes peninsula. A short distance from the southwestern end of the lake there is a high-temperature area on the mountainside at Seltún. It is usually named after the local farm of Krýsuvík. There are some shallow or closed drillholes but mostly natural steam and mud springs with access by good walking paths. Some years ago a drillhole exploded and caused damage to structures and the hot springs.

6. *Hengill-Nesjavellir*. Hengill is an active central volcano with two adjacent centres of volcanic activity (Ölkelduháls-Hrómundar-tindur and Grensdalur). Natural springs are widespread and there are many marked walking routes. At the Nesjavellir Power Plant, Reykjavík Energy produces hot water by heating cold water in heat exchangers and also electricity using steam turbines. Future plans include the building of another power plant south of Hengill (Hellisheiði Power Plant) and possibly one or two more. Access to the geothermal area is easy from the road which runs around Þingvallavatn and from the main road over Hellisheiði and from Hveragerði.

7. *Hveragerði*. This small town is located on the main (ring) road in southern Iceland. Several thermal fields are available for examination in the centre and surroundings, while a small visitor centre welcomes guests. Like several other villages in Iceland, Hveragerði bases its economy to a large extent on greenhouse cultivation and health facilities. A walk into the valley of Grensdalur behind Hveragerði is highly recommended.

8. The small thermal field at *Haukadalur*, where the two largest geysers (Great Geysir and Strokkur) form the main attraction, is visited by thousands on a fine summer's day. Strokkur erupts every 5–10 minutes (20–35 m) but Geysir only occasionally and irregularly (up to 30–40 m). There are several other interesting small geysers or hot-water springs in the area as well as a visitor centre.

Geysir erupting to a height of about 60 m in the
1930s. (GH)

9. *Kerlingarfjöll* is a remote and impressive group of brightly coloured
peaks. There are several hot springs, one of which, Ytri Hveradalur, borders on firn snow and a small glacier. The access route is off
the Kjölur highland road and a four-wheel-drive vehicle is
advisable. A visitor centre operates during the summer. The
nearby Hveravellir has some nice hot-water springs with lovely silica sinter deposits.

10. *Flúðir.* Besides the Flúðir village, a few other villages in the
southern lowlands attract visitors. Different geothermally based
facilities and extensive greenhouse gardening are the main
attractions but there are few natural hot springs to study due to the
high degree of utilisation of the geothermal resources.

11. *Deildartunga–Reykholt–Húsafell.* The region in the upper reaches
of the Borgarfjörður district offers different study sites, ranging
from natural springs, such as Árhver, to harnessed but still impressive springs like Deildartunguhver (the largest single hot-water
spring in Iceland) and the ancient cultural site of Reykholt, also

Natural steam vents (fumaroles) and clay mud
pits (solfataras) in the Kerlingarfjöll mountain
massif. (RTH)

based on geothermal resources. The resort at Húsafell bases some
of its activities on similar resources and is open all year round.

12. *Kverkfjöll*. The Hveradalur valley in the middle of the high
glaciated Kverkfjöll volcano is probably the most impressive
geothermal area in Iceland. Access is either from the south (long)
and requires the use of superjeeps, skidoos or skis, or from the
Kverkfjöll hut (Sigurðarskáli) to the north. This approach requires
a full day's hike, partly on snow, but is normally crevasse free
(700–800 m elevation difference, 20 km total distance).

The Kverkfjöll high-temperature geothermal area is associated with the central volcano by the same name on the northern edge of Vatnajökull. (RTH)

The Blue Lagoon is a well known spa not far
from the Keflavík International Airport. (RTH)

13. *Grímsvötn*. A very impressive glaciated caldera in the central snowfields of the Vatnajökull Ice Cap. The geothermal fields are partly visible in ice-free areas at the caldera rim and where recent volcanic eruptions have occurred. A visit to Grímsvötn requires some sort of vehicle transport from the west (Jökulheimar) or east (Jöklasel, Skálafellsjökull) or a long ski expedition and experience in glacier travel.

14. *Askja*. Askja is the ice-free counterpart of Grímsvötn. The geothermal fields are not easily accessible as they are perched on the steep slopes of the inner caldera rim, above the lake of Öskjuvatn.

15. *Krafla–Námaskarð*.While the central area of the Krafla Volcanic System is large and literally dotted with small and large thermal fields (steam vents, mud pots, etc.), it is also the site of recent volcanic eruptions and the Krafla Geothermal Power Plant. Námaskarð (or Hverarönd) is much smaller and lies closer to the Lake Mývatn area (and the main road) and is noted for particularly impressive solfataras. Still closer to the Reykjahlíð village is Bjarnarflag with the former diatomite factory. A fine geothermal health spa is located opposite Bjarnarflag (Lónið or Jarðböð), at Jarðbaðshólar. The Mývatn area is noted for tectonic fissures where eerie caves filled with warm water (sometimes too hot) have been used for bathing through the ages.

16. *Reykjanes*. This former site of a regional school in Ísafjarðardjúp is interesting in its own right. Natural hot springs as well as harnessed geothermal vents are found on the small peninsula in the large fjord. Springs with corals are located in the shallow beach area.

Selected bibliography

Surnames are written in italics. The Icelandic letters é, ó, á, ú, í and ý should be written as e, o, a, u, i and y, ö as ö, oe or simply o, æ as æ or ae, ð as d and þ as th when searching for references and papers in most databases.

H. *Ármansson* and H. *Kristmannsdóttir* 1993: Geothermal environmental impact. *Geothermics*, 21– 5/6: 869–880.

S. *Arnórsson*, S. *Sigurðsson* and H. *Svavarsson* 1982. The chemistry of geothermal waters in Iceland I. Calculation aqueous specitation from 0°-350°C. *Geochimica et Cosmochimica Acta*: 46: 1,513–1,532.

S. *Arnórsson*, E. *Gunnlaugsson* and H. *Svavarsson* 1983. The chemistry of geothermal waters in Iceland II. Mineral equilibria and independent variables controlling water composition. *Geochimica et Cosmochimica Acta*: 47: 547–566.

S. *Arnórsson* 1985. The use of mixing models and chemical geothermometers for estimating underground temperature in geothermal systems. *Journal of Volcanology and Geothermal Research* 23: 299–335.

S. *Arnórsson* and S.R. *Gíslason* 1990. Um uppruna lághitasvæða á Íslandi (with English summary: On the origin of low-temperature activity in Iceland). *Náttúrufræðingurinn* 60(1): 39–56.

S. *Arnórsson* 1995. Geothermal systems in Iceland. Structure and conceptual models. 1. High temperature areas. *Geothermics* 24: 561–601

A. *Björnsson*, G. *Axelsson* and Ó. G. *Flóvenz* 1990. Uppruni hvera og lauga á Íslandi (with English summary: On the nature of hot springs in Iceland). *Náttúrufræðingurinn* 60(1): 15–39.

Ó. G. *Flóvenz* and K. *Sæmundsson* 1992. Iceland. In: E. Hurtig, R. Haenel and A. Zui: *Geothermal Atlas of Europe*. Explanatory text. Hermann Haack Verlag, p. 48–51.

I. B. *Friðleifsson* 1979. Geothermal activity in Iceland. *Jökull* 29.

I. B. *Friðleifsson* 1995. Historical aspects of geothermal utilization in Iceland. *Proceedings of the World Geothermal Congress 1995*. Italy

A.T. *Guðmundsson* (ed.) 1989. *Energy resources and dams in Iceland*. The Icelandic Commitee on Large Dams, the National Energy Authority and the National Power Company. Reykjavík.

E. *Gunnlaugsson*, Á. *Ragnarsson* and V. *Stefánsson* 2001. Geothermal Energy in Iceland. *International Symposium in Izmir*, Turkey, 4–5 Oct. 2001. (www.or.is and www.samorka.is).

V.K. *Jónsson*, R.L. *Gunnarsson*, B. *Árnason*, and Þ.I. *Sigfússon* 1992. The Feasibility of Using Geothermal Energy in Hydrogen Production, *Geothermics* 21 – 5/6: 673–681.

H. *Kristmannsdóttir* and H. *Ármannsson* 1996. Chemical Monitoring of Icelandic Geothermal Fields during Production. *Geothermics*, 25: 349–364.

B. *Líndal* 1973. Industrial and other applications of geothermal energy except power production and district heating. *Geothermal Energy*. UNESCO LC 7279: 135–148. Paris.

Á. *Ragnarsson* 2000. Geothermal development in Iceland 1995–1999. *Proceedings of the World Geothermal Congress 2000*. I: 363–375. Kyushu-Tohoku. Japan.

V. *Stefánsson* 1992. Success in geothermal development. *Geothermics* 21: 823–834.

V. *Stefánsson* et al 1995. Geothermal reservoir management in Iceland. *Proceedings of the World Geothermal Congress 1995*, 3: 1,763–1,768. Florence, Italy.

S. *Þórhallson* 1988. Experience in developing and utilizing geothermal resources in Iceland. *Geothermics* 17: 205–223.

Ignimbrite from the late Tertiary period in
Berufjörður, eastern Iceland. (RTH)

10 A young country

The Earth's history is very long by human standards. It starts with the formation of the planet 4,500–5,000 million years ago. Plate-movement episodes with accompanying orogenic events, numerous large eruptions and ice ages occupied the first few billions of years. The maximum age of Iceland is 20–25 million years and the country is therefore among the Earth's youngest landmasses of a similar size. Examination of the strata, their composition and internal arrangement, many kinds of landforms (landscape) and many fossils makes it possible to retell the history of the Earth. One basic premise of the method is that the present is the key to the past. The same processes that can be observed at present have always been active on Earth.

Key words:

Late Tertiary • Quaternary Ice Age • glacial periods • interglacial periods • fossils • sea-level fluctuations • Holocene

The framework

The two most recent geological eras are the Quaternary, which began with the first global glacial period about 1.8–2.0 million years ago and the Tertiary, which was a much longer warmer era before it. The Tertiary era began around the time of the opening of the northern Atlantic about 65 million years ago. Around the same time the mammals came into their own and flourished. The Quaternary era is the era of man in Earth's history. The last third of the Tertiary era and Quaternary are in effect Iceland's geological eras.

Volcanic activity in an area close to the latitude of Iceland insured that there was a land-bridge between the eastern and western continental landmasses for a long time. Fossils of land mammals suggest this.

Late in the Tertiary era, about 30–35 million years ago, the hot spot close to Iceland and an active spreading ridge east of Greenland began operating jointly, in full. The build-up of volcanic rocks in this area was so great that a new land area appeared in the North Atlantic, which formed the beginnings of Iceland. This period began just over 20 million years ago. The oldest dated surface rock in Iceland, in the east and west, is just over 16 million years old. Ever since, volcanism has added to the country, competing with rapid erosion and weathering, but the land-bridge disappeared under the sea long ago. This history of plate movement, ocean volcanism and the wandering of the hot spot is described in the third and fourth chapters of the book.

For the first few million years of Iceland's history the mean annual temperature was up to 8–10°C higher than at present. Deciduous trees were dominant. About 9–11 million years ago, it became gradually colder and more rapidly so about 7 million years ago. Conifers increased in numbers. The climate in Iceland changed from being similar to that of the marine states of the eastern coast of the United States to that of the coast of southern Norway today. There were no glaciers on the mountains at this time. About 4 million years ago Iceland was for the most part covered in coniferous forest, following the disappearance of most of the large deciduous trees. The landscape was also less varied than it is now for most of the Tertiary era. It consisted of volcanoes and lava on extensive highland plains with some valleys, and the coastline

Lava enters the sea during the Surtsey eruption. This must have happened over and over again in the early geological history of Iceland (late Tertiary). (HB)

was probably indented by small fjords and coves. About 3.3 million years ago it had become so cold that the first glaciers began to form. The Ice Age had come to Iceland. For the northern hemisphere as a whole the Quaternary Ice Age is considered to have started 1.8–2.0 million years ago. Great climatic fluctuations began and became the norm as time passed. During glacial periods, usually of around 100,000 years' duration or more, 50–90% of the country was ice covered. There were probably over 20 glacial periods. Between them were warmer intergla-

363

cial periods when conditions resembled those of the last 10,000 years (the Holocene). The interglacial periods were mostly 10,000–20,000 years long. Great denudation took place during the glacial periods.

Different formations

It is customary in geology to divide the bedrock into main sequences or formations that have certain characteristics and are also in general of different ages. This is usually a definition process where the development proceeds from some general outlines to a more exact and complex picture. In Iceland, this work started in the early 20th century with recognition of the Quaternary Ice Age formations and progressed to the late 1980s. Slightly different approaches are still used, both in the geomorphological and petrological sense, and one encounters different names for some formations along with different definitions. It is customary to name bedrock formations after places or geological time spans. The following overview is a useful hybrid.

The oldest part of the country is known as the Blágrýti formation (*blágrýti* = dark rock). Another term sometimes used is Late Tertiary, or sometimes just Tertiary formation. In age this is equivalent to the final stage of the Tertiary era, from about 3.3 to 6.5 million years ago. The formation is characterised by thick dipping lava units with reddish interbed horizons (sediments), dyke swarms of varying density, plutonic intrusions and the remains of eroded central volcanoes. The rocks are either normally or reverse magnetised and span many reversal events.

Formations from the very end of the Tertiary era, ca. 2.0 –3.0 million years ago, and from the internationally defined Quaternary Ice Age period, are classified as two formations of different ages. The older is called the Older Grágrýti and Móberg formation or simply the Grágrýti formation (*grágrýti* = greyish rock and *móberg* = hyaloclastic tuff). The term dolerite for *grágrýti* may turn up in older literature. Another, more common name is the Plio-Pleistocene formation, as it bridges the Pliocene epoch of the Tertiary and far into the Pliocene of the Quaternary Ice Age. Its age is 0.78–3.3 million years.

Old lava layers (8–9 million years BP) in the east of Iceland. The landward tilt is related to istostatic movements. (RTH)

The younger formation, i.e. from late in the Quaternary, is called the Younger Grágrýti and Móberg formation (or simply the Younger Grágrýti formation). Other names sometimes used are the Late Quaternary formation or Upper Pleistocene formation. Its rocks are younger than 780,000 years but older than 10,000 years in age. The division by age is chosen to coincide with the last major geomagnetic reversal in geological history, which occurred 0.78 million years ago.

The characteristics of the older formation are lava piles, including lava-shield flows, greatly eroded móberg formations and marine or land sediments. The characteristics of the younger formation are fairly complete lavas (including lava shields) and individual eroded volcanoes, slightly eroded móberg (hyaloclastite) mountains and tuff formations, as well as marine and land sediments.

Rocks dating from the onset of the Pleistocene (about 2 million years ago) to the last magnetic reversal (780,000 years ago) classify as the Lower Pleistocene Formation but there has been little need for such a term because extensive glaciation had already occurred in Iceland by that time. However, the term Lower Pleistocene is seen in the literature, referring to this period of time.

The youngest major formation in the country is the Holocene formation, younger than 10,000 years in age. Composed of lavas or sediments, the rocks have not been left untouched by the ice sheet of the final glacial period.

The following sections describe the main features of the geological and environmental history by periods.

16–35 million years BP

Greenland had long moved with the North American plate to the northwest over the fixed hot spot, which was under the western edge of Greenland at the beginning of the period. Some time later Greenland was situated west of the hot spot and the mantle plume was then active underneath the sea floor east of Greenland. It became more active as magma rose beneath the spreading ridge, which was somewhat further to the east from Greenland, i.e. in the vicinity of Iceland. This meant that the magma was sufficient to add considerably to the build up of volcanics. The first volcanic formations in the Iceland area probably emerged 20–25 million years ago. The spreading ridge was consistently getting closer to the hot spot with a resulting increase in volcanic activity until the two practically coincided and activity probably reached levels similar to those of today or even more intense. There are no dated rocks from this period in Iceland, 18–20 million years ago, but they might be found in deep drillholes in the far east and west of the country or beneath the sea floor off the present coast in the east and west.

It is unclear where dry land and the sea floor lay 18–25 million years ago at the latitude of Iceland. Plate spreading over the mantle plume, isostatic vertical movement of the crust, increasing distance between the continents and global sea level would all have had an effect on the existence of a probable land-bridge to the east or west of the Iceland area.

6–16 million years BP

The primitive Iceland continued to enlarge from before 16 million years ago, although it is difficult to estimate the size of the country, say, between 12 and 9 million years ago. The rifting zone was first active in the west of the country (in its present form). The crust that formed at this time is for the most part formed of slightly dipping tholeiite basalt lavas, which form thick and extensive expanses. The lavas are from 1 m to 60 m thick. The lava sequences resemble stacks of cards, shifted sideways. Together the lava flows form slanting sequences or piles, up to 2,000–3,000 m thick, because the continuous spreading of the plates has caused a 5–15° dip towards the active rift zone. The total thickness is 10–12 km. It is possible to recognise individual volcanic systems from this time span in the pile. They distinguish themselves as large lenticular bodies with an activity centre, in the Tertiary formation. These units mainly consist of lava-flow sequences and a complex structural and petrological centre. Such central structures also seem to exist on the ocean floor to the northwest of Iceland (off the West Fjords), detectable from magnetic or gravitational surveys.

The main rift zone began its eastward "jump" about 7 million years ago. It appears that the southern part moved gradually to what is now the Southwestern Rift Zone and spreading commenced there. The process of such a rift-zone shift may have taken up to 2 million years. By around 5–6 million years ago, the northern part had also jumped east, and became fully active in what is now northeast Iceland.

As the lava layers on both sides of the new rift zone moved outwards and dipped slowly towards the active zone, large structural "flexures" were formed. This becomes evident as one crosses Iceland from east to west. Two broad "synclines" (troughs) appear in the western and central part of Iceland with a large "anticline" (a rise) between them. The easternmost of the troughs, albeit with a recent infill of volcanic rocks, contains the present, somewhat bent, rift zone. The older, now extinct, rift zone can be observed in the west by tracing another "syncline" from Snæfellsnes to the eastern part of Húnaflói bay in North Iceland. In between is the Borgarfjörður "anticline". Not to be confused with folding, these features are the obvious result of sinking (downward isostatic movement) and separation of rock strata within and close to an active rift zone.

The elevation of the old lava plateau probably never attained more than 500–1,000 metres above sea level, but with several 1,000–2,000 m high central volcanoes (a.s.l.) at any given period. As today, many eruptive fissures lined this volcanic landscape that we can only picture in our minds.

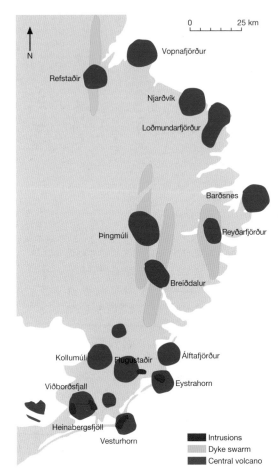

Tertiary central volcanoes in East Iceland. Prominent dyke swarms represent ancient volcanic systems. Dykes around intrusions may be less numerous or almost absent in some cases due to deep-reaching erosion and weathering. The names of volcanic centres vary in the literature. (Sources: G.P.L. Walker 1974 and Á. Guðmundsson 1998)

Commonly, the Blágrýti formation or Tertiary rocks have been thermally altered to different degrees, and pores and fractures are filled with secondary minerals; more so the deeper they are found. Different zeolite zones are tell-tale signs of different depth and temperature/pressure levels.

Since the volcanic activity was confined to volcanic systems and activity centres much like those we see now, many dykes stand out in the eroded Tertiary lava pile. Locally, they may account for up to 10–

15% of the bedrock. Vertical dykes represent magma infills in ancient fissure swarms. A few of them are feeder dykes to volcanic edifices, while dipping dykes are directly associated with tectonic and volcanic activity at volcanic centres, for example cone sheets and ring dykes.

About 40 ancient volcanic centres have been identified in the Tertiary formation on dry land. The central volcanoes are characterised by light-coloured acid volcanics, plutonic intrusions, for example granophyre and gabbro formations, and by high-temperature alteration of the bedrock. Thick tephra deposits are also known to be associated with the centres. The centres have been scanned for precious minerals and metals.

Faults and fissures criss-cross the Tertiary bedrock. However, they commonly strike north or northeast.

Sedimentary basaltic beds are widely found in the Tertiary formation, in between lava flows. Some contain fossils that enable a crude reconstruction of the Tertiary climate and flora. Volcanogenic interbeds are mostly tephra layers or, less commonly, sediments from pyroclastic flows, mudflows (lahars) and tuffs or breccias from subaquatic volcanic eruptions. Red interbeds are red and brownish lateritic topsoils with a varying clay and sand fraction, overrun by lava flows. They have been compacted and may range from less than a metre to less than 10 m thick. Few fossils have been found in red interbeds, except for quite a lot of vegetation remains, so nothing is really known about the birds and mammals that may have occupied Iceland at this time.

Lignite seams are intercalated with part of the Tertiary interbeds. Some may class as brown coal seams but they are thin (up to 1 m). In most cases, the lignite represents remains of wetland soil and vegetation. It is dark brown to black in colour (*surtarbrandur* in Icelandic) and has a low carbon content. Lignite is most common in the northwest of Iceland but is also found in the other Tertiary regions. At some locations pieces of wood are present in the seams. Despite being poor fuel, lignite was collected for domestic use and mined to a small extent in some areas until the early 20th century.

Lake sediments also form interbasaltic beds. The bulk is brownish layers of sand and clay with thin lignite seams. Imprints of leaves, stems

The almost horizontal lava layers that constitute this mountain (top), and form thick lava sequences, illustrate the basic building units of the uppermost crust in Iceland (Berufjörður, eastern Iceland). Red interbeds (old soil) are common. (RTH and HK)

and fossilised tree branches or trunks, along with seeds, are fairly common, with about 60 different species represented.

Four localities with fossilised fauna, chiefly with lake sediments, are the best known representatives of the Tertiary fauna. The oldest collection is at Þórishlíðarfjall by Selárdalur in the West Fjords with 14–15-million-year-old fossils. The findings include mammoth tree, pine, walnut tree, alder, beach, elm, lime tree and grapes. At Brjánslækur (on the northern shores of Breiðafjörður) the remains are around 12 million years old and comprise spruce, Sequoia, mammoth tree, birch, maple, alder, magnolia and sassafras. By then, the most thermophilic species had vanished. Old fossils at Brjánslækur show that the mean summer temperature was then still close to 20°C and the mean winter temperature above freezing. The mean annual temperature was 10–15°C, or at least 8–10° higher than at present, depending on region. This means that deciduous forest with coniferous patches, including even giant fir, covered the country where conditions were suitable, not unlike on the east coast of the United States at present. The younger fossils in Steingrímsfjörður (on the western shores of Húnaflói) include ferns (e.g. Osmondia), willows, walnut tree, birch, maple and hickory. Conifers were probably already more conspicuous than deciduous trees 10–11 million years ago. At this point it seems that the climate had started to cool off for good because at the Mókollsdalur fossil site,

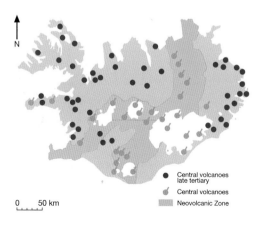

N

0 ____ 50 km

● Central volcanoes late tertiary

🍄 Central volcanoes

▨ Neovolcanic Zone

Ancient and recent central volcanoes. The main outcrops of large intrusions, some of which are parts of magma chambers, occur in the Tertiary formations. The still-active centres will eventually become inactive as they drift east or west of their present position. (Main source: Geological map of Iceland; Icelandic Institute of Natural History)

Eroded ruins of a late Tertiary volcanic centre
close to Borgarfjörður eystri in the northeast
(Dyrfjöll). (RTH)

south of Steingrímsfjörður, 8–9-million-year-old fossils show a slightly
hardier flora, consisting of, for example, alder and birch but less of
beech, maple, hickory and hazel tree. Many of the more thermophilic
species have vanished.

Around 7–8 million years ago the climate continued to cool, without
respite. The proportion of coniferous forest became even greater. This
can be seen from fossils from Hreðavatn in the west, which are 7–8 million years old. Representative plants in addition to birch are pine, alder
and willow, so that conditions were similar to those around the North
Sea.

As with the older fossil-bearing strata, no traces are found of birds or
mammals in interbeds of this age. One explanation is that bones are
poorly preserved in the volcanogenic Icelandic soils. A few insects have
been found in amber pieces, including the hickory louse (*Longistima
caryae*), now found for example in the southeastern parts of the USA.

3.3–6 million years BP

By about 6 million years ago a major change had already taken place in the tectonic activity since a new rift belt had begun to open further to the east in of the country. This evolution continued over the next few million years. It can be assumed that volcanism at this time was as active as before but in a new location. The cooling of the climate continued and conifers and hardy deciduous trees increased in number.

From this long period one fossilised mammal has also been found in Vopnafjörður in the northeast. It was found in interbasaltic sediments, which are thought to be 3–4 million years old. The find is of a small animal related to the deer. This at least suggests that a land-bridge existed between Iceland and the land to the east or the west some time earlier in the Tertiary era and relatively early in the history of the country.

About 3–4 million years ago the first significant glaciers appear, first in the southeast and presumably also on isolated high volcanoes elsewhere and then gradually in other places. Evidence for them is found in ancient till layers. There are in addition layers of possible till, for instance in the Geitafell volcano at Hornafjörður, which may be much older or 6–7 million years old. If correct, then it was also a very localised glacier.

Around 3 million years ago the first major formations formed by subglacial eruption appeared (móberg, breccia and pillow lava). Volcanism in the rift zone produced the Plio-Pleistocene formation now running as a narrow zone along either side of the active volcanic rift zone, due to the divergent plate movement. There are also volcanic formations in the area between the southwestern rift zone and the southern volcanic belt, a large area called the Hreppar formation. The Plio-Pleistocene formation is easily accessible along national route 1 between Kirkjubæjarklaustur and Lómagnúpur.

The characteristics of these formations are lavas and cube-jointed rocks formed by eruption on ice-free land, mixed with altered tephra (*móberg*), breccia and other volcanic formations which have erupted subglacially or in lakes. Central volcanoes were active in the areas of present-day Þjórsárdalur, Hafnarfjall/Skarðsheiði and Hvalfjörður. They can be seen on either side of the present active rift zone, for

Petrified wood and lignite or leaf imprints of tree and plant remains, found within the Tertiary lava succession. Most of the species require much higher mean annual temperatures than those prevailing today. (RTH)

The mountain Sandell in Fáskrúðsfjörður, East-
Iceland (light coloured) is defined as a typical
laccolith. (RTH)

example close to Þingvellir, and are older the further they lie from
active fractures.

The oldest sediments in the so-called Tjörnes succession date from
the very end of this period. Although the Ice Age had not begun in
earnest in the northern hemisphere, signs of it in Iceland are very clear.
This is also the time, 3.3 million years ago, of a magnetic field reversal
from the reversed Gilbert period to the normal Gauss period.

2–3.3 million years BP

Early in this period volcanism began in the area of present-day Skagafjörður (Skagafjörður Volcanic Formation), close to the old rift-zone
axis. It is possible that a new rift zone almost managed to form and the
reason could be a sudden increase in magma generation beneath the
country. Volcanism continued here for at least 1–2 million years and
the volcanic formations produced can be seen, for instance, in the far
north of the Skagi peninsula, on Drangey and Þórðarhöfði on the east
coast of Skagafjörður. Volcanism also resumed on Snæfellsnes a little
later, and is still active in three volcanic systems.

During this period climatic fluctuations become more pronounced
than before. The approaching cold period is presumably getting longer
and colder. Ice caps develop still further to the west from the southeast

of the country. Just over 2 million years ago the first glacial periods begin with extensive formation of glaciers in most parts of the country. This fits in with the beginning of the Quaternary Ice Age in the northern hemisphere as a whole. To start with, the glacial periods may have lasted for at least 20,000 years each and the greater part of Iceland disappeared under the ice, but there were also shorter interglacial periods in which the country was more or less ice-free.

The northern part of the new rift zone which was long since established in the northeast began to extend southwards, it is thought due to the effect of the hot spot which was at this time already situated near the centre of Iceland. About 2–2.5 million years ago the South Iceland Volcanic Belt became active ahead of this propagating rift. Gradually the northeastern rift zone continued to "eat" its way into the new volcanic zone, i.e. extended slowly into the Southern Iceland Volcanic Belt which itself slowly changes into a rift zone, first in the central highlands. At the same time the South Iceland Seismic Zone became active or at least more so than now. To start with it lay rather further north (in Hreppur) than at the present.

Active landscaping by the glaciers began at this time and the landscape changed greatly as mountains, valleys and fjords were formed under active outlet glaciers.

The Tjörnes layers are a key formation for interpreting Plio-Pleistocene history. Tjörnes is a short but broad peninsula in northeast Iceland. On the western side there is a 1,200 m thick tilted series of sediment beds and lava flows. The tilting is caused by tectonic movements. The oldest fossil-rich beds (Tjörnes beds, 500 m thick) are mostly clay or sand-rich shallow-sea sediments and fluvial, estuarian sandstones. They crop out with three distinct mollusc zones and are intercalated with lignite seams. The lignite layers show that the area occasionally rose above sea level. The whole series rests on an eroded pile of lava flows, 8 million years old.

The two lowest mollusc zones (*Tapes* and *Mactra*) are of late Tertiary (Pliocene) date and estimated to be about 3–4 million years old. They contain thermophilic species that indicate a marine annual temperature of 10°C which is 4–6°C higher than at present. However, the third and highest zone contains cold-water species (*Serripes* and *Macoma*) that indicate an inflow of cold water into the North Atlantic Ocean some 3 million years ago. The opening of the Bering Strait occurred around 3.3 million years ago and explains the changing marine scene and also the arrival of Pacific species in the Tjörnes area. These gradually take over and account for quarter of the 100 species found in all the beds. The very late Pliocene sea temperature was 2–4°C above the present figure.

These marine beds are topped by a series of lava flows (the Höskulds-vík lavas). The oldest lava is 2.5 million years old. Above it, some 250 m of additional lava sheets represent nearby volcanic activity over a time span of about 500,000 years. In the middle of the sequence rest two tillite beds (the Furuvík beds or Furuvík Group). Dated roughly at 2.2 million years BP, they are the first indicators of a major central ice cap in Iceland.

On the lava flows that cap the Furuvík tillites rests a 125–150 m thick series of marine sediments (with fossils), tillites and a few lava flows. This Breiðavík Group represents about 800,000 years of transgressing or regressing sea, the oldest interglacial marine sediments being 2 million years old.

At Mýrdalur (southern Iceland), 2–3-million-year-old strata with chiefly thermophilic molluscs indicate that the ocean stretched inland during a warm interglacial period prior to the growth of the large central volcanoes that reside in the area at present.

Some 2.3 million years ago another magnetic reversal occurred when the Gauss period (normal polarity) was succeeded by the Matuyama period (reversed polarity).

A long chapter of geological history is visible in
the sediments, lava flows and fossils that line
the western coast of Tjörnes. (RTH)

130,000 to 2 million years BP

The Breiðavík Group at Tjörnes partly reveals the Lower Pleistocene
geological history, from about 2 million to 1.2 million years ago. In this
time span, six long glacial periods become separated by shorter interglacial periods. Six tillite beds represent the glacial stages and marine
fossils in interglacial sediments directly above each of them indicate a
similar marine environment to that of today. The occurrence of the
cold-sea-loving *Portlandia arctica* high up in the Breiðavík Group
shows that the glacial periods were creating Arctic conditions in Icelandic waters. Pollen in the sediments shows that alder, willows and some

birch thrived during interglacials. The Breiðavík Goup is capped by a reverse-polarity lava flow (the Máná Basalt). Further north, along the Tjörnes coastline, more sedimentary beds occur, mainly tillites, above the Breiðavík Group proper and the Máná Basalt. Altogether six tillite beds have been identified there. This brings the total number of glacial periods represented at Tjörnes to 14. Combining this information with that from Plio-Pleistocene strata in other parts of Iceland (e.g. in Mt. Esja), as well as from the Upper Pleistocene, suggests that the number of glacial periods probably exceeds 20.

Subglacial eruptions were common at this time. The southern volcanic zone continued to evolve into a rift zone while the South Iceland Seismic Zone crept slowly southwards. In the volcanic zone the southern part extended gradually towards the Vestmannaeyjar area and the rifting part in the northeast reached approximately to the Torfajökull area.

Volcanic systems with active centres, 1–3 million years old, which crop out at present as highlands, were active at this time. Acid eruptives characterise these centres along with hyaloclastites intermingled with lava layers. The Hvalfjörður, Kjalarnes and Esja areas are typical of such formations. The western part of the long mountain of Esja is an eroded flank of the Kollafjörður caldera volcano which was active 2–3 million years ago. The volcano is almost completely eroded, with its centre in the fjord of Kollafjörður. The extreme eastern part of Esja and the neighbouring hills, such as Móskarðshnjúkar, show the remains of a younger volcanic centre, the Stardalur central volcano, which was active 1–2 million years ago.

Fossil-rich sediments from the first part of the Ice Age occur in a handful of places in the country. Such occurrences have already been mentioned in Tjörnes and Mýrdalur. A younger example is an up to 70 m thick succession of sandstone layers from a lake in Bakkabrúnir in Víðidalur in the north. Here some layers contain traces of alder, birch, willow, heather and grasses. Their age is estimated at 1–2 million years old. Still younger, or close to 1 million years old, is a series of marine and land-borne sediments on the northern shores of Snæfellsnes, between Kirkjufell, Stöð and Búlandshöfði. Together the sites reveal two distinct tillites that represent glacial periods. Between them lie interglacial sediments containing molluscs and strata with fossilised

Móskarðshnúkar (light-coloured, acid eruptives) connect to the Stardalur central volcano, northeast of Reykjavík, active 1–2 million years ago. (RTH)

alder and willow. They show a gradual warming of both climate and marine environment, as well as a marine regression.

The youngest of the well-known fossil sites is at Svínafellsfjall, at the base of the large Öræfajökull central volcano. The sediments are mainly lacustrine or lake sediments, probably from 700,000 to 500,000 years old. They are quite thick (120 m) and contain remains or imprints of plants including birch, rowan, alder and grasses.

The penultimate glaciation period (Saale) reached its height some 170,000 years ago. Volcanic activity beneath the ice shield created móberg (hyaloclastite) and pillow-lava formations.

13,000–130,000 years BP

About 130,000–140,000 years ago, Iceland was once again released to a large extent from the grip of the ice. New *móberg* (hyaloclastite) mountains rose from the ice-free landscape in the active volcanic zone and once again volcanic fissures and lava shields spread fresh lava over moraine material or lake and river sediments. Eroded lava shields and large lava flows can be found, for example in the southwest. Ok and Lyngdalsheiði, inland from Lake Þingvallavatn, represent eroded lava shields from the early warm Eem period. The Reykjavík bedrock is composed of denuded greyish lava flows from several effusive eruptions in the vicinity during the latest, the penultimate and maybe also older interglacial periods, i.e. they are 100,000–400,000 years old. The lava buried moraine material, fine-grained marine sediments and fluvial sands (indicating a regressing sea level) in the Reykjavík area. At Elliðavogur in Reykjavík, a sedimentary succession of this kind contains moor and pond sediments plus lignite, probably from the Eem interglacial period, with remains of a flora very similar to the present one and without any traces of alder.

The last glacial period (Weichselian) commenced 110,000–120,000 years ago. The climate was unstable for the whole period as indicated by ice cores from the Greenland ice cap, with pronounced temperature lows some 70,000 and 22,000 years ago. The cold climate fed a huge ice cap that finally covered most of Iceland and reached far out on to the sea-floor shelf surrounding the island. Submarine moraines are found more than 100 km offshore. The ice cap attained a thickness of 1,000–2,000 m with a main ice divide stretching east-west across the southern highlands. There were independent ice divides in the northwest and northeast, and small mountain glaciers, ice streams, promontories and nunataks characterised the highest and steepest regions close to the coast. Part of the flora may have survived in these ice-free areas. Another part may have survived in less elevated areas with low precipitation, like Langanes in northeast Iceland. The country thus resembled eastern Greenland as it is at present, while the Arctic Ocean extended far south of it with drift ice and icebergs.

The last glacial period reached a maximum glacier extent 19,000 – 20,000 years ago. Within the volcanic zone huge *móberg* (hyaloclastite) mountains accumulated in subglacial eruptions (cf. Herðubreið) as well as numerous other table mountains and móberg ridges. Around 14,000–15,000 years ago yet another far-reaching climatic change occurred and warm ocean currents stretched northwards to Iceland once again. The Weichselian glaciers started to retreat all over northern areas and the sea level rose rapidly, while the land responded to the lighter overburden with uplift.

This photo of East Greenland shows scenery that   of the last glacial period of the Ice Age
might have been typical in Iceland at the height   (Weichselian). (RTH)

9,000–13,000 years BP

About 15,000 years ago the Pleistocene glaciers started to retreat off northern Iceland and during the next 1,000–2,000 years the Icelandic ice cap shrunk rapidly in all parts of the country. It appears that shrinkage began a few thousand years after glaciers on the continents began to melt in earnest.

About 12,500–12,700 years ago, during the warm Bölling period, the ice-sheet edge already lay within the present-day coastline. Lowland coastal areas and headlands in Iceland were in places ice free and this development continued. Glacier melting elsewhere in the world added greatly to the water content of the oceans and the sea advanced rapidly in Iceland. A result is the occurrence of widespread shell remains in western Iceland at 20–135 m high, which have been dated as belonging to the Bölling period. Remains of a whale just over 12,000 years old have also been found in the mountainside at Akrafjall. In the north of the country there are remains of a strandline at 30–90 m above the present sea level. However, the land rose rapidly following the decreasing glacier overburden and the relative sea level fell rapidly during the Bölling period which came to an end 12,000 years ago.

In various places in the northern hemisphere there is evidence of a cold period about 11,500–12,000 years ago (Older Dryas period). The remains from this period are not clear and decisive in Iceland. Rather it appears that glacier retreat continued for up to 2,000 years or up until the end of the warm Alleröd period which occurred in the northern hemisphere in general 10,500–11,500 years ago. Over such a long period of time it can be assumed that the glaciers diminished greatly but did not disappear entirely, least of all in the central highlands and southeast.

Isostatic uplift was very rapid by the start of the Alleröd period and the strandline was below that of the present-day low-tide mark. These isostatic changes encouraged volcanism and it can be assumed that the youngest Pleistocene *móberg* (hyaloclastite) mountains were formed subglacially at this time, while on ice-free land effusive eruptions occurred, resulting in the first relatively young shield-volcano lavas. During this period there was a large acid tephra eruption in Askja while evidence of effusive lava eruptions can be found on the Reykjanes peninsula and in the northeast (Þeistareykir–Krafla).

Just over 11,000 years ago at the close of the Alleröd period, the climate got colder. The Fossvogur strata in Reykjavík date from his period. They consist of glacial till at the bottom and shallow marine sediments including varves, with low-arctic to high-boreal mollusc species that all live in Icelandic waters today, while further up coarse sediment appears that suggests an approaching glacier. The mean age of the sediments is just over 11,000 C^{14} years (the absolute age is somewhat lower).

By about 10,500 years ago, a 500–700-year-long cold period known as the Younger Dryas period had already started. The glaciers advanced rapidly over the centuries to largely cover the country, even extending beyond the shores in the south and southeast. In the east, valley glaciers extended to fill the fjords while there were cirque glaciers present in a fairly broad highland belt along the coast. Meanwhile the land sank under the greater weight of the glaciers and the strandline rose, reaching a maximum just over 10,000 years ago when it was on average some tens of metres higher than the present-day strandline. Distinctive delta sediments and shorelines from this period are widespread.

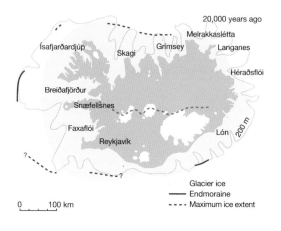

20,000 years ago

Glacier ice
——— Endmoraine
- - - - Maximum ice extent

0   100 km

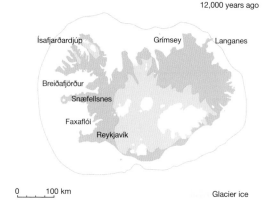

12,000 years ago

Glacier ice

0   100 km

The shaded area shows the
extent of glacier ice
according to model
calculations and sediment
mapping, 20,000 years ago
(LG-maximum), 12,000 years
ago (end of Bölling period),
10,300 years ago (Younger
Dryas period) and around
9,800 years ago (Preboreal
time). (Simplified after:
H. Norðdahl and H.G. Pétursson 2005, 2006)

In the Younger Dryas there was an enormous explosive tephra eruption in Katla with associated floods which carried ash and rock fragments out to sea and resulted in ash fall in Iceland and its surrounding
countries. This is known by various names including Vedde tephra and
Ash Zone 1. For some time this Katla tephra was thought to be somewhat older or 11,000–12,000 years old.

Again the climate became suddenly warmer and 10,000 years ago the
Preboreal period began, spanning the first few thousand years of the
Holocene, as it is called in geological terms. The glaciers retreated and

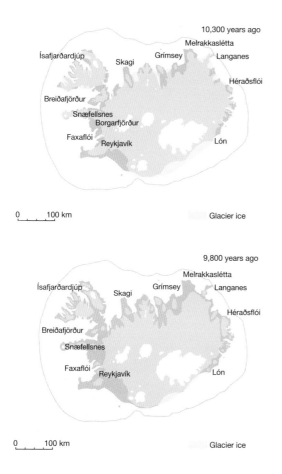

10,300 years ago

Melrakkaslétta

Ísafjarðardjúp   Grímsey   Langanes
          Skagi

               Héraðsflói

Breiðafjörður

   Snæfellsnes
    Borgarfjörður

  Faxaflói
     Reykjavík   Lón

0   100 km   Glacier ice

9,800 years ago

Melrakkaslétta

Ísafjarðardjúp   Grímsey   Langanes
         Skagi

               Héraðsflói

Breiðafjörður

  Snæfellsnes

  Faxaflói
     Reykjavík   Lón

0   100 km   Glacier ice

the strandline sank by about 25–45 m because landmass uplift was more than accounted for by what global ice melting added to the oceans.

The widespread climatic changes were not yet complete, however. About 9,800 years ago a cold spell began in Iceland and the glaciers advanced yet again, although not to the same extent as in the Younger Dryas. It can be assumed that the cold spell lasted for two to three centuries. The main ice sheet reached almost the same position as in the Younger Dryas, covering probably two thirds of the country, while

local glaciers either formed or increased outside this area. The strandline rose by up to 25 m due to land subsidence when the glaciers became thicker. Clear shorelines belonging to this cold spell are widespread 10–30 m below those of the Younger Dryas period. A large
lowland area in the west and north of the country was ice free but below
sea level in many areas.

Eruptions from shield volcanoes were common during this period
and important volcanic structures such as the Skjaldbreiður lava shield
are believed to date from Preboreal time. About 9,500 years ago the
glacier finally succumbed to a vigorous warm interglacial period,
although fluctuations continued for 2,000–3,000 years. The land rose
rapidly as soon as the overburden was removed and 9,000 years ago the
strandline was some tens of metres lower than today.

At around this time, or about 9,200 years ago, one or more strong
eruptions occurred in Grímsvötn. These produced, for example, the
Saksunarvatn tephra, which covered an area of over 1.5 million km^2,
and places where it is found include the Faroe Islands (whence the
name) and Germany.

Land areas freed of the glaciers and rivers were already covered by
vegetation during the Bölling period. The vegetated area grew and
shrank in keeping with climatic change and other conditions, right up
until late in the Preboreal period when vegetation gained a firm foot-
hold all over the country.

1,100–9,000 years BP

The mean annual temperature increased by 5–10°C during the above-
mentioned interglacial periods of the late Pleistocene. This seems very
pronounced during the Bölling period and also 9,000 years ago. Following the cold spell in the Preboreal period and for the next 1–2 millennia, the glaciers almost disappeared from the entire country, while
the vegetation spread rapidly. Uplift became slower, although increased
meltwater from the glaciers caused a higher strandline.

About 8,000–9,000 years ago the strandline was probably 10–15 m
lower than at present. When the Þjórsá lava erupted from a volcanic

Many younger Pleistocene volcanic structures are cone-shaped peaks or long, serrated ridges (Fjallabak), chiefly made of móberg or palagonite tuff and breccia (hyaloclastites). (RTH)

fissure in the south central highlands about 7,800 years ago, the highlands were largely or completely ice free and the strandline in the south and southeast was still many metres lower than at present. A number of other effusive eruptions producing large amounts of lava typify the first thousand years of the Holocene. Simultaneously, many large tephra eruptions occurred in central volcanoes (e.g. Hekla).

Sea-level increase (sea transgression) became slower and slower but continued for several thousand years. At Grótta on the Seltjarnarnes headland where there is now a small inlet, a freshwater lagoon formed shortly after the start of the Holocene. Peat began to form in it about 9,000 years ago and this continued for a long time. The youngest peat formed about 3,000 years ago by which time the sea level was approaching its present position although it was probably still 4–5 m lower than at present. A short time later the sea transgressed this lagoon and by the time of settlement it was doubtless salty and became known as Seltjörn. Shortly after this it became an inlet of the sea as the waves broke down a land barrier and started to erode the peat. Similar "beach peat" is found a short distance further east at the settlement of Kjalarnes.

In the Boreal period grass and heather species were widespread and dwarf birch (*Betula nana*) became established. It is possible that large eruptions, such as the one that occurred in Grímsvötn about 9,200 years ago, retarded the spread of vegetation somewhat, but it can be assumed that the spread of shrubs such as juniper, willow and dwarf birch then increased. A larger species of birch (*Betula pubescens*) appeared by the middle of the Boreal period and was probably conspicuous, forming low-profile forests. Birch probably reached its maximum distribution about 5,000–6,000 years ago.

The warm period of the Holocene may have reached its maximum temperature just over 7,000 years ago. It can be assumed that the land was almost completely ice free except for the highest peaks. After this the mean annual temperature decreased on the whole until the 20th century, although there were considerable fluctuations in temperature and precipitation.

There is some debate about the origin of the Holocene flora in Iceland. First it was thought that it had survived on nunataks and ice-fee land on the highland coastal headlands. It was also thought that seeds and spores been wind borne. Although none of these factors should be completely discarded, the general view today is that the shrubs originated in Scandinavia and were carried here by ice rafts, driftwood and flood debris from the decaying Fennoscandian ice caps. Further research will clarify how the colonisation occurred and where it originated.

When sections of deep Icelandic bogs are examined, they reveal a peat layer at the bottom which overlies some sort of sediment, either glacial, fluvial or lacustrian in origin. Above this there is generally a layer of birch remains. The birch bears witness to the most vegetated and warmest period of the Holocene, which passed around 6,000–8,500 years ago. A wetter and possibly cooler period then started just

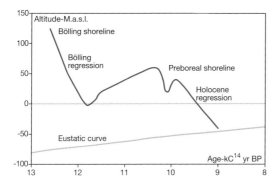

Relative sea-level changes in western and southwestern Iceland (upper curve) in late glacial and early Holocene times. The lower curve represents the eustatic sea-level development worldwide. (Simplified after: H. Norðdahl and H.G. Pétursson 2005, 2006; eustatic curve by Tushingham and Peltier 1991)

over 6,000 years ago and forests disappeared in many areas while bogs increased and heath vegetation spread. This can be seen from the thick peat layer that overlies the birch remains in sections. There are indications that glaciers then advanced or formed on the ice-free highland.

Another horizon containing birch remains, found much higher up in the bog sections, is about 4,500–5,000 years old and suggests that the bogs had then dried up to some degree and dwarf shrubs and forests were again thriving in a drier and somewhat milder climate, but only briefly. At this time there was a small marine transgression in both Iceland and Scandinavia.

It can be assumed that up to 60% of the country was well vegetated during the birch period, particularly in its earlier stages, with a flora consisting of various vascular plants, and furthermore that up to half this area of vegetation consisted of dwarf birch shrubs or true birch forest.

About 4,500–5,000 years ago there were further environmental changes. The bogs started to increase in size again, as did the glaciers. By this time the climate had cooled so much that it could be regarded as the beginning of Iceland's present-day glacier distribution. A new layer of peat formed on top of the later birch horizon and the associated climatic conditions continued until the last century, with minor but significant fluctuations. It is thought that at least four glacial advances occurred after 4500 BP, the last 1,200–1,500 years ago or just before the settlement of Iceland. The "Little Ice Age" in the years 1400–1900 was a historically significant climatic cold period, especially the

The deepest canyon in Iceland is Hafrahvammagljúfur (170 m), cut by a glacial river
now dammed and harnessed by the Kárahnjúkar
Hydropower Plant (690 MW). Extensive land
areas and interesting sediments were
submerged. The photo was taken before the
controversial project was realised. (RTH)

later part of it. The main glacial advances were in the 18th and 19th centuries. Everything suggests that the widespread shrub and forest areas which covered the country at the time of settlement were decimated during the first one to two centuries after a thin tephra layer fell in about 870 AD (Vö871, the "Settlement Layer"), but this damage was man-made rather than due to natural events.

As already explained, all kinds of soil and sediment evident on the surface of the country originate in the Holocene or last Pleistocene glacial period. Volcanic products from the Holocene are thought to amount to 400–500 km3 and many thousands of square kilometres of lava have covered older lavas, glacial till and other sediments, but have also flowed seawards and thus increased the land area.

On the whole the last 2,500–3,000 years were more a "period of expanding mires and glaciers" than a "period of birchwoods and ice-free highlands". In spite of warm spells at intervals, the mean annual temperature decreased over this time. This period may now coming to a close in the technological age and a new drier and warmer period of the Holocene may be commencing. This has, after all, been the pattern during the Holocene. A natural increase in temperature could thus partly explain the evident current global warming which is at present under debate and causing concern. If this is the case, then human activity and the emission of greenhouse gases is increasing a trend which has natural causes and has been linked to such factors as the changing intensity of incoming solar radiation to Earth. The human impact has been estimated as accounting for about a third of the global warming due to greenhouse gas emission and that is a conservative estimate. On the other hand, it seems fairly certain that the Holocene interglacial period must end sooner or later, to be replaced by cold, wet conditions once more. This would mean the start of yet another glacial period which would seriously affect life and conditions globally. It has been pointed out that vigorous warming in polar areas of the northern hemisphere could change the driving mechanism of the present northward-moving warm ocean currents and result in sudden cooling and the advance of the glaciers. Environmental factors and climate are therefore very important issues for mankind in our time.

Productive central volcanoes like Hekla (seen here from the northeast) and associated volcanic fissures have piled up the bedrock of Iceland for millions of years. (OS)

Shoreface terraces from interstadial and preboreal times are common in Iceland, implying a rather complex history of sea-level changes (Esja, north of Reykjavík). (RTH)

The Icelanders denote the past 1,100–1,200 years as historical times, beginning when the human settlement began to change Iceland. This is a mere trifle on any geological timescale. Even so, during that time-span, geological processes have had much impact on society and nature. The most pronounced influence is of course made by what one termes as natural hazards. These are for example volcanic eruptions, floods and earth or rock slides. New figures for the estimated volume of volcanic products have almost doubled in the last few years, from close to 50 cubic kilometres to more than 80. The lava and tephra surely put widespread marks on the island. But slower geological processes really do change our environment. Glaciers did advance for centuries and are currently retreating fast, revealing untrodden ground to us. Frost shatters rocks and global warming causes the sea to advance inland. The soil on steep slopes creeps downhill. The Icelanders like to point out that there are few places in the world where the influence of all these processes is as evident and easy to follow as in their country. The book is meant to illustrate that there is some truth in the statement and to rely information on the geology of the terra vivante – the living earth – of Iceland.

Selected bibliography

Surnames are written in italics. The Icelandic letters é, ó, á, ú, í and ý should be written as e, o, a, u, i and y, ö as ö, oe or simply o, æ as æ or ae, ð as d and þ as th when searching for references and papers in most databases.

Þ. *Einarsson* and K.J. *Albertsson* 1988. *The glacial history of Iceland during the past three million years.* Philosophical Transactions of the Royal Society of London 318, p. 673–644.

Þ. *Einarsson* 1994. *Geology of Iceland – rocks and landscape.* Mál og menning, Reykjavík.

J. *Eiríksson* 1980. Tjörnes, North Iceland: a bibliographical review of the geological research history. *Jökull* 30, p. 1–20.

G.Ó. *Friðleifsson* 1983. Mineralogical Evolution of a Hydrothermal System. Geothermal Resources Council, *Transactions* vol. 7, p. 147–152.

G. Ó. *Friðleifsson* 1995. Míósen jöklun á Suðausturlandi. In (eds) B. Hróarsson et al.: *Eyjar í eldhafi.* Reykjavík, p. 77–87.

W.L. *Friedrich* and L.A. *Símonarson* 1981. Die fossile Flora Islands: Zeugin der Thule Landbrücke. *Spektrum der Wissenschaft.* Oktober, p. 23–31.

G.R. *Foulger*, J.H. *Natland*, D.C. *Presnall* and D.L. *Anderson* (eds) 2005. Plates, Plumes and Paradigms. *Geological Soc. of America Special*, vol. 388, 861 pp.

Á. *Geirsdóttir* and J. *Eiríksson* 1994. Growth of an intermittent ice sheet in Iceland during the late Pliocene and early Pleistocene. *Quaternary Research* 42, 115–130.

Á. *Geirsdóttir* and J. *Eiríksson* 1994. Sedimentary facies and environmental history of the Late-glacial glaciomarine Fossvogur sediments in Reykjavík, Iceland. *Boreas* 23, p. 164–176.

H. *Guðmundsson* 1997: A review of the Holocene environmental history of Iceland. *Quaternary Science Rew.* 16, p. 81-92.

I. *Kaldal* and S.*Víkingsson* 1990. Early Holocene deglaciation in Central Iceland. *Jökull* 40., p. 51–67.

M. *Halldsóttir* 1995. On the pre-settlement history of Icel. vegetation. *Búvísindi* (Icel. Agric. Sci.) 9. p. 17–29.

H. *Norðdahl* and H. G. *Pétursson* 2005. Relative sea-level changes in Iceland: new aspects of the Weichselian deglaciation of Iceland. In (eds): Caseldine C., Russel, A., Hardardottir, J. and Knudsen O., Iceland- *Modern processes and past Environment*, p. 25–78. Elsevier, Amsterdam.

E. *Roaldset* 1983. Tertiary (Miocene-Pliocene) interbasalt sediments, NW and W-Iceland. *Jökull* 33, p. 39–56.

K. *Sæmundsson* 1979. Outline of the Geology of Iceland. *Jökull* 29, p. 7–28.

K. *Sæmundsson* 1986. Subaerial volcanism in the western North Atlantic. In: (eds) P.R. Vogt and B. E. Tucholke: *The geology of North America. Vol. M*: The western North Atlantic Region. Geol. Soc. Am., p. 69–86.

S. *Sigurðsson* and K. *Einarsson* 1988. Groundwater resources and demand. *Jökull* 38. p. 35–54.

L. *Símonarson* 1990. Fyrstu landspendýraleifarnar úr íslenskum tertíerlögum. *Náttúrufræðingurinn* 59, p. 189–195.

Index

K

L